HEAVENLY KHAN

A Biography of Emperor Tang Taizong (Li Shimin)

a historical novel

Victor Cunrui Xiong

D1295947

airiti press

華藝學術出版社

In memory of
Brigid Keogh (1909–2007),
educator, philanthropist, and missionary

HEAVENLY KHAN

Contents

List of Illustrations

Author's Note

I would like to express my sincere gratitude to those who made the writing of this book possible.

I owe a profound debt to the great writers of historical fiction of the past two centuries in the West and to students of History 3020 (World History to 1500) at Western Michigan University, who read with enthusiasm the historical fictions I assigned them.

Dr. Dongfang Shao of the Library of Congress recommended me to Airiti Press.

Adam Christopher Matthews of Western Michigan University reviewed and copy-edited the whole manuscript and saved me from quite a few embarrassments.

Stu Smith of Kalamazoo, Michigan, offered some insightful remarks.

The Burnham-Macmillan Endowment of the History Department, Western Michigan University, provided funding to defray the cost associated with the production of the book.

Lastly, my wife, Xiaoqing Li, gave me constant support and encouragement.

This book is a historical fiction. But it is essentially based on traditional historical sources. Although challenged by modern scholars in a few areas, these sources are highly reliable. Readers interested in the history of the period in question are referred to the modern studies in the Bibliography.

During Sui-Tang times, the Chinese had no concept of minutes or weeks. Traditionally, a day was divided into 12 instead of 24 sections. Nonetheless, I use such temporal terms as "minutes," "hours," and "weeks" for the benefit of the reader.

The traditional Chinese calendar was a lunisolar calendar and was approximately one month behind the Julian-Gregorian Calendar. In this book, I normally use Julian-Gregorian Calendar dates. When Chinese dates are given, they are expressed in ordinal numbers (e.g.: the 1st day of the 2nd month).

The traditional Chinese way of counting age regards a person at birth as one year old and adds one more year on the first New Year's Day. Thus, an age recorded in a traditional source is one to almost two years older than the real age. In this book, I convert recorded ages to approximate *real ages* by deducting one year.

In Western literature, China is sometimes referred to as the "Middle Kingdom" (*zhongguo*). To avoid confusion with its use associated with Ancient Egypt, I replace it with the "Central Kingdom."

The only traditional unit of measurement used in this book is *li*, which varied slightly from the first to the second reigns of the Sui, and from Sui to Tang, and is roughly equivalent to half a kilometer or slightly shorter than one third of a mile.

Place names are usually traditional ones followed by their modern equivalents in parentheses where necessary. However, in the case of large geographical regions, modern place names are sometimes used (Inner Mongolia, Shanxi, Shaanxi, Manchuria, and such like) instead of their Sui-Tang equivalents. Some Sui-Tang region names in this book such as Henan, Hebei, and Shandong have survived into present-day usage, but the areas they covered in Sui-Tang times were larger and less well defined than their modern namesakes.

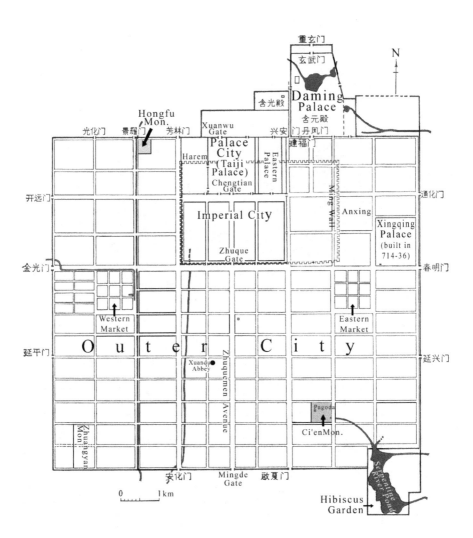

Fig. 1. Tang Chang'an (Sui Daxing City)

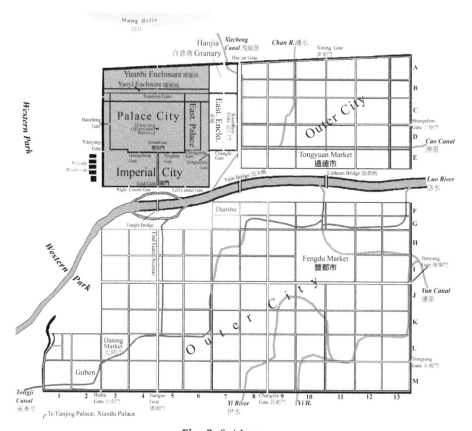

Fig. 2. Sui Luoyang

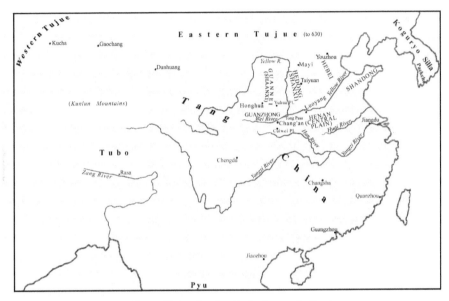

Map 1. Tang China in the Early Seventh Century

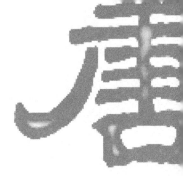

Part I.

Quest for the Throne (613–626)

1. The War of Daye 9

ONE MORNING IN LATE March, Daye 9 (613), the Emperor Yang, a soft-skinned man in his 40s, was speaking to a gathering of leading civil officials and top military commanders in the assembly hall of the Daye Basilica in Luoyang the Eastern Capital. He was sitting on a yellow silk throne beneath an ornate yellow baldachin. The throne was positioned atop a marble dais above two flights of stairs at the northern end of the commodious hall.

In a stately but factual tone, He spoke about, among other things, the widespread drought in the North, especially in Shandong, which had given rise to insurgency, and berated His generals for failure to stamp it out. Pausing briefly He continued in a raised voice, "Now about the Koguryŏ. They are inferior barbarians. Still, they have managed to humiliate our superior state—the Great Sui. If we so desire, we can pull up the Eastern Sea and remove Mount Tai, to say nothing of crushing these small-time bandits. We must launch another war against them."

The audience listened in awe.

"This time," He resumed, "I will lead in person."

Silence gripped the hall for a while before a high-pitched, feeble voice from the audience said: "Your Majesty, in my humble opinion, the Koguryŏ bandits are not strong enough to withstand another assault by our mighty army." With an emaciated face and tall stature the speaker Yuwen Shu carried himself with a military bearing despite his advanced age of over 70. As one of the key commanding officers in the War of Daye 8 (612), Yuwen had been brought back to Luoyang in chains after it had ended in ignominious defeat for the Sui. Only recently had he been reinstated by the Emperor.

"Your Majesty," Yuwen Shu continued, "it would be hard to imagine that any foreign power would be foolish enough to challenge the might of the Sui with its more than 1 million men under arms. Least of all little Koguryŏ, a country the size of a Sui Commandery with a tiny military."

"We concur," several in the crowd said.

Others remained silent except for an elderly-looking man of stout physique, who said, "However, our Central Kingdom has yet to fully recover from the War of Daye 8. Furthermore, one does not shoot a rat with a bow of a thousand pounds. How can the sovereign of our country, one of ten thousand chariots, condescend to fight such a pitiful enemy in person?"

"I appreciate your frankness and loyalty, Mr. Guo Rong. But My plan is to bring an overwhelming force to bear against Koguryŏ, and awe her into submission without much of an engagement."

Addressing the entire audience, the Emperor asked, almost rhetorically, "I suppose there is no more objection?"

When no one spoke a word, He continued, "Very well, preparations for the Daye-9 War against Koguryŏ are now underway."

THE KOGURYŎ WERE AN ancient Korean people. They founded their first state in 37 BCE. By the time of the late Sui, Koguryŏ had become by far the most dominant power of the Three Kingdoms of Korea (the other two being Silla and Paekche), with a territory that took up much of Manchuria and most of the Korean Peninsula.

In antiquity, after the Zhou conquest of the Shang around 1045 BCE, a member of the Shang royal family, Jizi (Kija), was enfeoffed in north Korea. Almost 1,000 years later, Emperor Wu of the Western Han set up four Commanderies in the Korean Peninsula and southern Manchuria in 108 BCE. These records provided a ready rationale for later Chinese sovereigns to engage in aggressive action.

Oftentimes, however, the invading sovereign was actuated by more immediate reasons. When the Emperor Yang Jian (Yang Guang's father) launched the disastrous first Sui invasion in 598, He wanted to rein in the defiant Koguryŏ sovereign, who had attempted to form an alliance with the nomadic Tujue, an act regarded as a threat to the Sui Empire's security. When the Emperor Yang Guang launched the Daye-8 (612) and Daye-9 (613) Wars, He was driven by an ambition to surpass His father.

RESTING ON TOP OF a hill, the parallelogram-shaped Liaodong City (Liaoyang, Liaoning), a strategic outpost in west Koguryŏ, was circumvallated with a ring of tall walls and a massive moat. It had a total of four gatetowers, each of which was fronted by a much taller watchtower. With hills and mountains to its north and east and rolling fields and woodlands to its south and west, this strongly fortified fortress-city seemed impregnable.

But the Emperor Yang Guang was not daunted. Having just arrived at the Liaodong front, He was determined to execute the invasion plan adopted at Luoyang one month earlier. To maximize His chances of success, He had mobilized a large expeditionary army comprised of three columns. The first column, placed under His direct command, had as its immediate target Liaodong City itself. The second column—the main force led by His top generals Yuwen Shu and Yang Yichen—was to march east across the Yalu River. The third column, comprised of naval forces, was to cross the sea from the Shandong Peninsula to land in the suburbs of Pyongyang. The second and third columns would then launch a joint attack on that city.

As the battle for Liaodong City—the first major engagement in the Daye-9 War—began in earnest, the Emperor launched a day-and-night assault from four directions. A whole range of missile weapons and siege devices were deployed, including arbalests, catapults, mangonels, battering rams, and scaling ladders. Even sapping was attempted; but it was soon abandoned for lack of progress—the protective moat was simply too deep.

For 23 days the Koguryŏ defenders held their ground.

Under the protection of archers, thousands of Sui conscripted laborers and construction soldiers began to frantically raise an earthwork close to the city wall. Despite constant enemy harassment, the "Long Ridge"—30-foot wide and as high as the city wall—was erected in two days with more than a million sacks of soil. Meanwhile half a dozen "Eight-wheelers"—mobile assault towers on wheels rising above the city wall—were slowly hauled to the front.

With crack archers deployed on the Long Ridge and the Eight-wheelers providing cover, the Sui forces launched another round of attacks early the next morning. By the late afternoon, the city defenders began to show signs of weakening, as the Sui commandos were storming one of the four city gates and breaching the city wall in two places.

Then, unexpectedly, the attack stalled, and came to a halt—the field commanders had just received an urgent edict to abandon the entire operation.

On the night of July 20, the Sui forces beat a disorderly retreat, leaving behind a mountain of materiel. Campaign tents and bunkers that had not been dismantled stood eerily still, silhouetted against glowing campfires scattered across the field.

The Emperor's decision to withdraw had not been made lightly. It was prompted by a secret dispatch from the interior concerning an armed revolt in the Central Plain. The leader of the revolt was Yang Xuangan, then President of the Board of Rites, who had been in charge of storing grain in Liyang (near Xunxian, north Henan, southeast of Anyang) and transporting it to the Koguryŏ front. His rebellious action had cut off much of the grain supply to the invading Sui forces, and posed an imminent threat to the Eastern Capital—Luoyang, in the heart of the Central Plain. Even worse, scores of sons of senior court officials and military commanders had joined him. This had left the Emperor no other choice.

The sudden departure of the Sui army left the beleaguered Koguryŏ defenders puzzled. For fear that a trap might await them, they did not give chase until two days later. By then the Emperor's main force was already deep inside Sui territory. It was near the Liao River that the pursuing Koguryŏ forces caught up with the rear of the Sui army and launched an assault, killing a couple of thousands, mostly of the weak and feeble.

AT THE START OF the Daye-9 War, almost the entire top brass of the army and all the leading court officials, regardless of rank or status, had gone north to Hebei or Liaodong (with the exception of a naval force that had left for Shandong). Duke of Tang Li Yuan, a most privileged member of the ruling elite, was among them. Now that the War was over, he joined hundreds of thousands of Sui officers and men in moving south, in the direction of Luoyang.

At 47, Li Yuan was already in the autumn of his life, but was in excellent physical form, which clearly distinguished him from most of his similar-age compeers often plagued by a variety of chronic ailments. Nonetheless, the screeching of the wooden wheels of ox-carts and horse-drawn carriages, and the thudding of hooves racked his nerves; and the continuous jolting of his own mount upset his stomach. More seriously, he was constantly oppressed by a sense of melancholy. The pervasive low troop morale did not help; and a recent personal mishap had left him in a deep state of depression. During the War, his beautiful Xianbei wife, Ms. Dou, who had born him four sons and a daughter and whom he loved and respected, had followed him all the way to Zhuo Commandery (north Hebei). But due to the harsh conditions of war, she had contracted a disease and succumbed at age 44.

At the start of the War, Li Yuan had been assigned to Huaiyuan Garrison (based in Liaozhong, Liaoning) to manage the flow of grain to the front. Now the War had ended abruptly and Luoyang was under attack, Li Yuan was unsure of what lay in wait for him once the long trek south was over.

The uncertainty of the journey was eventually resolved by the unexpected arrival of an Imperial envoy, who announced: Li Yuan was to go west to Honghua Commandery (based in Qingyang, Gansu) to take up appointment as its Commander with the responsibility to supervise the civil and military affairs of 13 northwestern Commanderies including Honghua. Li Yuan's appointment, although a provincial one in a remote area, was quite important, and gave him reason to look forward to a career full of challenge, responsibility, and reward.

Traditionally, a Commandery (*jun*) had been the intermediate-level local government lower than a Prefecture (*zhou*) and higher than a County (*xian*). Under the first Sui sovereign, this intermediate level was abolished. Only Prefectures (*zhou*) and Counties (*xian*) remained. But under the second sovereign Yang Guang, all "Prefectures" were renamed as "Commanderies." Thus in terms of power and prestige, a Commandery Governor now was the same as a Prefect under the previous reign.

2. Yang Xuangan

WHILE GROWING UP IN Daxing City as a "noble brat," Yang Xuangan was surrounded by power and privilege. His father Yang Su, until his death in 606, was the highest-ranking officer at court. His Yang clan, though not directly related to the royal house, acquired so much power that even the Emperor felt threatened and expressed His desire for its elimination. In fact, the Emperor's threat was one of the main reasons why Yang Xuangan had started his rebellion.

Having raised a large army, Yang Xuangan now needed a viable strategic plan to carry on the fight against the mighty Sui Empire. He consulted Li Mi, a fellow nobleman in his early 30s who had just arrived from Guanzhong. Li Mi was a magnanimous and charismatic character, and most importantly, a talented strategist.

"I have three strategies for you," Li Mi said, his eyes sparkling with excitement. "The first and best strategy: move north into Ji (based in Beijing) to launch with the Koguryŏ a two-pronged attack against the Sui main force, while using our rich grain supply to win over enemy officers and soldiers. We can prevail in less than 10 days in the North. Then we will be able to launch a southern expedition to conquer all under Heaven."

"The second strategy: make a bee-line for Guanzhong (the Wei River valley in south Shaanxi) to take the capital Daxing City (Xi'an, Shaanxi). While there we can rely on the surrounding natural barriers for protection and easily invade and dominate the Central Plain in the east. Of all the key regions in the realm, Guanzhong, no doubt, is of the greatest strategic importance."

"The third and least effective strategy: capture the Eastern Capital (Luoyang) nearby and use it as a military stronghold against the Sui forces. It will not guarantee a long-term success, because the Luoyang area is not really defensible."

Pausing to contemplate his options for a long while, Yang Xuangan responded, "In fact, your last strategy—to capture Luoyang—is the best one for me. Since the close relatives of the senior court officials all live in Luoyang, its fall will be a devastating blow to enemy morale."

Having thus made up his mind, Yang Xuangan moved south to lay siege to the Eastern Capital. While his troops were still forming a circle around the city, he ordered a general assault. His men soon penetrated the Outer City and started attacking the Palace City (or the Palace-Imperial City) in the northwest quadrant of Luoyang, still firmly in Sui hands.

But the arrival of Sui reinforcements took Yang Xuangan by surprise, who was forced to abandon the attack and retreat west.

It was then that he decided to adopt Li Mi's second strategy: advance on Guanzhong. But it was too late. Constantly pursued by hostile forces, his army suffered horrendous casualties and disintegrated along the way.

Yang Xuangan himself, seriously wounded, was now accompanied by only one man, his younger brother. Both had lost heir chargers, and were fleeing on foot. In a small township east of the Tong Pass, thirsty and exhausted, the Yang brothers took refuge in an abandoned farm cottage.

"Dear Younger Brother," Yang Xuangan said gruffly as he lay listlessly on a pallet, "I want you to do me a favor."

"Yes, Elder Brother?"

"Kill…me!"

The younger brother, who had always obeyed his elder brother, asked, in stupefaction, "Why?"

"I don't want to be insulted in a public execution."

The younger brother sat wordless for a while until he heard the thudding of hooves, growing louder by the moment. He hefted his broadsword to deliver the *coup de grace* before turning it on himself.

When the Sui pursuers found the Yang brothers weltering in blood, the elder one was already dead and the younger one barely alive. They brought both back to Luoyang. The younger Yang was beheaded in public, and the corpse of Yang Xuangan was carried to the city's main market, Fengdu, where it was ceremoniously "fifthed," that is, pulled apart by five horses going in five directions. His body parts were then chopped up, burned, and scattered.

By then a nationwide campaign had been underway to hunt down Yang Xuangan's followers. The law-enforcers taking their cue from the Emperor cast a wide web to capture as many accomplices and sympathizers as they could.

As this reign of terror spread, most court officials began to feel the heat. Li Yuan was no exception. But people around him knew that he had no need to worry, being the Emperor's maternal first cousin (their mothers were blood sisters). Besides, one of his nieces Lady Wang was a favored Imperial concubine. Since Li Yuan had never been close to Yang Xuangan in the first place, it was almost impossible to charge him with culpability by association, a fanciful crime that had brought down many an official. Moreover, his recent appointment seemed to confirm the Emperor's trust.

A man of gregarious temperament, Li Yuan had made many friends, mostly officials and local luminaries. But cautious by nature, Li Yuan did not want to make a wrong move and arouse His Majesty's suspicion. So when in the company of friends and acquaintances, he always refrained from voicing his views on court politics.

In summer, when the Emperor moved into His favorite summer resort, the Fenyang Palace north of Taiyuan (southwest of present-day Taiyuan, Shanxi), He requested key local officials in the region including Li Yuan to come for a semi-formal gathering. Li Yuan, still recovering from a recent illness, was too weak to make the journey. So he sent a message to His Majesty to apologize for his reluctant absence.

Several days later, Li received a secret message from the Fenyang sent by Lady Wang, which described the Emperor's reaction. As expected He was displeased with Li Yuan's absence. But, instead of flying into a rage, He simply asked: "So that uncle of yours can't come because of illness? Oh, is he going to die?"

The fact that His Majesty used the much-tabooed d-word did not seem to bode well. For days, Li Yuan was tormented by the fear of arousing Imperial suspicion. He then made a crucial decision: he would stop granting audiences to fellow officials and local big shots. From then on, he whiled away his time in the company of young female courtesans, who were his drinking companions, conversation partners, entertainers, and bedmates.

3. Li Min and Li Hun

AMONG THE FEW SENIOR officers allowed to stay behind in the Two Capitals

(Daxing City and Luoyang) during the Daye-9 War was Acting General-in-chief of the Encampment Guard Li Min. His main responsibility was to safeguard Daxing, particularly its Palace City. The fact that he was appointed to this vital post had much to do with his intimate connections with the Yang Imperial house. His granduncle Li Mu was a founding elder of the Sui, whose backing of Yang Jian—Yang Guang's father— was crucial for the successful founding of the dynasty. His father, as Commander of Youzhou Command in the northeast, had laid down his life defending the Empire against a Tujue raid. To show His gratitude, the Emperor Yang Jian brought the young Li Min, then known in his family by his pet name "Hong," into the Palace, where he was raised until majority.

In the 6th year of Kaihuang (Inaugural Sovereign) (586), when Li Min was about 20, the Emperor issued an unusual rescript that scandalized Daxing's noble society: All marriageable young noblemen were to take part in a contest to compete for the hand of Yuwen Êying, His favorite granddaughter. The mastermind behind the rescript was little Êying herself. At the ripe age of 12, Êying was the hottest catch in Daxing. She had resisted the "normal" way of spouse selection—matchmaking—which would allow the grownups to choose a man of power on her behalf, and instead insisted on having a hand in picking her own helpmate.

Êying was the only daughter of Yang Lihua and the Emperor Xuan (Yuwen Yun) of the Northern Zhou. Under the Northern Zhou prior to the Sui, Êying's maternal grand-father Yang Jian was a top-ranking court official. After ascending the throne in 578, Yu-wen Yun (Êying's father) began to exhibit increasingly bizarre behavior. He threatened to execute Yang Jian (Êying's grandfather) and repeatedly abused Yang Lihua (Êying's mother). One of the most serious grudges Yuwen Yun held against His wife was perhaps her inability to produce an heir. After Yuwen Yun passed away in His 20s, Yang Jian seized the throne and founded His own Sui dynasty (581).

Charming, clever, and strong-willed, little Êying was pampered beyond reason by her mother and grandpa. And it did not take long for her naïve idea to win the nod of both. But many self-proclaimed adherents of Confucianism at court opposed it. Not only did the idea have no precedent, it ran counter to the fundamental principle of Confucian ritual propriety, they argued. But all to no avail. Yang Jian had nothing but contempt for the bookish Confucians.

On the day of the contest, young men from some of the best families in Daxing flocked to the suburban Hongsheng (Royal Sage) Palace where the princessling and her mother resided. In a basilica courtyard, one by one they showcased their artistic and martial skills. All this while the princessling watched surreptitiously from behind the thick dark window curtains of the basilica. Eventually, out of more than 100 suitors,

Êying chose Li Min, which won her mother's instant approval. Although a member of the elite Swordsmen Guard, Li held no official rank. But Êying was attracted to him because he was a good singer and a good dancer, and a master of such essential martial skills as archery, horse-riding, and weight-lifting. Besides, he had strikingly good looks and graceful manners.

After the wedding Li Min moved into the Hongsheng Palace. It would be a few years before he was allowed to share the same bed with Êying. But as the husband of the Emperor Yang Jian's favorite granddaughter, he immediately basked in Imperial favors. The Emperor granted him one of the highest prestige titles, the "Pillar of State," with a fief of 1,000 households (at the insistence of Êying's mother) to match. Upon ascending the throne, the Emperor Yang Guang continued to treat him well, increasing his fief to 5,000 households and promoting him to a top position in the prestigious Encampment Guard. During the Yang Xuangan Rebellion, Li Min had the city walls of Daxing thoroughly examined and repaired. It impressed Yang Guang so much that He appointed him Chief of the Directorate for the Palace Buildings (*jiangzuo jian*), the top central government agency in charge of court construction projects.

BESIDE LI MIN THERE was another notable member of the Li clan who had been allowed to stay behind: his uncle General-in-chief of the Courageous Guard Li Hun. This good-looking man in his late 30s was noted especially for his beautiful whiskers and mustache. Not nearly as well connected as his nephew, Li Hun was nonetheless much richer. However, initially, he had been cut off from the family fortune, being the 10th son of the famous Li Mu. After Li Mu died in 586, his ducal title and dukedom went to one of his grandsons, whose father, Li Mu's eldest son, had died early. When the grandson himself died in the early 600s, Li Hun saw his opportunity. No one in the Li clan was nearly as qualified as he to inherit the title and dukedom, or so he thought. But he still had to convince the Emperor Yang Jian, who would make the ultimate decision in this matter. One person who could help was Yuwen Shu, his brother-in-law, known for his close ties to Crown Prince Yang Guang.

"Could you ask the Crown Prince to put in a good word for me with the Emperor?" Li Hun asked imploringly. "You helped him get appointed as heir apparent. He owes you."

"I'm not sure if the Emperor will listen," Yuwen Shu said irresolutely.

"Yes, He will," averred Li Hun. "Nobody can have the ear of the Emperor like the Crown Prince."

Sensing his brother-in-law's reluctance, Li Hun made him a generous offer, saying, "If you can help me obtain my father's fiefdom, I'll go 50-50 with you on its revenue every year."

"All right, I'll see what I can do," Yuwen Shu said begrudgingly.

In less than a month, an Imperial edict was issued that appointed Li Hun as the successor of his father's ducal title and dukedom. Li Hun was pleasantly surprised to find that the dukedom was an enormous wealth generator. Reveling in his newfound riches, Li Hun seemed to have forgotten the offer he had made to Yuwen Shu, whose good offices were crucial in gaining the Imperial approval. On several occasions, Yuwen Shu discreetly reminded his brother-in-law of his promise. Each time Li Hun assured his benefactor that he would still make good on his offer, but never got round to actually doing it.

4. Peach Plum Master

AFTER THE YANG XUANGAN Revolt of 613, the political situation of the Empire greatly deteriorated. From the northeast to the northwest, from Guanzhong to Shandong, from the Central Plain to the Yangzi valley, the fire of rebellion was raging. The Emperor Yang Guang, who had succeeded His father Yang Jian in 604, was loath to hear reports of rebellion. But even He had awakened to the reality that government efforts at suppression had been by and large ineffectual. In the North, each of the more than half a dozen major rebel leaders commanded a force in excess of 100,000 and some of them had the support of the redoubtable Tujue further to the north. Recently, armed rebels were even sighted in the suburbs of Luoyang where the Emperor resided.

As worry about security increasingly occupied His attention, the Emperor began to take a greater interest in various auspicious and inauspicious omens, particularly one that took the form of an enigmatic ditty, which had been making the rounds in the streets of Luoyang:

Peach Plum Master!
As the sovereign circles around Yangzhou,
He tosses and turns in the garden.
Stop talking nonsense! Who says so?

The Emperor had it sent to An Qieluo, one of a small group of elite theurgists hand-picked by the court to provide exclusive service to the throne. An Qieluo lived in "Daoshu," a residential Ward in Luoyang that exclusively housed the royal occultists. There were a total of 103 Wards inside the city. Each was like a mini-city, enclosed by four walls and regulated by curfew. But Daoshu was the only one guarded by Palace guardsmen and off-limits to ordinary city inhabitants. For the theurgists living inside, contact with the outside world was strictly forbidden. The Emperor was afraid that, should their magic power lose its exclusivity, it would stop working.

The theurgist An Qieluo was the best among them. He divined the future with a variety of techniques: Yin-Yang and Five Phases, tortoise-viewing, astrology, *Yijing*, *chen*-prognostication, and such like. Prior to the Daye-9 invasion of Koguryŏ, the Emperor had consulted him. Mr. An then observed the erratic movement of Mars in the third month that had overshadowed the sun in Tail (Wei) and Winnower (Ji) Stellar Lodges (*xiu*). Both Lodges had Yan (in the northeast) as their "Allotted Field" on earth. So he predicted a major conflict in the Yan area, but was ambiguous about the outcome. However, that was enough to convince the Emperor of his prophetic power.

The appearance of the Luoyang ditty could not have been more timely. There had been a recent solar eclipse that took place in Well (Jing) and Ghost (Gui) Stellar Lodges. Both Lodges shared the same Allotted Field on earth—Qin—where were located the main capital, Daxing, and the ancestral home of the Yang Imperial house. In the correlative cosmology of ancient China, the 28 celestial regions known as the Stellar Lodges (or Mansions) were scattered along the Zodiac and the celestial equator, and were matched with various provinces on earth known as "Allotted Fields." Celestial events that took place in the Lodges would have a direct impact on their corresponding Fields down below and on people closely identified with them, and contrariwise.

Obviously, the recent solar event suggested that someone was posing a threat to the throne in Daxing. And the ditty provided the crucial corroborative evidence. So far efforts to reveal its full meaning, however, had not been very satisfying. While the second and third lines suggested that the Emperor would end up in the South (Yangzhou) where He would fall in a garden inside the Palace, the first and last lines seemed little more than prattle. By deploying the *chen*-prognostication technique, which foretold the future through interpreting enigmatic texts or sayings, An Qieluo soon came up with a different reading. Therewith he went rushing to the Palace and was immediately granted an audience. When he entered the Imperial study inside the Daye Basilica, the Emperor had been waiting.

"So you've got something interesting?" the Emperor asked, at once impatient and expectant. "It'd better be good."

An Qieluo replied, "Yes, Your Majesty. I think I have deciphered the ditty. In the first line, *Tao li zi* (Peach Plum Master), the character *tao* (peach) means 'Taotang,' the name of Yao (the first of the Three Sovereigns in far antiquity); the characters *li* and *zi* together point to a certain Master Li. The whole ditty suggests that a man of extraordinary leadership ability from the Li clan will overthrow the throne."

The Emperor was stunned, and asked, "Are there any countermeasures?"

"The only way to counter it is to exterminate *all* the males of the Li clan regardless of age."

"That is impossible." The so-called Li clan was one of the largest surname groups, with many clans, lineages, branches, and households.

Having sent the theurgist away, the Emperor asked his most trusted adviser Yuwen Shu, "What do you think of An's work?"

"Well, it sounds plausible," answered Yuwen. "But I can help Your Majesty find out more about it."

"How about Li Yuan?"

"He does have the physiognomy of a king. But…"

"But what?"

"He is your cousin."

"Yes. But sons will kill fathers, and brothers will kill each other when the throne is at stake."

"Indeed. Should I keep a close watch on him, Your Majesty?"

"Yes. But don't disturb him yet."

ABOUT A MONTH LATER, the Emperor received the much-awaited confidential report from Honghua sent by a court agent who had secretly investigated Li Yuan's activities. It turned out that Li had spent most of his days with young women of ill-repute, and neglected government business. Clearly he was blameworthy, but there was no sign of his involvement in a conspiracy. The Emperor was at once relieved and disappointed. Relieved that His cousin was not scheming against Him; disappointed that the throne-challenger was still at large.

Just as the memories of the unpleasant ditty were beginning to fade, the Emperor received another secret report, which read,

It is an open secret that His Majesty has been concerned with chen-prognostications lately. One of them is about Emperor Wen (Yang Jian), *who dreamt about the old city of Chang'an* (located to the immediate northwest of Daxing) *being inundated by a deluge* (hong). *Li Min, whose pet name happens to be Hong, seems to be a match for the prognostication. After the "Peach Plum Master" ditty had begun to spread, it caught Li Min's attention. He and his supporters subsequently formed a secret clique with the aim of making him King in response to the ditty.*

Intrigued, the Emperor called in its author, Yuwen Shu, for questioning. "Are you sure about this? Li Min—Êying's husband?"

"Absolutely, Your Majesty," answered Yuwen Shu.

"Who else?"

"Li Hun."

"Your own brother-in-law?" the Emperor asked, beyond belief.

"For me, your subject, loyalty to the throne always trumps family ties. I do not enjoy doing this at all. But here is an exposé letter by Êying herself."

The Emperor took the letter from Yuwen Shu, and started reading,

...In a conspirators' meeting, Li Hun said to Li Min [her own husband], "You are the answer to the chen-*prognostication, and must be the next Son of Heaven. Our current Emperor is a warmonger and has caused much grief to all under Heaven. If He starts another Koguryŏ War, you and I can use the opportunity to launch an uprising against the Sui. Together we can immediately raise an army of 50,000, and members of our Li clan can serve as commanders...*

At the end of the letter was the unmistakable seal of the princessling. Visibly shaken, the Emperor held Yuwen Shu's hand and said, "Had it not been for you, Shu, the rule of the Imperial house would have been subverted."

Immediately thereafter, an edict was issued whereby Li Min and Li Hun were summarily executed, as were all male members in the Three Clans of the two Lis—those in their father's generation, their own generation, and their sons' generation. Between the two Li houses, a total of 32 men lost their lives while more distant relatives and dependent women were banished to the far south for life.

Li Min's wife, Êying, as the Emperor's niece, was allowed to live in Daxing. But, with the death of her husband, she sank into a slough of despond. She bitterly regretted that she had allowed her seal to be affixed to the long document presented by Yuwen Shu, which had virtually become her husband's death warrant. A few months later, she received an Imperial rescript ordering her to end her own life. She willingly obliged by drinking poisoned wine.

5. The Vicegerent of Taiyuan

THE PEACH PLUM MASTER ditty scandal finally subsided. Li Yuan was appointed in quick succession to two crucial positions, Grand Commissioner of Pacification of Taiyuan Circle (*anfu dashi*) and Vicegerent (*liushou*) of Taiyuan in early Daye 13 (617). The latter appointment in particular allowed him to exercise authority as the top civil and military leader of a vast region that included Shanxi and its surrounding areas on behalf of the Emperor. With its north merging into the Mongolian steppes, the mountainous Shanxi held the key to the security of the Two Capitals, Daxing and Luoyang. To assist in Li Yuan's administrative duties and to keep an eye on his activities, the Emperor appointed two of His men, Wang Wei and Gao Junya, as Deputy Vicegerents.

By then China was embroiled in a total civil war and the Emperor had settled permanently in the Southern city of Jiangdu (Yangzhou) in the lower Yangzi River valley where the situation was less desperate.

The North was plagued with numerous anti-government groups and bands of robbers and outlaws. Shanxi, as one of the main Northern regions, was seriously affected.

One group of banditti posed an immediate threat to the Vicegerent's government in Taiyuan. These were the 20,000 troops from neighboring Hebei sent by Wei Dao'er (nicknamed "Flyer across the Mountain" [Lishanfei]) to capture lands in Shanxi. Having seized Shangdang (Changzhi, Shanxi) and cut off Li Yuan's main supply route, they were now marching north towards Taiyuan.

Li Yuan decided to take a stand. But Wang Wei had serious misgivings.

"We are grossly outnumbered by the enemy," said Wang. "We only have 5,000–6,000 infantry and cavalry."

"But these bandits," replied Li Yuan, "fight for loot only. After a couple of recent victories, they think they are invincible. This actually makes them vulnerable. And the generalship of their commander is poor. Of course, it is impossible to defeat them by a frontal attack, but we can win by wisdom and strategy."

Thus, ignoring Wang Wei's concerns, Li Yuan deployed his troops south of Taiyuan near the head of the Queshu Valley (Sparrow and Rat Valley), west of Jiexiu, Shanxi. The long stretch of road running through the Valley formed a vital link between Taiyuan and the Tong Pass. It derived its name from a widely-held belief that it was so treacherous that only sparrows and rats could pass through it. Approximately 140 *li* long, it was comprised of three parallel pathways, flanked by steep mountains and cliffs, and deep ravines.

Having divided his men into three columns, Li Yuan ordered Wang Wei to command the central column consisting of foot soldiers, drummers, and horn-blowers. They carried with them most of the banners and much of the non-combat materiel. Li Yuan himself, however, had under his direct command the left and right cavalry columns hiding in two wooded side vales. As the bandit army came into view in a line stretching over 10 *li*, it immediately took notice of Wang Wei's central column moving slowly, with horns blaring, drums pounding, and a sea of banners fluttering. The bandit army attacked and the central column beat a hasty retreat, which soon became chaotic. Wang Wei himself fell off his horse and had to be rescued by a guardsman on horseback, who snatched him up and galloped away. The enemies followed in hot pursuit. Suddenly, battle cries erupted as Li Yuan's left and right columns debouched from the two side vales to fall on the flanks of the enemies, putting them to rout.

BEFORE LI YUAN HAD time to celebrate his victory he was alerted to a massive Tujue invasion from the north. Descendants of the Dingling in antiquity, the nomadic Tujue, like the Seljuks, Mamluks, and Ottomans of later times, were Turkish in culture and language. They first gained prominence in Inner Asia in the 6th century when they threw off the yoke of the Avars, another nomadic people of the steppes. (Some Avars migrated west, and intermixed with other peoples, especially the Slavs, along the way. Their cavalry, widely known for their prowess, joined forces with the Sassanians in the siege of Constantinople in 626.) In late Sui times, the Tujue military, with its formidable cavalry, was the most effective fighting force in East and North Asia.

It was hardly surprising that the Tujue invaders thoroughly defeated Wang Rengong, the Sui Governor of Mayi Commandery (seat: Shuozhoushi, Shanxi) on the frontier. Suddenly, Li Yuan's own life was hanging in the balance. As Wang's boss, Li Yuan would be ultimately held responsible for the defeat. He could only hope that his recent victory and his blood ties with the Emperor would incline the latter to leniency. When the much-anticipated Imperial edict finally arrived, his jaw dropped. It demanded that Governor Wang and Vicegerent Li Yuan himself be placed under immediate arrest. The former would be executed on an auspicious day, and the latter would be transferred to the court in Jiangdu for interrogation.

ANTICIPATING HIS ARREST AT any moment, Li Yuan urgently summoned his second son, Li Shimin, to his study, and said, "The days of the Sui dynasty are numbered. I thought I would start a revolt in response to the prophecy as soon as your two brothers joined me. But before a messenger was sent to your brothers, the Imperial edict came. Now it is all too late. My son, promise me this: after I'm gone, you, together with your brothers Jiancheng and Yuanji, will raise an army of your own."

"I promise, Father," Li Shimin responded, becoming ruffled. "But we can still go to the Mangdang Mountains together like Liu Bang." The Mangdangs straddle the four modern provinces of Henan, Shandong, Jiangsu, and Anhui, and are virtually in the middle of nowhere. It was a hotbed for outlaws even in peaceful times. Eight hundred years before, Liu Bang and his rebel followers had taken refuge there before they went on to conquer the realm and found the mighty Han dynasty.

"What about your brothers? I can't leave without them," Li Yuan said. "Besides, escape is futile if Heaven can't protect me. I firmly believe my fate is now in the hands of Heaven. I trust Heaven will help me survive this. Don't lose hope…"

The talk was interrupted by the tramp of heavy steps and the clang of weapons in the hallway. The door flung open and in came Wang Wei accompanied by six armed guardsmen. Resignedly, Li Yuan allowed himself to be taken into custody.

Li Shimin followed his father and the guardsmen all the way across the courtyard to the outside, where a carriage was waiting to take his father away. Shimin watched quietly as his father mounted the carriage, which rolled away. By that time he could no longer hold back his tears. He knew that his father stood almost no chance of surviving the ordeal.

Two days later, a prison cart was ready to transport Li Yuan to the South under the escort of a troop of mounted guardsmen as Wang Rengong was languishing in a Taiyuan prison cell waiting for his execution. Then a new edict arrived that pardoned both of them.

6. Liu Wuzhou

COMMANDANT LIU WUZHOU WAS greatly relieved when he heard that Governor Wang Rengong had been pardoned and was about to return to Mayi. During the Governor's imprisonment in Taiyuan, Liu Wuzhou, a gregarious man of imposing stature in his 30s, had been responsible for safeguarding Mayi City.

Escorted by a few hundred mounted troops, Liu warmly greeted the arrival of his boss about 30 *li* south of the city. Wang Rengong was deeply moved that his most trusted officer had braved the bitter cold of early spring to welcome him, and was relieved to find that Mayi City, the Commandery seat, was still firmly in the hands of the Sui. Obviously, his biggest fear, another Tujue invasion, had not come to pass.

"There were no serious disturbances," said Liu Wuzhou as he briefed his boss, "except for a few lootings and robberies by local bandits. The main problem seems still to be the shortage of labor in the fields. That already took a toll on the harvest last year. Most people can hardly feed themselves."

"I know. It was a pressing issue even before my departure for Taiyuan."

"But the Commandery and County granaries are full of millet."

"Yes, they are. However, we can't simply open these granaries to the masses without an edict from the Emperor. That is a capital crime."

"I'm afraid, without food, people may make trouble."

"First thing first, Wuzhou. My present worry is not popular unrest but invasion by the Tujue. The Emperor has driven that point home in His recent edict."

Liu Wuzhou stopped talking, looking sullen.

"Come on, Wuzhou," resumed Wang Rengong, in a raised voice. "In fact, you've done a great job keeping law and order. I wish we had more officers like you—daring, generous, and loyal. That would make our job so much easier."

"Thank you for the kind words, Governor."

"I've heard that you have close ties with some community leaders and village braves."

"Yes, Governor. You know, although my folks are migrants from the east, I grew up locally. Many of them I've known for years. Almost all are now in the military."

"Are some of them in the regiment under your command?"

"Yes, most of them are."

"Great! These connections may stand us in good stead. Now I'm giving you a new assignment. Are you ready?"

"Yes," Liu answered expectantly.

"I want you to move into my home and some of your troops quartered in the neighborhood."

"Yes, Governor."

MAYI CITY WAS SITUATED in the upper valley of the Sanggan River. Enclosed by a ring of walls, the city proper was large, but had relatively few inhabitants. The Commandery territory outside the city consisted of flatland, hills, and mountains. Its north part was linked to the Mongolian steppes.

The Governor's home was in the north central part of the city. It was comprised of a dozen or so adjoining courtyards. Liu Wuzhou moved into the southernmost one where the south-facing main entrance was. He lived in the principal house of the courtyard located in the northernmost part. His bodyguards and attendants occupied the east and west wings.

A buxom maidservant in her late teens was assigned to take care of Liu's household chores and to act as the Governor's eyes and ears. But, gradually, frequent contact between Liu and the maid gave rise to a sense of familiarity. Once Liu made a suggestive move, she flounced away in a huff. In the following weeks, she tried to keep a respectful distance from her new master. But when spring arrived in earnest, she gave in to his persistent overtures and got herself entangled in an amorous relationship.

The secret of the illicit liaison eventually leaked out. A furious Wang Rengong locked up the maidservant and threatened to court-martial his favorite officer.

Liu was frustrated by his inability to rescue his lover, and was fearful of the punishment that awaited him—fornication with civilian women under the draconian Daye Code was punishable by flogging. One night, when everyone in the Governor's mansion was asleep, Liu slipped out into the city streets and made his way back to his old home in town.

On the following morning, Liu woke up to find the courtyard of his home swarming with well-wishers. The main hall (similar to a drawing room) in the principal house was large enough to hold three-dozen people. Still, it was too small for the crowd. Liu got outside, stood in front of the door, and improvised a thank-you speech, which soon evolved into a tirade against Wang and the tyranny of his government.

"People are starving," one voice in the crowd responded.

"There are corpses in the streets," another echoed.

"But the granaries are full!" the third one shouted angrily.

Gradually, this informal gathering morphed into an anti-government rally and people began to pour out their grievances against the powers-that-be. In the end, the whole crowd was whipped into a frenzy and a booming voice shouted, "Down with Wang Rengong!"

WITH LIU WUZHOU AT their head, the agitated crowd made a beeline for the Governor's Office compound. At the gate, the mobsters demanded to see the Governor.

Only Liu was allowed in and was soon brought face to face with Wang Rengong, who, flanked by guardsmen and chastisers, was holding court in the audience hall.

"Your reckless conduct is a disgrace, and it won't go unpunished," Governor Wang began.

"I'm not here to listen to your lecture," Liu retorted.

Stunned by the blunt answer of his subordinate, Wang was speechless for a few moments before he stammered out, "You…you arrogant bastard! Guardsmen! Arrest him!"

Before Wang's men could make a move on Liu, a gang of mobsters had already broken into the hall, their swords in hand. Dashing across the hall, they dispersed the guardsmen and chastisers, and tackled Governor Wang to the floor. Wang struggled like a trapped animal, screaming and kicking, until his hands were securely bound up by rope and his mouth gagged by a rag. He was then dragged to his feet. After haranguing him briefly about his abuse of power, Liu cocked his eyebrow to give a signal for action. One of his men kicked the back of Wang's knees to force him down. Another hefted a broadsword and chopped off his head.

Under the armed escort of his close followers, Liu went on a horseback tour of the key cities in the Commandery. Whenever he stopped at the main gate of a city, he would request to see its garrison Commander. When the Commander appeared on the gatetower, one of Liu's attendants would hold up Governor Wang's severed head for him to see while Liu lectured on why Wang deserved to be killed. None of the Commanders uttered a word of protest.

Encouraged, Liu declared himself Governor of Mayi Commandery.

No longer beholden to a higher authority, Liu announced his first order: "All Commandery and County granaries shall be opened to allow millet to be doled out to the starving multitude."

The residents of Mayi were excited and tens of thousands of young and middle-aged men volunteered to join Liu's army.

As for the old nemesis of Mayi, the Tujue, Liu sued for peace with them. Shibi Khan (Qaghan), their leader, responded by recognizing the new regime, granting Liu the title of "Yang-suppressing Khan" (Ding-Yang Qaghan). Of course, here "Yang" referred to the Imperial house of the Sui and its head, the Emperor Yang Guang.

7. The Jinyang Palace

SOUTHWEST OF PRESENT-DAY TAIYUAN, the Taiyuan of Sui times was by far the most important city in Shanxi (a modern province about the size of Michigan). It had been the summer capital of the Northern Qi dynasty in the sixth century, and was now the seat of Taiyuan Commandery and Taiyuan Circle (a circle was an ad hoc local administrative division usually comprised of dozens of Commanderies or Prefectures). More importantly, Taiyuan was host to the largest palace complex—the Jinyang Palace— outside the Two Capitals and Jiangdu (Yangzhou).

Not long before Liu Wuzhou's rebellion, Taiyuan residents had witnessed a miraculous event at the Jinyang one midnight in the first month of Daye 13 (617). A brilliant crown of light flashed out from the northwest of the Palace as a purple-colored vapor shot up into the sky to reach the Great Dipper.

A professional aeromancer caught sight of the phenomenon and concluded that the crown of light was the aura of a Son of Heaven. This was irrefutable evidence that in Taiyuan a future Emperor was in hiding.

When Pei Ji, Director of the Jinyang Palace, was informed of the aeromancer's claim, he did what he could to conceal it. There had already been too many rumors in circulation that might implicate his old friend Li Yuan.

Although a middle-ranking official, Pei occupied a fairly important local position: he was responsible for provisioning the palace residents and for recruiting young beauties as palace ladies. An excellent manager and administrator, Pei Ji had done his job very well. But his reputation was somewhat tainted by his gambling habits.

Recently, Pei had been keeping company with certain Mr. Gao, a local County Magistrate. They gambled by playing backgammon (*shuanglu*). Mr. Gao had already lost a small fortune, but was far from ready to quit. One afternoon, after Pei had won another round in a local tavern, Mr. Gao took him for a walk outside.

"How much have you won recently?" asked Mr. Gao.

"I don't know," answered Pei Ji. "Anything wrong with that?"

"Nothing. But do you know why you've had such a long winning streak?"

"Luck, I suppose."

"Not only that, Mr. Pei. Do you remember the young man who sat at the table the other day?"

"Yes, the tall man you call 'Young Master.' "

"All the money you've won is his, not mine!"

"Get out of here!" exclaimed Pei in disbelief.

"As a matter of fact, I have been instructed by the Young Master to lose money to you."

"Who is he, anyway?" asked Pei in astonishment.

"His name is Li Shimin."

"The second son of the Vicegerent?"

"Exactly."

"What does he want?"

"A private meeting with you."

"I am looking forward to it."

"WHAT CAN I DO for you?" Pei initiated the conversation when he was alone with Li Shimin. The latter was a young man in his late teens with a relatively tall stature and broad shoulders, which seemed to indicate physical maturity. But his burgeoning facial hair gave away his young age.

"I'm sure you know Liu Wenjing," Li Shimin said, his bright piercing eyes gleaming.

"Yes, the Magistrate of Jinyang County. He is now in jail because of marriage ties with Li Mi."

"Li Mi was once Yang Xuangan's top adviser. Now he is the leader of the largest rebel army."

"Of course, the Wagang Army."

"They recently seized the Huiluo Granary. Anyway, Li Mi's threat was the main reason that the Emperor sent His favorite officer Wang Shichong from Jiangdu to Luoyang—to beef up its defenses against the Wagang Army. Li Mi treats his underlings like family, and uses the grain from the Huiluo to bribe local residents. Not surprisingly, he now has a large following."

"All the more reason the court should go after him. Many of his former associates and relatives, Liu Wenjing included, have been thrown into jail. By the way, how is Liu doing?"

"Liu is doing fine. In fact, we just visited him in prison. He's given much thought to the current situation. In fact," continued Li Shimin in a grave tone, "he's of the opinion that the Sui dynasty does not have long to live."

"He is not!" said Pei, looking somewhat startled.

"The current Emperor," Li Shimin resumed, "has already forfeited His right to rule. He abuses the people with back-breaking public works projects. Luoyang, the Great Wall, and the Grand Canal, to name a few. To say nothing of his disastrous wars against the Koguryŏ. Hundreds of thousands of men were pressganged into the army, and many of them perished as a result. Only the old, the weak, and the women are left to till the fields. Farming is destroyed, the economy is in a shambles, and the whole country is in revolt."

"Wait a minute, this talk is treasonous," Pei Ji interrupted with a seriousness in his voice.

"That is Liu's view."

"Do you agree with him?" asked Pei Ji.

Li Shimin hesitated for a moment, then asked back, "What if I say I do?"

"Can you tell me why?"

"One considers loyalty to the throne as a fundamental tenet of Confucianism and a highest moral principle. Mencius, however, teaches another principle, that is, the rule of a Son of Heaven is only justified by the Mandate of Heaven, something Heaven can give, but can also take away. Because of the atrocities He has committed, this Emperor has completely lost His Mandate of Heaven. Don't you see?"

Pei Ji paused to ponder for a few moments, then said, "Mencius is the great Confucian sage. I can't argue against him. But what does it have to do with me?"

"Well, as confirmed by heavenly signs, the Sui will be replaced by a new dynasty. And the only person that can make it happen is my father. When Father's life was threatened by the Emperor, he was quite sympathetic to the idea of rebellion. But after he was pardoned, he became a loyalist again. Could you try to persuade him to join us in rising against the Sui? No one else, not even his children, can grab his attention the way you can."

After a long meditation, Pei Ji said resignedly, "What can I say? If it is the will of Heaven, how can I refuse it?"

8. The Righteous Uprising

THE DEATH OF WANG Rengong and the loss of Mayi to the rebel regime of Liu Wuzhou greatly complicated Li Yuan's task as the highest-ranking court-appointed official in Taiyuan Circle. Liu Wuzhou had already pushed south and captured the Fenyang Palace. Li Yuan organized a counter-offensive, but it was soon defeated. Liu Wuzhou's army, numerous and motivated, clearly outmatched the Sui forces under Li Yuan's command. To make things still worse, Liu Wuzhou was backed by the mighty cavalry of the Tujue. Under orders from Jiangdu, Li Yuan was forced to constantly engage the rebel army. It was a fool's errand so long as Jiangdu failed to send the much need reinforcements.

One evening, an anxiety-ridden Li Yuan sought out his confidant Pei Ji and over a pot of wine poured out his woes. After a few attempts to comfort him, Pei Ji suggested, "Maybe it is time that one found a solution."

"What solution?" Li Yuan asked, semi-tipsy.

"Replace the sovereign."

"Conspiracy against the throne?" Li Yuan asked suddenly, in a knee-jerk reaction. "It is a crime punishable by the extermination of the Nine Clans!"

"But Heaven has spoken," said Pei Ji firmly. "The crown of light from the Palace suggests the hidden presence of a future Son of Heaven. Besides, it is supported by a new reading of the 'Peach Plum Master' ditty."

"Is it?" Li Yuan asked inquiringly.

"According to An Qieluo, the first character, *tao*, is short for 'Taotang,' the name of the early sovereign Yao. But a new interpretation draws attention to the second character of

Taotang–Tang. It is the name of your place of enfeoffment. My lord, you, the Duke of Tang, are the future Son of Heaven!"

"Go on."

"Besides, if you fail in your current mission to defeat Liu Wuzhou and the Tujue, in the best-case scenario, you will be banished together with your family to the miasma-infested far south; in the worst case, you will be beheaded together with your sons, and your family assets will be confiscated."

Li Yuan sank into a brown study for a long time before he came down to earth and said with a sigh, "Indeed, what you have just said makes sense. I will not defy destiny, nor should I. As a matter of fact, I've given much thought about it myself. The Emperor's edict has left me no choice. However, I don't want to take the throne."

"Do you still want to start an uprising?"

"Yes, but it is an uprising against the usurpers."

"That is an excellent idea, my lord."

"What do you think if I call it the 'Righteous Uprising?' "

"The 'Righteous Uprising'? It sounds great to me."

A FEW DAYS LATER, Li Yuan went to see the most respected Daoist master of the age, Wang Yuanzhi, the Patriarch of the Mount Mao school, through one of his staffers. Well over 100, Wang was the most ancient man alive in China and a top expert in all branches of wizardry. More than 20 years before, when he was residing in Mount Mao (in south Jiangsu), he was invited by then Prince Yang Guang to his Viceroy's residence in Jiangdu. Of short stature, Wang Yuanzhi sported a long white moustache, a white goatee, and bushy white eyebrows that shadowed his eyes. And his head was topped by thick coat of white hair. The shiny whiteness of the master frightened the young Prince, who immediately sent him away. Later, during the Daye-9 Koguryŏ War, Yang Guang, now the Emperor, summoned him to the northeast. Thereafter, Wang Yuanzhi stayed in Luoyang. Only recently did he journey north to Taiyuan.

When Li Yuan was led into Wang's room, he walked up to the master in quick steps. Making obeisance, Li said, "I have heard so much about you, Master. I am so pleased to see you in person."

"The pleasure is mine. I was told that you are interested in a physiognomic reading."

"If you don't mind."

After Li Yuan motioned his attendants to get out of the room, Wang examined Li's facial features, and closely studied the lines, patterns, markings, and shapes of his palms and fingers for about half an hour. Then he whispered, "Congratulations! You're going to be the next Son of Heaven!"

"Heaven forbid. You will get my entire clan extirpated!"

"Let me tell you what I have seen. The wide forehead itself is indicative of high power, and the lines on it form the character 'king' (*wang*). The long and plump earlobes, the bulbous nose, and the tall nose bridge that merges into the forehead—altogether they suggest that you possess a royal physiognomy. Your palm lines tell very much the same story."

"Unbelievable," Li Yuan responded in seeming astonishment. "But as far as I'm concerned, I'm a loyal subject of the Sui."

"That may be the case today, but you'll never know what is going to happen in one or two years. Besides, I've got other evidence to back me up."

"What evidence?" Li Yuan asked, intrigued.

"In one of my sacred communications with the Beyond, I received a holy message from Lord Lao Himself. It said, *The Sui dynasty will be replaced by a dynasty founded by one of my descendants. Let him worship me, and I will make sure that the new dynasty will endure.* Of course, the surname of Lord Lao is Li, the same as yours, and the descendant is none other than you."

"That can't be true."

"This is what I've received. I only serve as the messenger."

"Well, don't tell another soul what…"

"Don't worry. Let Heaven and Earth be our witnesses. What I've told you today will never leave the four walls of this room."

WANG YUANZHI'S PROPHECY NOTWITHSTANDING, Li Yuan knew very well that if founding a new dynasty was in his future, he still had a long way to go. He immediately set about making preparations for his "Righteous Uprising." On his orders, Li Shimin, his second son, was to raise an army locally; and Li Jiancheng, his eldest son and heir, and Li Yuanji, his fourth son, were to secretly leave Hedong Commandery (in south Shanxi) and move north to join him in Taiyuan.

In a matter of days, Liu Wenjing, fresh out of prison, mustered for his friend Li Shimin an armed force of 10,000, independent of the high command in Jiangdu. Li Shimin then helped solve its logistic problem by fabricating an Imperial edict that gave it access to the provisions and military stores of the Jinyang Palace.

Deputy Vicegerents Wang Wei and Gao Junya were alarmed at the burst of activity around them. They suspected foul play. The threat of Liu Wuzhou and the Tujue was still ever-present—their vanguard forces had been recently sighted in the northern suburb of Taiyuan. But Wang and Gao felt by intuition that something sinister was afoot right here inside the city. They formed a secret plan to arrest Li Yuan in the Jin Shrine (in Taiyuan), during a previously scheduled supplication-for-rain ceremony. One of Li Yuan's acquaintances got wind of the plot, and tipped him off.

On the morning of June 23, in the audience hall of the Vicegerent's office, a middle-ranking officer arrived to deliver an exposé letter. Li Yuan, Wang Wei, Gao Junya, and

Liu Wenjing were there. Li asked Wang Wei to receive the letter. But the officer insisted, "It is for the eyes of the Vicegerent only."

Li Yuan took the letter and read it. With a surprised look on his face, he turned to Wang Wei and said, "It accuses you and Gao of conniving with the Tujue!"

Gao Junya exploded, "Balderdash! The conspirators have cooked it up to frame us!"

Liu Wenjing shouted, "Tie them up!"

Several guardsmen rushed forward and overpowered the two unfortunate Deputy Vicegerents. A few moments later, their heads rolled.

To a massive gathering assembled at the main gate of the Vicegerent's Office Li Yuan publicly denounced the treasonous crimes of Wang and Gao—collusion with the Tujue. Thereupon, the Righteous Uprising was born.

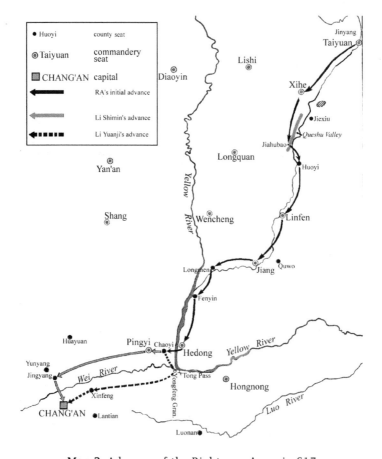

Map 2. Advance of the Righteous Army in 617

9. Xihe

THEN CAME THE GRAVE news that a massive Tujue army was advancing on Taiyuan. But Li Yuan was calm as he remarked to his generals, "It is a godsend, isn't it? The Tujue invasion proves our point: Wang Wei and Gao Junya were pro-Tujue traitors."

"That is indeed great news, my lord," said Pei Ji, now Li Yuan's right-hand man. "But how are we going to deal with the invaders?"

"Well, we are outnumbered at least five to one. To try to defend the city is suicidal. And we should employ the 'Empty Fortress Strategy,' following Zhuge Liang's example." (That is probably the most famous of the Thirty-six Strategies of the celebrated third-century strategist.)

On Li Yuan's orders, Pei Ji and Liu Wenjing were to hide most of the troops from the enemy; and Wang Kangda, a local rebel leader who had recently joined forces with Li Yuan, was to set up an ambush with a thousand cavalry near the northern gate. Wang's mission was to spring a surprise attack on the Tujue and capture as many horses as possible.

The ferocity of the Tujue warrior on horseback was legendary. The very sight of him—with his long flowing hair, his tight-sleeve caftan that extended to his knees, his cowhide tall boots, and his scimitar—could inspire terror among men and women living in settled communities south of the Great Wall. To top it all, his ram's horn bow had a much longer shooting range than the Chinese bamboo or wooden counterpart, and was thus a vastly superior weapon.

EARLY THE NEXT MORNING, amidst the thunderous pounding of horse hooves, a massive horde of Tujue cavalry swept across the northern suburb of Taiyuan, raising a cloud of red dust. Encountering virtually no resistance, they charged right through the northern gate to penetrate deep inside the city. About noontime Wang Kangda and his men fell on what they believed to be the rear of the enemy, only to be surprised by the arrival of more Tujue cavalry. Sandwiched by two enemy forces, Wang and his men frantically made for the Fen River to the east. While crossing the River, Wang Kangda was unhorsed and killed, and his troops were butchered almost to a man.

The Tujue sack of Taiyuan did much to convince the city's inhabitants of Wang Wei's and Gao Junya's culpability and solidified their support for Li Yuan. Li Yuan, however, in spite of the loss of Wang Kangda and his cavalrymen, refused to be swayed by passion. He gave strict instructions to his forces not to accept battle from the Tujue. In his view, "Heaven has sent the Tujue to make a point. After the point has been made, Heaven will send them away."

In the Outer City of Taiyuan, the Tujue riders could not find Li Yuan's main force to fight. They went rushing to the gates of the Inner City, where the government offices were hidden behind well-fortified high walls. Suspecting trickery, they turned around and poured into the Wards and the market. After pillaging many homes and stores, they went away, carrying a rich haul of loot with them.

Li Yuan then wrote a letter addressed to Shibi Khan, the Tujue leader, which read:

I heard you when you came; I saw you when you went. You came and went of your own accord. It was the will of Heaven, was it not? Because I understood the will of Heaven, I did not give chase. Judging by the way you moved, you, too, must have understood the will of Heaven. Nowadays, with the Sui in turmoil, I have launched the Righteous Uprising in order to pacify all under Heaven. For the sake of mutual interest, I would like to propose that friendly relations between our two peoples be restored and you be allowed to keep whatever you gain in future expeditions, including women, jades, and silks, so long as you do not harass the masses.

Respectfully,

Li Yuan

ON READING THE LETTER, an aide was concerned, saying, "This is probably not the appropriate way to deal with a barbarian chieftain, my lord. May I suggest that 'respectfully' be omitted?"

"No," Li Yuan answered firmly. "This is called 'Bowing to a one person but standing tall above ten thousand.' Even if they ask for ten thousand pieces of gold, we should give them, let alone a single word."

So this letter of appeasement, as was originally written, was delivered to the Tujue Khan.

Shibi's reply, which arrived not long afterwards, clearly showed the Khan's pleasure with Li's gesture. He promised to lend support to Li on condition that he would replace the Sui sovereign as Son of Heaven.

Thrilled with Shibi's letter, many of Li Yuan's officials congratulated him as the next Son of Heaven. To this Li Yuan responded, "Even the barbarians want me to do this. However, as a Sui subject, I have to maintain my integrity. The purpose of the Righteous Uprising is not to replace the throne."

"But people in Taiyuan have been singing the 'Peach Plum Master' in the streets of Taiyuan, my lord," said Pei Ji. "Clearly they are expecting a new sovereign. And the aura of the Son of Heaven confirms that. If this is not 'the will of the people,' I don't know what is. "

"Don't you see," Li Yuan rejoined in a raised tone, "the real intention of the Khan when he asked me to become a Son of Heaven? He wants to have me in his pocket. Wasn't

Liu Wuzhou declared Son of Heaven and Yang-suppressing Khan? What is he now? Little more than a frontman for the Tujue."

"But," interjected Liu Wenjing, "it is probably not wise to snub the Khan right now."

"No, we won't snub him. Instead, we will send an emissary to parley with him. I think he will understand my position. Now then, I wonder who can best accomplish this mission."

There was a silence for a few moments until Liu Wenjing spoke, "If, in your opinion, my lord, I am up to the task, I would like to go on your behalf."

"You would?" Li Yuan asked, delighted.

"Yes, my lord. It will be a great honor to be of service to you."

"Excellent!"

DESPITE THEIR DIFFERENCES ON the issue of enthronement, Li Yuan and his advisers had reached a consensus on the long-term strategy of the Righteous Uprising: "To capture Xianyang and from Xianyang to dominate all under Heaven." Xianyang was the ancient name of Chang'an, now called "Daxing City," the largest metropolis in China.

Soon Li Yuan's "Righteous Army" (RA) began to push southwest towards its destination. But not far south of Taiyuan was a large Sui garrison at Xihe that threatened to obstruct the progress of the Righteous Army.

Li Yuan wanted to avoid unnecessary bloodshed, so he made an attempt to win over Gao Deru, the Deputy Governor in charge of the garrison. Gao replied promptly, claiming, "I will not betray the trust of the court. Furthermore, I recently saw a giant simurg, which, as you know, is an auspicious sign for the Sui." Now Li Yuan had no choice but to remove Gao by force.

The city of Xihe, where Gao was based, was the seat of its eponymous Commandery. It sat on the main road that extended all the way south to the Tong Pass.

At first blush Xihe seemed well protected. But the fortifications were not particularly strong and its garrison force was outmatched by the RA in numbers and almost certainly in morale. If Li Yuan launched an attack now before Sui reinforcements arrived, he probably could win a prompt victory. But he was more interested in giving his two sons—Jiancheng and Shimin—an opportunity to gain valuable experience in real combat and generalship.

"I have been thinking of letting one or both of you take command of the Xihe operation," said Li Yuan to his two sons. "But you are young and inexperienced. I am not sure if you can do it."

"Yes, I can, Father," said Jiancheng resolutely. At 27, the eldest son was anxious to prove his military worth.

Not one to be left behind, Shimin also said, "Yes."

Turning to Shimin, Jiancheng said, "Brother, you are too young for a battle of this magnitude."

"Not any more," said Shimin sharply. "I am already 17."

"In fact," said Li Yuan, "this can be a great opportunity for both. You can go together, can't you?"

"If you wish, Father," murmured Jiancheng.

"All right, you two will be the co-commanders of this campaign. To execute it successfully, you need to keep in mind that there are three fundamental elements, namely, 'the time of Heaven, the benefits of Earth, and the harmony among men.' All three are present now. But the most important is the last one. Specifically, I am talking about harmony between the RA and the masses, between officers and men, and especially between you two brothers."

"Yes, Father," said Jiancheng. "Since we have been enlightened by your teachings and guided by your instructions since childhood, we are not going to fail in the forthcoming engagement."

"Enough of your compliments," said Li Yuan. "Are there any specific issues you want to address?"

"Discipline, Father," said Shimin. "It is the most important aspect of war next to military strategy and tactics. Thus we must make sure that orders are strictly followed. Violators will be punished in accordance with army laws."

"That's more like it," said Li Yuan. "Don't you ever forget to enforce army laws. It is essential to army discipline and to our relations with the masses."

"Yes, Father," the two brothers answered almost simultaneously.

BOTH LI JIANCHENG AND Li Shimin were eager to establish rapport with and authority over the troops. Both insisted on marching with the rank and file, and eating their meals and taking their rest with them. They gave strict orders that officers and men alike must pay for foods and drinks offered by the locals. When caught taking food without payment, the Righteous Army men were not necessarily punished, but efforts were made to locate the owner and pay him. In one instance, some local peasants set up small tables with dishes of beef and cups of wine to feast the Righteous Army soldiers; but the latter, hungry and thirsty, had to reject the hospitality for fear of violating the army laws.

By the time the troops arrived at Xihe, their reputation as a disciplined army had preceded them. The locals lined the streets to watch them march by. They did not show any fear of this rebel army, and were pleasantly surprised to see the two young commanding officers marching armorless in the ranks.

As Jiancheng and Shimin started to environ Xihe, they did not stop the flow of people. Anyone, male or female, old or young, was allowed to freely exit or enter the city.

This show of magnanimity encouraged the city residents to pour out in multitudes. Even Sui loyalist officers and soldiers began to defect.

After their last appeal to Gao Deru fell on deaf ears, the two Li brothers jointly issued a general assault order. As the Righteous Army siege soldiers started to storm the city walls using scaling ladders, they encountered little resistance. Soon their advance troops entered the city, and, guided by Sui officials, headed straight for the compound of the Governor's Office, where they took Gao Deru into custody.

A few moments later, Li Jiancheng and Li Shimin arrived. They berated Gao Deru for his senseless resistance and his erroneous claim about seeing the simurg, and issued a joint order whereby Gao was executed.

All those who had fought *under* Gao, however, were let go in the name of Benevolence and Righteousness.

Li Yuan was elated with the Xihe victory, especially with the seamless cooperation of his two sons, and with the mature way they had handled the post-victory situation.

" 'Rare indeed are brothers,' " Li Yuan cited the *Classic of Songs* as he spoke to his generals. "Jiancheng and Shimin have worked together beautifully. Nothing pleases me more."

AFTER XIHE, THE RIGHTEOUS Army became numerous. Li Yuan divided it into two columns, with the Left Column under the command of Li Jiancheng, now the Duke of Longxi; and the Right Column under the command of Li Shimin, now the Duke of Dunhuang.

As the Righteous Army continued its march south, Li Yuan received intelligence that Liu Wuzhou supported by the Tujue had been advancing on Taiyuan. Li Yuan halted the progress of the Army and called an emergency meeting with his top commanders.

"If Liu Wuzhou and the Tujue," said Li Yuan, "launch a two-pronged attack, Taiyuan is in danger. Our garrison force there is simply not strong enough."

"However, Father," said Li Jiancheng, "I distrust the source of the information. The Tujue sent us an olive branch only recently. It is unthinkable that they should attack Taiyuan."

"I agree," said Li Shimin.

But no matter how hard his two sons tried, Li Yuan could not be persuaded.

"We'd rather err on the side of caution," said he. It was thus decided to march the Army back north to rescue Taiyuan.

At the fall of dusk, Li Yuan retired into his tent and fell asleep immediately, only to be awakened by the sound of someone wailing outside. In a fit of rage, he stormed out of the tent and was surprised to see his second son Li Shimin.

"What is your problem, my son?" asked Li Yuan.

"I am sorry to disturb you, Father. But the Righteous Army is in danger."

"How so?"

"Our declared goal is to move south to capture Daxing so as to pacify all under Heaven. If we back down from that commitment, our army will lose momentum. As Master Sun's *Art of War* says, 'An army with momentum wins the battle.' An army without momentum is more likely to lose it."

"I never thought of that before," Li Yuan said contemplatively. "Are you suggesting that we should not be distracted by Taiyuan after all?"

"Yes, Father. If we move swiftly to capture Daxing City, we can rely on the natural barriers of Guanzhong to protect ourselves, and take back Taiyuan later. If we return to Taiyuan right now, we may never be able to take Daxing, and eventually lose Taiyuan as well." With these words, Li Shimin fell on his knees, saying, "Father, I beseech you."

"All right, I'll listen to you this time. Let me go back to sleep."

As Li Yuan was about to open the tent's flap, he turned his head and said, "But remember, this is your call. And you will be held responsible if it doesn't work."

"Of course, Father."

Early on the following morning, the southward march of the RA continued.

10. Huoyi

AT HUOYI (HUOZHOU, SHANXI), a heavily fortified small city in a deep valley south of Taiyuan and Xihe, the Sui general Song Laosheng and his 30,000 men were dug in. Song had been sent by Prince of Dai Yang You, the Sui royal nominally in charge of Daxing City, to provide the first line of defense against the Righteous Army.

Having won several victories against local rebels, Song was confident of his ability to defend the city.

Meanwhile, the Righteous Army was advancing steadily towards Huoyi. But its progress was very slow. Because of the intermittent rain in August, the road was covered with mud, knee-deep in some places.

Before reaching Jiahubao, an outpost 50 *li* northwest of Huoyi, Li Yuan ordered his advance troops to slow down in preparation for battle. With the towering Huotai Mountain (east of Huozhou, Shanxi) to its east and the Fen River to its northwest, Jiahubao was the best place to intercept the RA. But Li Yuan was puzzled when his troops encountered no enemy forces at all. Anyone familiar with the terrain would not have given up the outpost so easily.

"Well, Song Laosheng is either a military genius or a lightweight. We'll find out soon," said Li Yuan to his aides.

Just as the RA forces were about to encamp for the night, an attendant reported to Li Yuan, "A man with white hair and beard clad in white robe requests an audience. He says he carries a divine message from the Huotai Mountain."

"Thanks, but no thanks," said Li Yuan, who was agnostic towards Buddhism and Daoism, and was not interested in minor mountain cults at all. "I don't know this man, and I don't want to see him." With these words, Li Yuan walked towards his tent and was surprised to see the old man in white standing by the roadside in the distance. *Let me find out what the heck he wants*, Li Yuan thought as he went up to him and said, "Old man, how can I help you?"

"Greetings, my lord. I have got a divine message for you."

"You are not a god, how can you offer me a divine message?"

"In a ritual service to the mountain god, I heard a voice that said, 'Go and tell the lord of Tang: If he wants to go to Huoyi, he should take the mountain road. The rain has impeded his progress so far, but it will stop because of my intercession. The lord of Tang may want to set up a shrine to me later.' True, the mountain road ahead has quite a few twists and turns. But it will keep the army from view and allow it to reach its destination by sunset tomorrow. If instead the army takes the main road, it will expose itself to enemy attacks."

"It sounds very interesting," Li Yuan said to his aides, after sending the elderly man away. "But I am not really convinced."

Early the next morning, the RA was on the move again in a steady mizzle. The glum-faced Li Yuan slogged with his officers and soldiers along the swampy road. Soon the march slowed down, then came to a halt. A vanguard officer came rushing to ask for instructions: there was a fork in the road ahead with one branch leading into the mountain. Li Yuan looked at the overcast sky and saw a ray of the sun peek through the clouds. Imperceptibly, the rain had stopped. Without further hesitation, Li Yuan said, "Take the mountain road." And the march resumed.

The RA completed the rest of the journey to Huoyi without incident before dusk. Thereupon, Li Yuan instructed his aides to rear a shrine to honor the god of the Huoyi Mountain.

AFTER THE TROOPS PITCHED camp outside the city, Li Yuan held a war council with his commanders in his campaign tent.

"If we try, we probably can take Huoyi by force," Li Yuan began. "But the cost may be way too high. Doesn't Master Sun's *Art of War* teach us that sacking a city is always the last resort?"

"Yes, Father," answered Li Jiancheng, "but what are our options?"

"We wait," said Li Yuan, "until the enemies are tired of waiting."

"Do we have enough provisions, Father?" asked Li Shimin.

"I suppose so. Our grain supply can last up to a month."

It was thus decided that the main force of the Righteous Army, the Left and Right Columns, would stay out of sight, while about a dozen squadrons of foot and cavalry would be deployed around the city as decoys.

The presence of bands of RA troops so close to the city wall was irritating and suggested to Song Laosheng that an attack was imminent. Commanding a force that at least matched the enemy in number, Song believed that a surprise sortie would help him gain the initiative. He mustered the best of his troops, and sent them thundering out of the Eastern and Southern Gates into the suburban open fields. Li Yuan, who happened to be in the east suburb, was caught somewhat off guard, and had to make a frantic retreat east under the escort of a light cavalry squadron. Song and his men chased after him. It was then that the main force of the RA led by Jiancheng and Shimin launched a coordinated attack near the city and started to close in on the Eastern and Southern Gates. Before the ceremonial beating of drums was over, the RA men were already falling on the enemy, kicking up a maelstrom of red dust.

"Song Laosheng is killed!" an RA officer shouted, hoisting a severed head impaled on a pike for the defenders atop the city wall to see. Although the Sui officers could not positively identify the head as that of Song, they hurriedly pulled up the drawbridges outside the eastern and southern entrances and closed the city gates.

Song Laosheng, now trapped, fought his way to the edge of the moat outside the eastern entrance, and jumped off his horse and ran into the waterless ditch. An RA general caught up with him and hacked him down.

In a matter of hours, the RA forces sacked the city—the remnants of Song Laosheng's troops were either butchered or forced to surrender.

When the dust had settled, Li Yuan, triumphant, rode on horseback to the battlefield east of the city. Against the fading streaks of sunlight at dusk, he could still make out the mutilated corpses and body parts of Sui soldiers scattered all over the place, as the cloying stench of blood filled his nostrils. Suddenly, he broke into tears, saying, "Those poor souls—they did not gain fame when alive, and were consumed with hatred at the moment of their death. Had they not been deceived by Song Laosheng, they would have joined our righteous cause. It aches my heart to even think of that. From this day forward, we must try to win over the people with cultivated virtue and put an end to war altogether."

Pausing momentarily to wipe off his tears, he resumed, "This, of course, is not to make light of the distinguished service rendered by those brave RA officers and men in the battle for Huoyi. On the contrary, they shall be handsomely rewarded."

ON THE MORROW, WHILE in the Governor's Office, Li Yuan found time to sit down to read a few petitions and official communications. Two documents caught his eye. The first one raised an unexpected issue: whether to grant rewards to bondservants. Under the existing Sui law, a bondservant was a kind of property that could be sold by his owner, and was at best subhuman. The document elicited a passionate response from Li Yuan, "The Righteous Army men are from all walks of life and from different classes. They have among them a number of bondservants. In the past, a slave with a branded face rose to become King. What's wrong with making rewards to bondservants serving in the Righteous Army?" The slave-turned-king Li Yuan alluded to was Ying Bu, who, despite a brand on his face (indicating ownership by his master), made general and was enfeoffed as "Prince" or "King" of Huainan under Liu Bang.

The second one was a memorial that asserted that titles granted to the former Sui officials were too high, and suggested a more moderate approach. In response, Li Yuan said to his aides, "The Han rose to prominence because it was never stingy with the granting of titles and rewards. If every household deserves a fief, we will grant it, so long as it adds to the growth of our virtue. If we share with the people the fruits of our righteous labors, we will surely redound to the benefit of all under Heaven and prevail."

The remarks, recorded by Li Yuan's attendants, were communicated to the officers of the Righteous Army to be implemented as policy.

IN THE EARLY AFTERNOON, Li Yuan found himself in the compound of the Governor's Office, where were gathered a large crowd of prisoners of war comprised of Song Laosheng's civil officials and military officers as well as their dependents. In an agitated voice, Li Yuan began his address:

Who is to blame for the carnage of war that devastated the city? Song Laosheng, and Song Laosheng only. I won't blame it on anyone else. Some of you may be unwilling to switch allegiance to me and the Righteous Army. That is completely understandable. But there is no reason not to treat you with humanity and sincerity.

For those of you who are willing to join us, you are not only welcome, but are encouraged to bring your original ranks with you. Although you will serve under the overall command of the Commanders-in-chief of the Left and Right Columns, you are allowed to form your own combat units commanded by your own officers. Under no circumstances will you ever come under suspicion.

Many of you are from Guanzhong and are homesick. If you want to return to your hometowns or home villages, you may leave at any time. Before you go, you will be granted a rank-5 prestige title (sanguan) *and enough rations for the road.*

At this point, most in the crowd broke into tears; and some cried uncontrollably as Li Yuan's own eyes grew wet.

As for Song Laosheng, he brought suffering to Huoyi. He was our enemy. But he fought bravely for his master. And I respect him for his courage, loyalty, and integrity. Let us give him a proper burial, a burial that befits his rank and dignity.

The audience fell silent, too shocked for words. Then someone shouted, "The Duke of Tang!" The entire crowd echoed in unison, "The Duke of Tang! The Duke of Tang!"

11. Hedong

ON SEPTEMBER 20, LIU Wenjing caught up with the Righteous Army at Longmen, in southwest Shanxi. Having accomplished his Tujue mission, he brought back with him a Tujue emissary, 500 Tujue cavalry, and 2,000 Tujue horses. Li Yuan was thrilled—these assets would greatly enhance the fighting capability of the Righteous Army as it moved south to capture Guanzhong.

Soon, the RA troops reached the suburbs of Hedong (southwest of Yongji, Shanxi), where was massed a significant concentration of Sui troops under General Qutu Tong. Unlike Gao Deru, a light-weight, and Song Laosheng, a mediocre officer, Qutu was a formidable adversary and the highest-ranking Sui general tasked with the defense of Daxing. His presence at Hedong indicated the enemy's resolve to stop the RA's southward advance.

Not sure how to deal with Qutu, Li Yuan asked his aides at a war council, "Can we apply Master Sun's principle of 'winning war without fighting a battle'? I am really not interested in taking on this man."

"My lord, that probably won't work," said one aide. "Qutu Tong is intensely loyal."

Turning to the local gentry and officials present, Li Yuan asked, "What do you think?"

A local notable by the name of Xue Dading said, "In my humble opinion, the RA should ignore Qutu Tong altogether. Instead it should immediately cross the Yellow River into Guanzhong to capture the Yongfeng Granary, the main grain storage facility in the area. With the granary under control, you, my lord, will be able to dominate entire Guanzhong and the taking of Daxing will be just a matter of time."

"How about you?" Li Yuan asked his commanders.

"I disagree," said Li Jiancheng. "Heading directly for Daxing could expose the rear of the Righteous Army to Qutu Tong's attack."

"Do you agree with Jiancheng?" asked Li Yuan, turning to other generals.

"Yes," they replied in unison.

"All right, we will remove Qutu Tong first."

As Li Yuan deployed his troops to encircle Hedong a new concern arose: the morale of his troops was excessively high as a result of their recent Huoyi victory. *That is usually a sign of trouble, since pride goeth before the fall*, thought he.

Li Yuan then went to the front to survey the enemy defenses.

"The city is extremely well fortified for a Commandery seat," said Li Yuan to his aides, pointing to the tall and solidly built city walls.

"Yes, my lord," answered one of the generals, "but the RA can take it by storm. We can use the siege machines that proved quite effective in the battle for Huoyi."

"All right," Li Yuan said. Begrudgingly, he gave the go-ahead for a general assault.

In the initial engagement, the city walls and gates proved to be too strong to storm. Then a rainstorm hit, and the assault came to a halt.

"Stop the attack and pull back!" Li Yuan bellowed his order.

After the troops were safely back in camp, Li Jiancheng asked his father, "Are we going to resume the attack when it stops raining?"

"No," answered Li Yuan. "We have made our point. It will deter Qutu Tong from venturing out of Hedong any time soon. Furthermore, his best way to enter Guanzhong is through the Pujin Bridge on the Yellow River to the west, but that Bridge has been destroyed. If Qutu wants to rescue Daxing, he has to go south and west through the Tong Pass."

"But the Tong Pass is not in our hands."

"No. But it is now only guarded by a small troop of Sui soldiers. We'll take it and deploy a significant force there to protect our rear."

12. Daxing City

FROM HEDONG THE RIGHTEOUS Army marched west to the east bank of the Yellow River. Since the Pujin Bridge had been burned, thousands of boats had to be borrowed to ferry the RA men over to Guanzhong, which was no mean feat. But the task was made much easier by the enthusiastic support of the local populace.

At the small town of Chaoyi immediately west of the River, the RA reassembled only to split again into two columns. The Right Column led by Li Shimin was to move west through Pingyi to Jingyang, before turning south towards Daxing; and the Left Column led by Li Jiancheng was to go south to capture the Yongfeng Granary, from where one detachment would be dispatched to seize and guard the Tong Pass, and the rest would move west to head for Daxing.

Both Columns proceeded according to plan and arrived in the suburbs of Daxing in a matter of weeks, where they were entrenched, readying themselves for the final attack on the city.

Daxing City, the Western Capital, was the greatest prize of the war. It was located to the immediate southeast of the abandoned Han capital, Chang'an (or Han Chang'an), in the heart of Guanzhong (Within the Passes). For centuries, the Chang'an area had rivaled the Luoyang area in the Central Plain (present-day Henan) to the east as the premium location for the national capital. The founding Emperor of Han, Liu Bang, was initially based in Luoyang until He was persuaded by His advisers of the strategic significance of Guanzhong, and moved His capital to Chang'an, where the mighty Han Empire was based for 200 years. After a disruptive civil war, however, the newly restored Han court (Eastern Han) based itself in Luoyang. From that point on, Luoyang was favored over Chang'an until Yang Jian of Sui came to power. Yang Jian built a new capital near Han Chang'an, and named it after his ducal title, Daxing.

For Li Yuan, the capture of Daxing was absolutely essential: it would give him a sense of legitimacy like no other and provide him with a defensible area protected by formidable natural barriers and supported by the riches of the Wei valley.

Along the way to its final destination, the Righteous Army picked up a considerable number of recruits as the downtrodden, the destitute, and the homeless swelled its ranks. By the time Li Yuan arrived in Bashang, an outpost in the southeastern suburb of Daxing, he was commanding an armed force of 200,000.

Now the primary concern was no longer lack of manpower, but how to achieve the military objective without causing too much disturbance for the local populace. Li Yuan gave out strict instructions that all military units should encamp in the open fields rather than villages and hamlets.

As his troops moved closer to the city, Li Yuan declaimed, "What I hope to achieve is to pacify the world, and the use of the force of arms is the last resort. Let it be known that the Seven Chambers of the Imperial Ancestral Temple of the Sui as well as the persons of the Prince of Dai (Yang You) and other royal relatives are absolutely inviolate. Anyone who violates these rules will be punished by the extirpation of his Three Clans."

WITH AN URBAN SPACE of 84 km^2, Daxing was the largest walled city in China and the world. The Sui defenders were unable to man the entire length of the city walls more than 36 km long. Instead, they huddled in a large enclosure inside the city—the combined area of the Palace City and the Imperial City, protected by their own walls and fortifications.

Now the RA began to form a tight ring of encirclement around the city, with Li Jiancheng's Left Column approaching from the east and south, and Li Shimin's Right Column approaching from the west and north. After the RA penetrated into the Outer City, almost unopposed, Li Yuan set up his headquarters in Anxing Ward in the northeast quadrant.

By then Qutu Tong had marched most of his troops south in an attempt to rescue Daxing, leaving his lieutenant Yao Junsu to defend Hedong. Unexpectedly, the progress of Qutu's troops was halted at the Tong Pass. To his grief, this formidable natural barrier was now guarded by a sizeable RA troop under General Liu Wenjing. Repeated attempts to storm it had so far failed.

Meanwhile Li Yuan's RA forces now began to lay siege to the last stronghold inside Daxing. As final victory was drawing near, he became increasingly concerned with how to achieve his military objective in a morally justifiable way, taking a page directly from the playbook of his famous predecessor Liu Bang. When Liu entered Chang'an more than 800 years before, he announced the Three Article Law that would severely punish the acts of killing, wounding, and looting civilians, acts that an occupying army often committed.

An upshot of this relentless drive for discipline was the soaring reputation of the Righteous Army. Far from being an oppressive burden, it became immensely popular with the local residents. It was amid this atmosphere of widespread support that the final battle for Daxing commenced.

After the RA advance troops stormed the Jingfeng Gate, the eastern main entrance of the Imperial City, the Sui resistance simply collapsed. By December 13, 617, the RA had seized control of the entire city.

On entering the Imperial City, Li Yuan instructed his two sons, Jiancheng and Shimin, to immediately take over and safeguard the Imperial storehouse and archives. He then issued an order to outlaw any activities that could interfere with civilian life, including the taking of civilian captives, and looting. In addition, he authorized the opening of the Grand Granary to relieve the hunger of the city's starving residents.

As the new master of Guanzhong, Li Yuan soon got the situation under control. Still, he was haunted by a troubling concern: what had happened to the ancestral temple and tombs of the Li clan in the suburbs of Daxing? He was required by custom to pay homage to them regularly, which he had not been able to do for quite some time because of widespread turmoil. As soon he settled down in the city, he sent his underlings to find out about them. When their report finally came in, Li Yuan was horrified. The temple had been thoroughly destroyed and all the known tombs of his ancestors were dug open and their remains scattered. He broke down in a paroxysm of grief and guilt. Not only did he fail in fulfilling the responsibility of safeguarding these sacred structures, thereby committing a cardinal crime, he was forever deprived of the divine guidance, sanction, and protection of his ancestral spirits, indispensible for the prosperity of his family and descendants.

When Yin Shishi and Gu Yi, the two Sui commanders responsible for the destruction of the temple and tombs, were caught and identified, Li Yuan ordered their execution, together with two other top officers who had stubbornly rejected his request for surrender.

Their ceremonial beheading was to take place on a scaffold set up at the northern end of the north-south thoroughfare, Zhuquemen Avenue. When the slaughterers, with a sweep of their broadswords, sent the heads of the condemned rolling onto the ground, loud cheers went up from the watching crowd. For Li Yuan, however, the spectacle did not provide any solace at all. Instead, he felt trapped in a state of despair by the loss of the temple and tombs and his ancestors' remains.

When Li Yuan was approached by an adviser with a fresh request for his enthronement, he felt nothing but annoyance, and firmly turned it down. Instead, on his insistence, Prince of Dai Yang You (grandson of Yang Guang) was elevated to the throne with pomp and circumstance in the Daxing Basilica. Known in history as Emperor Gong, Yang You was then 12 years old. The current Sui sovereign, Yang Guang, now residing in the South, was named "Honorary Emperor." A general amnesty was announced while the reign title was officially changed from Daye (Great Enterprise) to Yining (Righteous Peace).

13. Qutu Tong

AFTER THE FALL OF Daxing, Qutu Tong's rescue mission lost its purpose. Some of his advisers even suggested surrender to the Righteous Army. To that Qutu responded, "The two Emperors (Yang Jian and Yang Guang) have treated me well. To betray their trust—this is something I will never do."

When the advisers persisted, Qutu growled, "From this point forward, any talk of surrender will be punished by death." Raising his right hand to slash across his neck, he continued, "I will rather do this for the sake of the country than surrender."

It was then a RA spy was captured, and on Qutu's orders, brought into his office. Claiming to be Li Yuan's manservant, he said that his master wanted Qutu to join the Righteous Army and offered him the post of President of the Board of War. Unmoved by the offer, Qutu Tong had him executed.

When the news of Guanzhong's fall reached him, Qutu Tong led his main force east in the hope of joining Prince of Yue Yang Tong, another grandson of the Emperor Yang Guang, now based in Luoyang. Sang Xianhe, Qutu's deputy, remained at the Tong Pass to fight the rearguard action.

At Chousang (near Lingbao, Henan), Qutu Tong's forces were overtaken by a RA cavalry force. Qutu urgently ordered his troops into battle position. Instead of launching an attack, the RA side sent a white-flag waving envoy with a demand for surrender. As soon as he learned of the envoy's intention, Qutu berated him and sent him packing. It was then that Qutu heard a familiar voice calling, "Daddy!" It was from his teenage son Qutu Shou, who was now with the enemy. *Shou wants to persuade me to surrender!* an incredulous Qutu Tong thought.

"Go to hell!" snarled Qutu Tong, before shouting to his men, "He is not my son. Shoot him!"

A barrage of arrows flew in Qutu Shou's direction, but none hit the target.

Then Sang Xianhe, Qutu's second-in-command left at the Tong Pass, made a surprise appearance. Accompanied by RA officers and sitting on horseback, he began to address the Sui officers and soldiers:

As you can see, I have joined the RA. It is because the RA is fighting for a right cause and the Sui has forfeited its right to rule. Besides, Li Yuan, the RA leader, is a great man. He has treated all of us well. Like most of you, I am from Guanzhong. Now that Guanzhong and the capital have been taken, where can you go? If you join the Righteous Army, the Duke of Tang will allow you to hold on to your original ranks and will keep your families from harm. And he is a man of his words.

To Qutu Tong's surprise and horror, within hours, his men all but deserted him. Realizing that the end had come, Qutu Tong got off his horse, dropped on his knees, and kowtowed three times towards the southeast in the direction of Yang Guang's city, Jiangdu. Between sobs, he said, "Let Heaven and Earth be my witnesses. Not that I, your subject, am not worthy of Your Majesty, but that I have been defeated after having done my best." He then allowed himself to be taken into custody.

LI YUAN WAS SITTING in the Daxing Basilica when Qutu Tong, his hands tied in rope, was brought into his presence. Li Yuan rose to untie him, and invited him to sit down.

"I am so pleased that you've finally joined us," said Li Yuan, with a smile on his face.

"I am eternally grateful for your leniency, my lord."

"This is not leniency. We need people like you."

"But I have committed crimes."

"Such as the killing of my manservant?"

"Yes, my lord."

"It was a terrible loss. But what can one do about it? Besides, at that time, you were still loyal to the Honorary Emperor in Jiangdu."

"Even today, I feel I have let him down."

"We greatly appreciate your strong sense of loyalty. But the Honorary Emperor is a lost cause."

"What are you going to do with him?"

"Mark my words, we will never harm him."

There was a silence for a few moments before Li Yuan said again, "Well, in spite of your loyalty to him, or perhaps because of it, I'll keep my word and appoint you President of the Board of War. For now, you'll work under Li Shimin as his Chief Administrator. Will that do?"

After pondering the offer briefly, Qutu answered, "Yes, my lord."

14. The Tang

IN THE REAR BASILICA of the Daxing Basilica, Li Yuan and the Emperor Yang You, accompanied by the entire court, were attending a state mourning service for the Honorary Emperor Yang Guang, who had been murdered at age 49 in Jiangdu about a month before in April of Yining 2 (618). Overcome with sorrow, Li Yuan wailed incessantly.

When a remonstrator realized Li Yuan was not merely acting out his part as the chief mourner, he became worried and said, "My lord, don't let your grief get to you."

"I was His servant, wasn't I?" Li Yuan asked, with tears rolling down his cheeks. "How can I not be sorrowful while mourning for Him?"

The remonstrator did not answer and the wailing continued. The service went on for three days. Each day Li Yuan was dutifully in attendance. The Emperor Yang You was deeply moved by Li Yuan's affection for His own grandfather. No doubt, Li Yuan would continue to give support to the throne. But the Emperor's advisers saw the writing on the wall. With Yang Guang's death, the rationale for Yang You's continued occupation of the throne vanished. Encouraged by His advisers the young Emperor, who had never been comfortable sitting on the throne, issued an edict to abdicate in favor of Li Yuan. As before Li Yuan rejected it. However, unlike in the past, the rejection was not accompanied by a vehement argument. Pei Ji, the leading proponent for Li's enthronement, saw his chance. He presented a long remonstrative memorial, bearing the signatures of more than 2,000 court officials, to once again urge Li to take the throne. The memorial cited a host of supernatural evidence that pointed to the rise of a new dynasty, of which Li Yuan was the natural founder. Overwhelmed by the request, Li Yuan finally gave in, or so it seemed.

ON THE *JIAZI* DAY of the fifth month (June 18, 618), Li Yuan assumed the Imperial mantle in the Daxing Basilica of the Daxing Palace. Both palace and basilica were renamed as Taiji (Grand Culmen). The dynastic title of "Sui" was replaced with

"Tang," and a new reign was announced, that of "Martial Virtue" (Wude). A general amnesty followed. The capital Daxing City reverted to its ancient name, "Chang'an." All Commanderies (*jun*) would be called Prefectures (*zhou*) again. These symbolic measures were intended to distance the Tang from the dynasty it had replaced and to forge its own identity.

After the coronation in the Taiji Palace, the Emperor Li Yuan proceeded with the Imperial procession south to the Xuandu Abbey—the leading Daoist institution of the capital—located a few Wards south of the Imperial City on the west side of Zhuquemen Avenue. There a sacrificial rite was held at which the Emperor personally made offerings to Lord Lao and enunciated to all under Heaven that Lord Lao, né Li Er, who sanctioned the Tang dynasty, was now the divine ancestor of the royal Li clan.

THE EMPEROR'S "ALL UNDER Heaven," however, sounded rather hollow, for the Tang was only one of more than half a dozen independent or semi-independent powers active in China proper and beyond. To the east Qutu Tong's lieutenant Yao Junsu still controlled the city of Hedong and its environs. To the west Xue Ju and Xue Rengao, father and son, were carving out a small empire that threatened Guanzhong. Further to the west, Li Gui dominated the Hexi Corridor in west Gansu. In north Shanxi and Shaanxi the Tujue-supported warlords Liu Wuzhou and Liang Shidu controlled their own expansive domains. In the Central Plain Li Mi, with the largest military force, the Wagang Army, constantly fought the Luoyang-based regime under Wang Shichong for dominance. To their north was the overlord of Hebei Dou Jiande, who had under his command another numerous rebel army. The South was divided among a number of rebel forces, with the strongest one under Du Fuwei.

Nevertheless, there were a few things going for the Tang. First, they were based in the best-protected metropolitan area. Second, their leader Li Yuan was not only a great strategist, but also a great visionary who would not rest until the entire realm was brought under His sway. Last, He had attracted a core group of talented and dedicated followers who served as His senior court officials and commanding generals.

15. Xue Ju

THE INVASION OF JING Prefecture northwest of Chang'an by the warlord Xue Ju on July 7, Wude 1 (618), did not come as a surprise. The Tang were aware that Xue had been looking for an opportunity to expand. But the timing caught them somewhat off guard. The dynasty was barely 20 days old.

On the Emperor's orders, Prince of Qin Li Shimin was put in charge of the counteroffensive with troops from eight neighboring Area Commands.

Xue Ju was no stranger to the Prince, who had fought him successfully in late 617, immediately after the Righteous Army had taken Chang'an. This time, however, Xue was a much more formidable foe because of the support of the Tujue.

Having had his troops billeted in the city of Gaozhi (Changwu, Shaanxi), the Prince met with his senior officers to discuss strategy.

"Xue Ju has cut deep into our territory," the Prince began. "But his grain supply is low and his troops are tired."

"That gives us a great opportunity for attack, does it not?" asked Liu Wenjing, now the Prince's Chief Administrator.

"I don't think so. The time is not ripe."

"What are we supposed to do?"

"We stay put."

"What if the enemies actively seek combat?" asked Yin Kaishan, the Prince's Aide-de-camp.

"We must refuse battle outside Gaozhi under any circumstances," the Prince answered with decision.

The task at hand was to make Gaozhi impregnable to enemy attack. Situated in a plain, Gaozhi depended on man-made fortifications for its defense. The Prince ordered his troops to repair and reinforce old trenches and redoubts, and to construct new ones in and around the city. Other than that, there was not much to do except to practice combat skills while waiting patiently in hopes of wearing out the enemies.

Then the Prince noticed a discomfort in his abdomen, accompanied by fever and cramps and frequent bowel movements. Within a week, he became so weak that he could hardly stand up, let alone ride a horse into battle. He summoned Liu Wenjing and Yin Kaishan into his campaign tent. Propped up on his pallet and looking scrawny and wan, he said to his two lieutenants, "I thought I could ride it out. Obviously, I was wrong."

"What did the army physician say, Prince of Qin?" asked Yin Kaishan.

"It is caused by the blocking of pneuma and blood in the bowels. It may take up to a month to cure. The coptis boluses he gave me work, but ever so slowly."

"We do hope you get well soon, Prince of Qin," said Liu. "Meanwhile what do you expect us to do?"

"As a matter of fact, I have to leave and hand over command to you. Wenjing, you will be the acting Commander-in-chief; and Kaishan, you will serve as his lieutenant."

"Yes, Prince of Qin," said Liu and Yin one after another.

"Remember, it is essential that you don't respond to enemy provocations. Wait until I come back."

"Do not worry, Prince of Qin," said Liu Wenjing.

"We will not let you down," said Yin Kaishan.

Not long after the conversation, the Prince departed secretly in a carriage under a light cavalry escort for Chang'an.

"DO YOU KNOW WHY the Prince kept asking you not to engage the enemies?" asked Yin Kaishan when he was alone with Liu Wenjing in the latter's tent.

"This is his father's favorite strategy," answered Liu. "To wear them out before attack."

"I think otherwise. He actually distrusts your ability. The problem is, sooner or later the enemies will learn about the Prince's departure and make an aggressive move."

"What do you think we should do?" asked Liu.

"We should make a show of force to prevent them from taking the initiative," answered Yin.

"But that would countermand the Prince's orders."

"Yes, that would. But we can't worry about that now. The survival of our troops is at stake."

"How can we make a show of force then?"

"By positioning most of our troops here," said Yin Kaishan while pointing a finger at an area southwest of Gaozhi on the map. Fixing his gaze on the spot, Liu Wenjing contemplated for a long moment, before making up his mind to give Yin's plan a try.

On the morrow, on Liu Wenjing's orders, the three Generals-in-chief and eight Area Commanders under his command led a total of 80,000 troops out of the base camp into the city's southwest suburb. After the troops were positioned in redoubts and trenches, they made sorties to deflate the enemy's arrogance. The tactic worked. Xue Ju was forced to move his troops to the west of the Jing River, and harassing attacks on the Tang forces dwindled to zero.

An uneasy stalemate ensued. Then Xue Ju made a sudden assault on the flank of the Tang army from the Qianshui Moor (NE of Changwu, Shaanxi) nearby. Liu Wenjing counterattacked with an overwhelming force and the enemies retreated. When the Tang troops, infantry and cavalry, were crossing the Moor, they bogged down in the marshy swamps. Enemy archers lying in wait suddenly emerged from the reeds and showered them with barrages of arrows. And the Tang troops broke in rout.

By the time Liu Wenjing and Yin Kaishan withdrew into the city, more than half of their troops had been felled by arrows, trampled to death, or taken prisoner. Among the Tang captives were the three Generals-in-chief and eight Area Commanders.

Gaozhi suddenly found itself under siege and attack by Xue's vicious army. Clearly, the disheartened defenders would not be able to resist the relentless onslaught for long. When it became obvious that the city was falling Liu Wenjing and Yin Kaishan fled with the remnants of the Tang army.

Having captured Gaozhi, Xue Ju ordered his men, following an ancient, but gruesome, tradition, to erect a monument called "Giant Mound" (*jingguan*), a pyramid piled up with the corpses of Tang soldiers (many of whom had been slaughtered in captivity) and covered with a thick coat of earth. Standing atop this macabre monument, Xue staged a grand ceremony to celebrate his decisive victory over the Tang.

16. Xue Rengao

WITH XUE JU'S THREAT looming larger every day, the Emperor Li Yuan was pleasantly surprised when Li Mi, one of His most serious adversaries, requested to join the Tang, and granted his wish with alacrity. Li Mi led 20,000 of his battle-hardened Wagang Army men into Chang'an. This once proud commander of the largest military force in the realm had suffered a devastating defeat at the hands of Wang Shichong. His dream of dominating the Central Plain dashed, Li Mi had turned to the Tang in desperation.

For his senior adviser, Wei Zheng, however, arriving in Chang'an marked a new beginning. Honest, loyal, and highly knowledgeable about history and politics, Wei had made numerous suggestions to his boss on strategic and tactical dispositions and on policy. Li Mi had rejected them all as being unconventional. *The Emperor is different—He is more open to new ideas*, Wei thought. So he submitted a memorial to draw attention to the strategic importance of Liyang (in north Henan) with its supersized granary and offer his service to bring it into the fold. To his pleasant surprise, his proposition received the Emperor's prompt approval. He then set off as the Emperor's legate. Not one to mince words, on arrival in Liyang, Wei Zheng raised the issue of joining the Tang with his old friend Xu Shiji, who had been Commander of the local garrison under Li Mi. Xu accepted Wei's advice on one condition: Liyang should be donated to the Tang in the name of Li Mi. He did not want to be seen as using his master's land to win favor. The Emperor granted Xu not only his request, but also the rare honor to assume the royal surname "Li" as a way to laud his exemplary loyal behavior. From then on, Xu Shiji would be known as Li Shiji.

AS XUE JU WAS busy preparing for the conquest of Chang'an, unexpectedly he suffered a stroke or "was struck by wind," and succumbed on September 3. His son Xue Rengao took over command of his army. In spite of his recent setback in Ning Prefecture (seat: Ningxian, east Gansu), Rengao was able to make further inroads in Tang territory. Compared to his father, he was a better general and thus posed a greater threat to Chang'an.

The Tang general sent to fight him was none other than Prince Li Shimin. Fully recovered, the Prince arrived in Gaozhi at the end of the year, bringing with him a much larger army. His strategy remained the same, refraining from engaging the enemies in an attempt to wear them down. To his subaltern generals who asked for permission to strike, the Prince responded, "Our army was recently defeated and demoralized. It will take a while to recover. Meanwhile, the enemies have grown arrogant. Sooner or later an arrogant army will fall. If we wait until later—when we build up our morale and the enemies become even more arrogant—we will be able to crush them."

More than 60 days passed, and neither side made a significant move.

One night when the Prince was already asleep, one of his adjutants woke him up to report that a high-ranking officer from Xue's camp had defected, bringing 2,000 troops with him. Li jumped out of bed to debrief him. The officer provided a vital piece of intelligence: Xue's grain supply was running dangerously low. It immediately spurred the Prince to action. He deployed a detachment under General Liang Shi in the Qianshui Moor (NE of Changwu, Shaanxi), whose swamps had dried up somewhat in winter. As Liang Shi and his men hid themselves behind earthworks, they sustained a furious enemy attack, lasting on and off for several days. Cut off from water supply the beleaguered Tang soldiers and horses were beginning to die of thirst. But the enemies were on the verge of total exhaustion. It was then that the Prince started a counterattack. He first sent a small advance force to the Qianshui Moor at dawn. Attacked by a much larger enemy force, the advance force was apparently worsted. As the enemies began to give chase, the Prince unleashed his main force in a surprise assault from north of the Moor. Leading the charge was the Prince himself riding a rave-black steed under the escort of several dozen cavalry.

When Xue Rengao attempted to pull back his troops from the Moor to outflank the Tang main force, he was horrified to find them in disarray. He had no choice but to beat a hasty retreat west. The Prince and his cavalry followed him in hot pursuit until they reached the south bank of the Jing River. Beyond the River was Zhezhi City (northeast of Jingchuan, Gansu), into which Xue and his forces had withdrawn.

The Prince waited until his main force fell into position along the south bank of the River; he then ordered a forced crossing. The Tang troops soon established several bridgeheads on the north bank, and started laying siege to Zhezhi City.

With the city granary depleted, the Zhezhi residents began to pour out in a steady stream. There were civilian refugees with shoulder-poles carrying bundles or baskets, or pushing wheelbarrows piled up high with belongings. There were also small bands of troops led by officers waving white flags. One group of foot soldiers walked at the head of a procession of carriages that trundled slowly out of the eastern gate. One of the carriages had a lacquered exterior coated in dark red, yellow, and black colors. On the carriage flagpoles were flying a white flag and a black banner with a medallion at the center emblazoned with the golden character "Xue." The passenger of the carriage was none other than Xue Rengao himself. Eventually, more than 10,000 of Xue's army and 50,000 of the city residents were brought into the fold. However, the capitulation came too late to save the warlord himself. Xue Rengao, together with his top generals, was hauled to Chang'an's Western Market and beheaded in public.

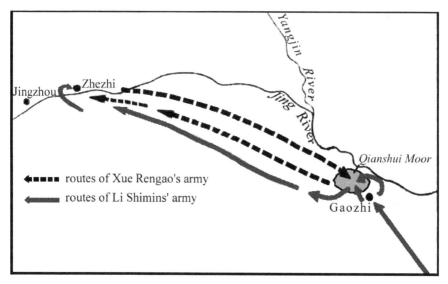

Map 3. Battle of Zhezhi City (618)

17. Li Mi

FOR LI MI, GETTING adjusted to life in Chang'an as a Tang official turned out to be extremely difficult. Paying obeisance to the sovereign, as was required by court ritual, was downright demeaning—Li Mi himself had been a sovereign only recently. His appointment by the Emperor as Director of the Court for Tributaries (*honglu qing*) was a bitter disappointment. The post was for the leader of a third-tier central agency, much less prestigious than that of President of the Board of War currently held by Qutu Tong.

"The Emperor and I," Li Mi said to his myrmidon Wang Bodang, "share the same surname. Besides, once He even suggested to share power with me. I deserve to be Vice Premier of the Department of State Affairs, or at least a Board President. I don't understand why He only made me a Court Director."

"That was then. Now He is the Emperor."

"I have to appeal."

"I wouldn't do that if I were you."

"Why?"

"First, it is getting too crowded at the top. Perhaps there is not a single Board-President position left. The real trouble is that the Emperor doesn't trust us at all."

"You think so?"

"As a matter of fact, our Wagang Army men have not been given a decent treatment. Sometimes, we received no provisions for days."

"Really? I was not aware of that."

"Nobody has bothered to tell you. But I swear, on the honor of the Wagang Army, that is absolutely true."

"If that's the case," Li Mi said ruefully, "Chang'an is probably not for us after all."

SUBSEQUENTLY, LI MI WROTE a long letter to the Emperor. In it, instead of complaining about his appointment, he asked for permission to lead his troops on a mission to the east. He would bring Li Shiji—nominally a Tang subject, but de facto an independent warlord—into the Tang camp. On his way back, with the help of Li Shiji, he would capture Luoyang for the Tang.

To his relief and surprise, the request was promptly approved. Li Mi lost no time in leading the 20,000 Wagang Army men out of Chang'an. For fear that the Emperor should change His mind they marched swiftly towards the Tong Pass. Along the way, they could feel the extensive reach of the Emperor's power in Guanzhong—all the cities they passed by were heavily garrisoned by His men.

When Li Mi was just 30 *li* from the Pass, an Imperial envoy caught up with him. The edict he brought ordered Li Mi to leave half of his troops inside (west of) the Pass. Li Mi had no choice but to comply.

After Li and his men had gone through the Tong Pass without incident and arrived at a village in Chousang, they breathed a collective sigh of relief. The vast area beyond was familiar territory, not in the hands of the Tang.

Then a second envoy arrived with another edict:

It is hereby ordered that Director of the Court for Tributaries Li Mi return by himself to the Imperial court for an assignment.

"What do you make of this?" an irritated Li Mi asked Wang Bodang.

"It is an ominous sign."

"What should we do now?"

"Continue to go east and make a junction with Li Shiji."

"If we don't, I am sure we'll be killed. Let's do it."

After a pause, Li Mi resumed, "Listen, Bodang. Select a small group of loyal riders and gather enough women's clothes for everyone."

"Yes, my lord."

"We'll meet here," Li Mi continued, pointing to a massive locust tree by the road.

That night after dark, about three dozens of Wagang officers and soldiers, dressed as ladies and maids, gathered at the designated place. Led by Li Mi, they quietly sneaked out of the village and moved east.

Before reaching a small town called Taolin, they stopped at a post house. Once inside, they pulled out daggers and poniards hidden in their red garments and skirts and overpowered the guardsmen.

After a warm meal and a good night's sleep, Li Mi and his men proceeded to Taolin, where they raided the headquarters of the local garrison, seized several dozen horses from its stable, and galloped away.

Before long, they found themselves passing through a ravine hemmed in by steep cliffs. They all dismounted and started to gingerly pick their way along the bottom strewn with scree and boulders. All of a sudden, a shower of arrows rained down and they crouched for cover. An ear-piercing war cry rose from the cliffs and reverberated down as a band of Tang commandos descended to make short work of them.

LI MI'S BOTCHED ATTEMPT to escape the grip of the Tang complicated the situation at Liyang. The Tang court was no longer sure of the loyalty of its Commander Li Shiji. The Emperor dispatched another envoy to secure his allegiance. When Li Shiji saw Li Mi's severed head the envoy brought with him, he broke down. The envoy then took great pains to explain why Li Mi had to be killed. The Emperor could be generous to His former enemies who joined Him, but could not afford to show mercy to those who betrayed Him. Still, Li Shiji was inconsolable for hours. In the end, Li quieted down, and the envoy communicated the Emperor's demand for his allegiance. Surprisingly, Li Shiji offered no opposition. The only thing he requested was a proper burial for his former master, which the envoy instantly approved on behalf of the Emperor.

On the day of the burial, the body and head of Li Mi were brought together and placed in an elaborately painted coffin, to receive funeral obsequies that befitted a sovereign. The entire garrison, dressed in white, came to bid goodbye to their former Commander-in-chief. With the breaking of a pottery basin, ritual wailing commenced, led by Li Shiji himself. Many of the officers and men sobbed so violently that their tears became bloody.

18. Song Jingang

BY THE TIME OF Li Mi's death in early Wude 2 (619), the Tang's drive to unify all under Heaven had gathered momentum. Hedong was essentially defanged after its loyalist Commander Yao Junsu had been murdered by his subordinates following the death of the Emperor Yang Guang; Xue Rengao had been executed, and his lands annexed; and Li Gui further to the west had recognized the Tang's hegemony. However, three powerful warlords still posed a serious challenge to the Tang's dominance in the North: Liu Wuzhou in north Shanxi, Dou Jiande in Hebei, and Wang Shichong in Henan.

The rise of Dou Jiande was particularly alarming. As the King of Xia, Dou had been gobbling up independent powers in the area. Song Jingang, a minor warlord based in Shanggu, Hebei, felt threatened. It was in Song's interest to see Dou weakened. Thus when Dou Jiande clashed with the warlord Wei Dao'er (Lishanfei), Song Jingang sent his troops to support the latter. Like Dou's army, Wei's army was a hodge-podge of bandits, destitute peasants, and vagabonds. But unlike Dou's army, it was poorly trained and even more poorly led. Soon it was worsted and Wei Dao'er himself, killed. Song Jingang's own army, originally 10,000 strong and now decimated, apparently would be doomed to the same fate.

Song Jingang retreated into the Western Mountain with 4,000 men. A letter from Dou Jiande followed. Upon reading it, Song was in tears. Waving the letter in the air, Song said to his generals, "Brothers, this man has killed Wei Dao'er. Now he is coming after me. If you like, you can have my head and get rich." Hefting a broadsword, Song made an effort to slash it across his neck. In the tussle that followed, several of his generals pried the sword away from his hands. Song, a mass of a man with a stout physique, started sobbing like a little boy. The generals tried to comfort him, only to start sobbing themselves as they huddled together.

"Tell us where to go," one of the generals said.

"There is nothing for it except to go west and join Liu Wuzhou," Song Jingang said. "But there is no way of telling whether he will be kind to us."

"Still," the general said, "it is far better than staying here and waiting for death."

"You're probably right. Sooner or later, Dou Jiande will find us."

"So we are going?"

"Yes," Song answered resignedly.

SONG'S WORRIES WERE COMPLETELY dispelled when Liu Wuzhou welcomed him with open arms. Whereas Liu prized the 4,000 battle-tested troops Song had brought with him, he prized Song himself even more, who had a reputation for being an excellent strategist and field commander. Liu appointed him his lieutenant and married off his prepossessing sister to him.

Song was grateful beyond measure for his sudden change of fortune. To show his gratitude, he proposed to Liu a bold strategy:

"Your Majesty, we can strike south to capture Taiyuan and link up with Hedong."

"Tell me more about it," replied Liu, apparently interested.

"Taiyuan is now in the hands of Li Yuanji, the fourth son of Li Yuan. He is corrupt and unpopular. If we move swiftly we can take the city by a surprise attack."

"How large a force do we need for the operation?"

"Taiyuan is the first home base of Li Yuan, and it is protected by a significant Tang army. We need a vastly superior force to sack it. The main force of our army should be brought to bear."

"How about a coordinated attack? I myself will lead the main force, and you lead a detachment of 30,000 comprised of both cavalry and infantry."

"Excellent, Your Majesty."

FROM MAY TO JULY, Liu Wuzhou's army pushed relentlessly south as far as the suburbs of Taiyuan. Song Jingang led his troops further down to Jiexiu. By order of the Emperor Li Yuan, Pei Ji led a rescue force north to check Song's advance but was worsted near Jiexiu and retreated back into Guanzhong.

The task of defending Taiyuan fell on the shoulders of Prince Li Yuanji. At 16 Yuanji was an accomplished master of horse-riding and the spear, but not much else. Although now a Prince, he had been born under an ill star during the Sui when his father Li Yuan was away on assignment. Because of his hideous looks, his mother ordered a maid to get rid of him. The maid disobeyed the order and raised him secretly. Later she made an attempt to return Yuanji to his father, but the latter insisted that she should continue to raise him. Always feeling unloved and abandoned, Yuanji grew into a young man with few moral scruples. Once he had a quarrel with his foster mother; on the spur of the moment, he had her killed by his underlings, an act he bitterly regretted later.

After Pei Ji's retreat, the fear of being left in the lurch haunted Yuanji day and night. His urgent requests for reinforcements seemed to have gone unheeded. So he decided to flee. Abandoning the city without the court's approval would certainly bring Imperial wrath upon himself and probably result in severe punishment. But that would be far better than being captured by a vicious enemy.

One night in October, under cover of darkness, a convoy of carriages—carrying his wife, concubines, and most of his staff—stole out of the western city gate and moved west. They were escorted by the best troops of Taiyuan Garrison commanded by Prince Li Yuanji himself. A small force mostly of the old and weak was left behind to defend Taiyuan under Aide-de-camp (*sima*) Liu Dewei.

Within days of Li Yuanji's departure, a pro-Liu Wuzhou local magnate, with the help of a small group of men, overpowered the remaining Tang troops from within, and welcomed Liu Wuzhou's army into the city. Liu Dewei was taken captive and forced to shift allegiance. It would be years before he would rejoin the Tang and serve as its President of the Board of Justice.

19. Liu Wenjing

LIU WENJING, THE MASTERMIND of the Righteous Uprising and until recently Chief Administrator under Prince Li Shimin, was in jail again, charged with libel. The Emperor Li Yuan appointed a special tribunal comprised of top officials to investigate. Heading the tribunal were Pei Ji, Vice Premier of the Department of State Affairs, and Xiao Yu, President of the Secretariat. After his defeat near Taiyuan, Pei Ji had been reprimanded and disciplined by the Emperor, and only recently had he wriggled his way back into favor. Xiao Yu was the only one from the inner circle of the previous regime who had survived the dynastic change with his reputation intact and his status improved. Opinionated and honest, he could serve as a countervailing force against Pei.

At the start of the interrogation in prison, Liu, at the request of Pei and Xiao, gave his own account. He said, "At the time of the Righteous Uprising, Mr. Pei Ji and I were of the same rank. But later, when Mr. Pei was promoted Vice Premier and moved into a mansion, I remained a Board President. On numerous occasions, I went on expeditions, leaving my old mother behind in a shabby home in Chang'an. Over time, I became bitter."

"You were later appointed President of the Chancellery, weren't you?" asked Pei Ji.

"Yes, but that was still different from the Vice Premier," replied Liu Wenjing.

"Didn't you say you wanted to behead Mr. Pei?" asked Xiao Yu.

"Never!" said Liu emphatically.

"But we have proof."

"What proof?"

"We got it from a reliable source."

"Who?"

"Your second concubine."

Liu Wenjing fell silent, realizing the futility of continued denial. He regretted that he had not treated her better after the arrival of his third concubine. But it was all too late. Now he had to fight for survival.

"I made that casual remark when I was inebriated," said Liu. "By the bones of my ancestors, I swear I had no intention of ever harming Vice Premier Pei."

The interrogation went on for several hours. Xiao Yu and Pei Ji left without answering Liu's question whether his life would be spared. It was now in the hands of the Emperor.

TWO DAYS LATER, AT a meeting with a small panel of key officials, the Emperor said, "I've read the report submitted by the interrogators. It seems that Liu Wenjing did harbor the intention of inciting sedition."

"Your Majesty," said Xiao Yu. "Judging by what I have heard and seen, Liu Wenjing has no such intention."

"I agree, Your Majesty," said Li Shimin. "In the old Taiyuan days, Liu Wenjing was the first proponent of the Righteous Uprising. He single-handedly negotiated a favorable treaty with the Tujue, and brought the much-needed Tujue horses and troops to the Righteous Army. He defended the Tong Pass heroically, which made the successful capture of Chang'an by the Righteous Army possible. Never once did he entertain the idea of sedition, even though he had plenty of opportunities. I would like to vouch for his character."

Turning to Pei Ji, the Emperor asked, "What do you think, Vice Premier?"

"Your Majesty," answered Pei Ji, "there is no doubt that Liu Wenjing is a talented administrator and a good general. But he has a treacherous personality. In this age of turmoil, we can ill afford to keep him."

"But because of his merit, he has been issued with not one but two Iron Plaques," said Li Shimin. The Iron Plaques were only awarded to those select few meritorious individuals whose exploits were considered absolutely essential for the survival of the Empire. One Plaque could be used to save its recipient from one execution.

After a pensive contemplation, the Emperor issued His order: Liu Wenjing, with his death-sparing privilege revoked, was to be executed; his family assets were to be confiscated; and all female members of his family were to be forced into bondage in the Palace.

20. The Queshu Valley

THE EMPEROR FOUND PRINCE Li Shimin's dogged defense of Liu Wenjing quite annoying. It left Him in an irascible mood for days. But soon He was distracted by something far more serious: Prince Li Yuanji's desertion and the loss of Taiyuan. Infuriated, He ordered the execution of one of Li Yuanji's mentors for failing to remonstrate, but stopped short of carrying it out when He was told that the mentor had indeed attempted to stop him, albeit without success. He also threatened to inflict a severe corporal punishment on Yuanji himself, but could not bring Himself to issue the edict. Frustration turned into worry when he heard that Song Jingang had linked up with Hedong in the southwest corner of Shanxi. Song Jingang's next move was likely to break through the Tong Pass to attack Guanzhong. How to prevent the situation from getting out of hand was foremost on his mind when He summoned His second son into the Liangyi Basilica.

Li Shimin had lost much sleep in recent days after the death of Liu Wenjing. As he entered the room, he looked haggard and tired.

"I too regretted the death of Liu Wenjing," the Emperor said to His son. "But as sovereign, I could not tolerate his menacing behavior towards other officials."

"I understand that, Your Majesty."

"That's more like it. I hope you've got over it by now."

"Yes, I have, Your Majesty."

"Good." After a brief pause, He resumed, "Have you heard about Song Jingang's recent move?"

"Yes. After the capture of Taiyuan, he has moved south."

"He is now in control of Hedong, and is poised to enter the Pass. And I want to stop him in his tracks. Shimin, can you help me do it?"

After pausing for a moment to ponder, Li Shimin said, "Yes. But I need a force of 30,000."

"That shouldn't be a problem. In fact, if 30,000 is not enough, you can have more."

"For now, that is all I need, Your Majesty."

IT WAS IN DECEMBER of Wude 2 (619) that Prince Li Shimin and his men crossed the Yellow River into Shanxi to reach Longmen (Hejin, Shanxi). Prominent among his top commanders was Li Shiji. After his submission to the Tang, Shiji had continued to garrison Liyang for some time. But soon, his father was taken hostage by Dou Jiande, and he himself was under attack by Dou's superior army and was forced to surrender. Later he found an opportunity to slip away and rejoin the Emperor in Chang'an. His checkered past did not bother the Prince, who valued his talent as a field commander.

In Baibi (southwest of Xinjiang, Shanxi) further to the east, the Prince and his men encamped right on the edge of enemy territory. With his food supply running low, Song Jingang did not want to stay in the area for long, and was anxious to take on the Prince. The Prince, however, was not in a hurry to accept battle. Instead, he decided to degrade the enemies' fighting capabilities by waiting while sending out small bands of troops to play cat-and-mouse games with them.

One morning the Prince went on a reconnaissance mission with a squadron of armored riders. In the process he got separated from all of them except for one. As the Prince and the rider were taking a nap on a hillside, the rider was awakened by something that touched his face: a rat had just scampered across as a snake chased after it. He cursed his bad luck and was about to go back to sleep when he saw Song Jingang's men surreptitiously closing in on them.

"Enemy!" the rider shouted in panic.

The Prince rose to his feet, and he and the rider jumped on their horses and sped away. Song Jingang's cavalrymen chased after them. The Prince turned his body around, while on horseback, to shoot at his pursuers. Suddenly, Song Jingang's Cavalry General, the commanding officer of the operation, tumbled off his horse, having been hit in the head by an arrow, and died on the spot. The enemies halted the chase as the Prince and his companion galloped to safety.

In the month that followed, the Prince authorized only two small-scale attacks. Both were successful. In the second attack, the Prince led 3,000 light cavalry in person and worsted the cavalry forces commanded by Yuchi Jingde and Xun Xiang, two of Song Jingang's top generals, as they attempted to rescue Hedong.

Several of the Prince's generals then came forth with suggestions to seize the momentum and "strike the iron when it's still hot." But the Prince turned them down. He was determined to wait until the enemies were thoroughly exhausted.

Four more months later, in May of Wude 3 (620), Song Jingang ran out of grain and was forced to retreat north. The Prince saw his chance and decided to attack with full force. As always, he was to lead the charge in person. But his decision ran into strenuous opposition from a high-ranking officer, who argued, "Now that you have acquired enough merit by dislodging the enemies, you should by no means risk the safety of your person to go after them. What's more important: since our officers and men are semi-starved, it would be far more prudent to wait for the arrival of more provisions."

The Prince replied, "Song Jingang has run because he is at the end of his resources. The morale of his troops has simply collapsed, leaving them vulnerable to attack. This is a golden opportunity. We must seize it before it slips away."

"But you don't have to lead the attack in person," said the officer.

"Don't worry. I can assure you that my time has not come yet. Besides, in the unlikely event of my death, I'll acquire immortal fame."

MARCHING AT BREAKNECK SPEED, the Tang troops caught up with the enemies in the Queshu Valley. With high morale and strong leadership, the Prince calculated, his army, even without a numerical superiority, could take on Song Jingang's forces and win. In the course of a day, he launched eight attacks. On every occasion, the Tang army, although poorly fed, worsted the enemies, who had virtually had nothing to eat for days.

On that night, the Tang troops bivouacked west of the Valley on a plain for a much-needed rest. The Prince was able to take off his armor for the first time in three days and to have his first bite of food in two. The army chefs butchered and cooked the last sheep saved for the commanding officer. But on the Prince's insistence, the mutton was shared among the officers and men working for him.

At Jiexiu, the strategic outpost north of the Valley, Song Jingang deployed a force of 20,000 outside the city's western gate. In the morning, the Prince and his top general Li Shiji launched a two-pronged attack that thoroughly routed the enemies after disrupting their battle formation. Song Jingang fled east on horseback. The Prince chased after him for miles as far as the village Zhangnanbao. Having lost sight of his quarry, the Prince turned around and declared to his adjutants, "The battle is over for now. It is time for a nice meal." Returning to camp, the Prince sat down to have a dinner—hot flat-cakes with a pork and vegetable stew, a bowl of soup, and wine. It was not a sumptuous repast by his standards, but the Prince could not remember having eaten anything so satisfying his entire life. In fact it was his first full meal for days.

Meanwhile two of Prince Li Shimin's top commanders—Prince Li Daozong and Yuwen Shiji—were preparing for an attack on Jiexiu. Li Daozong was a second nephew of the Emperor Li Yuan and a great general in his own right. Yuwen Shiji, son of Yuwen Shu, exceled as an administrator and as field commander.

Song Jingang's flight had left Jiexiu in the hands of Yuchi Jingde, a doughty general known for his death-defying courage in battle. While the Tang commanders maintained a tight siege of the city, Tang agents suborned Yuchi's closest advisers. It did not take long before the suborned officers convinced Yuchi to stop fighting for a man who had abandoned him. On Yuchi's orders, the gates of Jiexiu were thrown open to welcome the Tang troops.

Prince Li Shimin, feeling exultant, headed straight for the County Magistrate Office compound. Yuchi Jingde and his associates were waiting at the gate. As soon as Li dismounted, Yuchi fell on his knees to perform the kowtow ritual. The Prince, who did not want to give himself the air of a triumphant victor, rushed to help him to his feet.

That night the Prince held a banquet to honor Yuchi and his associates. By then, the Prince had learned much about Yuchi's past. The son of an ironsmith, Yuchi had made a living as an ironsmith himself before joining the Sui army. Like many young Sui officers in north Shanxi, he later joined Liu Wuzhou. The moment the Prince met him he was struck by Yuchi's uncouth manners and straightforward temperament. Having received hardly any literati education, this swarthy-faced daredevil brought to mind a simple rustic. Obviously, he was not someone to discuss literature with. But, on the other hand, there was no reason to distrust him. As soon as the banquet was over, the Prince appointed him General in the Tang army, commanding the 8,000 troops he had brought with him.

WHEN LIU WUZHOU GOT news of Song Jingang's disastrous defeat, he fled north to the Tujue. Song Jingang himself made an attempt to regroup the remnants of his army but failed. He too went north. Having lost most of their mighty army, Liu and Song were now of little value to their Tujue supporters. Liu and Song felt unwelcome, and went south to start anew. Before they could cross into Tang territory, they both got killed. The Tang went on to solidify their grip on the entire Hedong region. The only holdout was Hedong City in the southwest corner. When it eventually fell, an overjoyed Emperor paid a visit to the outpost and personally supervised the execution of its defiant Commandant.

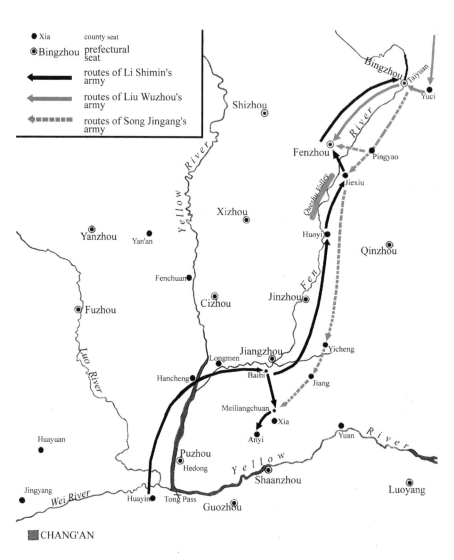

Map 4. War Against Liu Wuzhou and Song Jingang (619—620)

The capture of the entire Hedong (Shanxi) region gave the Tang a forward base to thrust its military power into Hebei and the Central Plain in Henan, and allowed them to set their sights on the second biggest prize of the war—Luoyang.

21. Wang Shichong and Dou Jiande

LUOYANG, THE CROWN JEWEL of the Central Plain. It was Emperor Yang's answer to His father's Daxing City (Chang'an). Although just about one half the size of Chang'an, what it lacked in urban space was more than compensated for in architectural extravagance. In its Palace City and suburban Western Park, lavishly designed structures—basilicas, pavilions, loft-buildings, terraces, and others—abounded.

Easy access to the vast riches in the neighboring areas and to grain and goods from the South via the Grand Canal was Luoyang's greatest advantage. But there were no meaningful natural barriers like the Tong Pass to keep an invading army at bay. With the Hedong region (Shanxi) and Guanzhong under their control, the Tang had already formed a semi-circle around the city.

But Luoyang was not ready to surrender. The Luoyang-based warlord Wang Shichong had emerged as a power to be reckoned with, having trounced Li Mi's Wagang Army, and intruded into Dou Jiande's Kingdom of Xia. With an aquiline nose and pallid countenance, he descended from the Yuezhi, a people of Indo-European extraction. Jiangdu in the lower Yangzi had been his home base, where he had welcomed Emperor Yang in Daye 12 (616) and been responsible for His personal safety. Wang's transfer to Luoyang was indirectly responsible for the deterioration of Palace security and inadvertently contributed to the Emperor's murder.

Alarmed by the Tang invasion from Guanzhong, Wang had set up a numerous garrison at Cijian 40 *li* west of Luoyang.

The Tang general in charge of the Luoyang campaign was Prince Li Shimin, now the most formidable general of the Tang army with a near-impeccable track record.

By August of Wude 3 (620), the Prince had massed an army of 50,000 (including the original 30,000 and reinforcements) near Cijian. In response, Wang Shichong beefed up his garrison with 30,000 more troops.

Having set up camp, the Prince and Li Shiji, his second in command, ventured out on a reconnaissance mission, under the escort of 200 light cavalry. As they were trotting on an undulating field in the western suburb, suddenly, a band of enemy cavalry emerged from a patch of woods nearby led by a burly giant of a man wielding a spear.

"Prince of Qin!" Li Shiji shrieked out. "He is Shan Xiongxin! Be careful!"

Too close to draw his bow, the Prince lunged his long sword to engage Shan in a one-on-one combat. A swift thrust of Shan's spear scraped across the flank of the Prince's horse, causing him to wobble, and nearly throwing his rider off the saddle. It was at this juncture that two Tang Carriage-and-Horse Generals with a small band of riders rushed to the rescue. As Shan charged headlong toward them, the Prince turned his horse and galloped away.

When the Prince, Li Shiji, and the surviving Tang cavalrymen reached the gate of the stockaded Tang camp, it was already late afternoon.

"Open the gate," shouted the Prince in a hoarse voice. "This is Prince of Qin."

The camp sentries saw only an indistinct human figure on horseback covered with dust from head to toe and were not sure of his identity.

"Prove yourself," they shouted back.

"It is me!" the Prince shouted again in frustration, taking off his helmet.

After some hesitation, the sentries threw open the camp gate, and the Prince and his men rushed in.

THE INITIAL ENCOUNTER WITH the enemies that had nearly cost the Prince his life and resulted in the loss of dozens of his best riders, including the two Carriage-and-Horse Generals, was far from being a victory. But there was an unexpected upshot: Wang Shichong pulled his garrison forces out of Cijian. Upon capturing this outpost, the Prince started deploying his troops around Luoyang: in the Mang Hills to the north, at the Hulao Pass to the east, and near the Longmen Hills to the south. Two detachments on two separate missions seized Huiluo and Luokou with their famous granaries northeast of Luoyang.

The loss of Luokou on the south bank of the Yellow River was especially devastating to Luoyang's defenders, because the famous Luokou Granary had been their main storage facility for grain shipped from the North China Plain and the South. Cutting off access to the Granary effectively stopped the flow of grain into the city, which from then on was forced to live on its own dwindling grain reserves.

Having abandoned Cijian, Wang Shichong's army dug in at Qingcheng inside Luoyang's immense Western Park while Prince Li Shimin's army positioned itself to its west. The two camps were separated only by a small band of water. In desperation, Wang Shichong requested a parley with the Prince.

"After the fall of the Sui," Wang shouted on horseback to the other side, "the Emperor of Tang was set up in Guanzhong; and the Emperor of Zheng was set up in Henan. I as the Emperor of Zheng have not taken an inch of land from the west, why has the Prince of Qin invaded the east with a massive army?"

"I will tell you why," Yuwen Shiji, the Prince's deputy, declaimed. "All within the Four Seas have submitted themselves to the enlightening Imperial authority, with one exception—you. I would like to ask: why do you alone stand in the way of enlightenment?"

Wang asked back irrelevantly, "Can't we mend the fences and become peaceful neighbors?"

"Our Imperial edict," answered Yuwen Shiji, "instructs us to take the Eastern Capital but not to mend the fences."

Obviously, the dialogue was going nowhere. Wang Shichong turned back and withdrew into his camp crestfallen.

OF ALL THE GREAT heroes of the age, Dou Jiande most resembled Robin Hood. Born in an area that bordered on modern Hebei and Shandong, he raised the standard of rebellion in Daye 8 (612) and soon assembled a large army thanks in no small part to his clement policy towards war captives and his largesse towards his followers. His practice of robbing the rich to help the poor had won him many recruits from the bottom strata of society.

From Hebei he had been closely watching the situation in Henan and turned down repeated requests from Wang Shichong for assistance. There was no love lost between Dou and Wang. As recently as a year before, Dou's Kingdom of Xia had been invaded by Wang. With an army at least equal in size to that of the Tang, Dou was hoping to benefit from the Tang-Zheng war, which would weaken both belligerent parties. Recent developments, however, showed that most of Wang Shichong's local leaders had defected to the Tang and that Wang's regime in Luoyang might soon collapse.

Persistent pleas by his advisers finally awakened Dou Jiande to the sobering fact that the fall of Wang Shichong would jeopardize Xia's own existence, and forced Dou to abandon his policy of neutrality and come to the rescue of his former rival.

While waiting for Dou's rescue forces, Wang Shichong adopted the strategy of "taking the battle to the enemies" to keep the Tang army from gaining more ground. But he was worsted repeatedly, and lost in a matter of weeks, in succession, Qingcheng, the entire western suburb, and the Outer City of urban Luoyang. Eventually, the area under his control was reduced to the Palace City.

Upon entering the Outer City, Prince Li Shimin sent some of his troops to guard the three markets and the 100-odd residential Wards to prevent looting and harassment of businesses and residences. Having environed the Palace City, he launched a general assault from four sides. Several super-sized mangonels capable of hurling stones of 50 pounds for 200 paces pounded the Palace gates and wall battlements. Bolts of enormous size and weight—with heads as large as small adzes and stems as thick as carriage pokes—were propelled from gigantic crossbows.

In a span of two weeks, the Prince launched no less than 13 attacks by specially trained commandos on the gates and walls. But none was successful and most of the commandos perished in action. The exhausted Tang officers and men were demoralized.

"The army can do with a break," suggested one of the Prince's advisers.

"No," said the Prince firmly. "We must attack with full force to finish the enemies once and for all. Their Prefectures in the east have already surrendered. Luoyang is now an isolated city and cannot survive for long. We should not give up when victory is almost within reach!"

"But our soldiers are extremely tired. They need to return to camp for at least a brief rest."

"The enemies are even worse off. We have come so far already, and all we need now is a final push."

Still, petitions to suspend the campaign kept coming in. At length, the Prince had to issue an order to the entire army to stop them:

The army shall not return until Luoyang is sacked. Anyone who dares to speak of returning again shall be beheaded!

All potential remonstrators were silenced. But the Prince was caught by surprise when he received a secret rescript by the Emperor for immediate withdrawal. The Prince had no choice but to bring his troops back into camp. The Emperor was mainly concerned with the high casualty rate and Dou Jiande's rescue forces. After the Prince's military adviser Feng Deyi had made the case for his strategy, the Emperor relented and authorized the resumption of the campaign with the proviso that Dou Jiande should be intercepted long before he reached Luoyang.

The Prince sent an ultimatum to Wang Shichong in an effort to persuade him to surrender. Wang, however, encouraged by Dou Jiande's move, did not even bother to respond.

Meanwhile Dou Jiande was marching west and stopped at a place 20 *li* east of Hulao. From there he sent a letter to the Prince. Addressing himself as King of Xia, Dou offered peace on condition that Li retreat to the west of the Tong Pass, threatening to head west with an army of 300,000 if his offer was rejected.

The Prince was not intimidated by the letter, since he knew Dou had grossly exaggerated the size of his army, much of which was of dubious fighting value. Nonetheless, it attracted the Prince's attention. He decided to take on Dou first, and rode east to the Hulao Pass with 3,500 crack cavalry in April of Wude 4 (621).

For more than 20 days, Dou's army made no progress at all. Several of his advisers, supported by his wife, suggested an alternative. Instead of attempting to effect a junction with Wang Shichong, Dou's army should skip Luoyang altogether and move north to capture Shanxi, which would pose a direct threat to Chang'an and in turn lift the siege of Luoyang. While Dou clearly grasped the strategic rationale of the plan, he was more concerned with fulfilling his current commitment. "A promise is a promise," said he. "Right now, we are obligated to help Wang Shichong."

On the early morning of May 28, Dou's massive army began to move determinedly toward the Hulao. Marching to the accompaniment of drums, it stretched out over a distance of 20 *li*. Watching from the vantage point of a hilltop, Prince Li Shimin observed, "These bandit troops are not well disciplined at all. Since their rebellion in Shandong, they have not yet encountered a worthy adversary and clearly underestimated our strength. Just avoid combat with them for a while, their morale will sink. We can then strike, and clinch the victory."

On the east bank of the Si River, Dou's army came to a stop. Having arrayed his troops along the River, Dou sent 300 light cavalry across to challenge the Prince to a preliminary fight. They were met head-on by a Tang cavalry force of 200. After much cat-and-mouse action, both sides withdrew. Then, suddenly, Wang Shichong's general and envoy to Dou Jiande, Wang Wan, trotted onto the scene on the east bank. He was riding a tall white horse, who was immediately recognized as a favorite steed of Emperor Yang. As the horse caracoled and curveted up and down, the shining armor and long sword of his rider dazzled the eye under the morning sun.

"What a great horse!" the Prince could not help exclaiming.

"Let me capture the son of a bitch!" said General Yuchi Jingde, who had noticed Wang Wan's lack of escort.

Before the Prince could stop him, Yuchi was already galloping away on his bay horse, accompanied by two pursuivants. Their sudden move across the River took everyone by surprise. Before the enemies could react, Yuchi and his men had already seized hold of Wang Wan and his horse and galloped back to the west bank.

About noontime, Dou's troops, having been without food for the entire morning, showed signs of restlessness. Scuffles broke out here and there over drinking water. The Prince saw his chance and ordered General Yuwen Shiji to lead a squadron of 300 light horse across the river. Their task was to move south and distract the enemies. If the enemies stayed put, they should immediately return. If the enemies went after them, they should ride east as a decoy.

As soon as Yuwen Shiji landed on the east bank of the river, commotion broke out in the enemy's camp. "Charge!" the Prince yelled out his order to his adjutants, as he led a troop of light cavalry into battle. The Tang main force of horse and foot soon followed.

Dou Jiande was still holding court with his generals and officials in his campaign tent when the attack hit. Before he had time to array his men in battle formation, the

Tang vanguard forces launched a fierce attack. On Dou's orders, his ill-prepared troops made a frantic retreat, which soon turned into a debacle.

Dou frenziedly galloped east for 30 *li*, sustaining a few spear wounds along the way, until two Tang Chariot Generals overtook him and knocked him off his horse. As one of them held up his long spear to deliver the final thrust, Dou suddenly shouted, "I am the King of Xia. Don't kill me." The two Generals dismounted to seize him. By then Dou's mighty Kingdom of Xia had fallen.

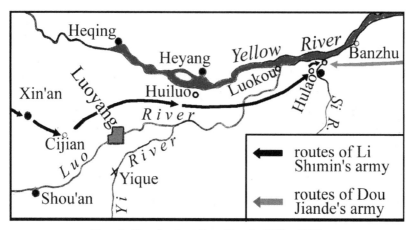

Map 5. War Against Dou Jiande (620−621)

22. The Battle for the Palace City

THE SITUATION INSIDE LUOYANG'S Palace City was beyond miserable. Of the 30,000 households recently forced into the enclosure, only about 3,000 remained. Food shortage was so severe that a bolt of silk could only buy three pints of grain. Jewelry and ornamental pieces were simply worthless. The area had been completely denuded of vegetation—all weeds, roots, and tree leaves and barks had been consumed for food. But Wang Shichong still refused to lay down his arms.

One morning, Wang mounted the south-central gatetower of the Palace City and saw in the distance a number of war captives being paraded in chains by the Tang troops. When he spotted Dou Jiande among them, his world crumbled.

On June 4th, Wang Shichong, dressed in white, emerged from the southern main gate of the Palace City. Walking closely behind was his Crown Prince, followed by Shan Xiongxin and 2,000 army officers and court officials. They proceeded slowly south across the Heavenly Ford (Tianjin) Bridge to the south side, where Prince Li Shimin, fully armored, was waiting on horseback.

Prostrating himself before his conqueror, Wang could not speak a word for a long while as sweat beaded his forehead.

"Come on, Shichong," said the Prince. "We used to play together when we were kids. Why so much formality? I am just an old play pal."

Kneeling up, Wang Shichong kowtowed repeatedly before he began to speak in a voice that was a hardly audible, "I deserve to die for having resisted the Tang army."

"Don't worry," said the Prince dismissively. "The court will never execute someone who surrendered his city."

Wang and his men were taken into custody. Prince Li Shimin's men spread out to take over the Palace City. Record Keeper (*jishi*) Fang Xuanling with a team of staffers and soldiers went straight to the Secretariat and Chancellery, to seize control of Sui archives and edicts. But none were found. Obviously, they had been destroyed by Wang Shichong. Xiao Yu, leading another team, headed for the Imperial storehouses. With the Prince's approval, the storehouses were briefly opened to allow some gold and silk to be taken out to reward meritorious officers and men, before they were locked and sealed.

On the following morning, the Prince entered the Palace City, where he was greeted by a cluster of imposing basilicas. The most spectacular of them was the Qianyang, the main hall of the Palace City. With tiered hipped roofs, flying eaves, and glazed yellow roof tiles, this edifice looked majestic and splendid from afar. The roofs were supported by a complex system of bearing blocks and bracket sets. Resting on an immense granite platform of 9 feet high, the basilica measured from ground to the owl-shaped rooftop ornament 170 feet in height, and 30 bays (a bay is similar to a Japanese *tsubo*) by 29 purlin spaces in area. Its three flights of steps were equipped with balustrades with studded railings and figured edging. The façade consisted of a colonnade with intricately carved round columns so thick that each one of them took 24 people to link arms around it. Once inside, one could not help noticing the cloud-patterned crossbeams and embroidered columns, ornate rafters, and jade finials.

A series of stone steps to the west led to the Guanwen Basilica (the Basilica for the Observation of Literature), dwarfed by the Qianyang in size, but distinguished by its ingenious design. Its two entrance halls were book halls, each of which had 12 bays. Each bay held 12 treasured bookcases. In front and back, there were bunk beds of fragrant wood, bedecked with gold and jade. Spanning across the 12 bays from north to south was the "lightning window," with wondrously carved numinous dragons facing one another. Gold knockers and jade rafter finials, elegant ceiling panels and luxurious rafters were dazzlingly brilliant. For every three bays there was a square double door. The door was covered with embroidered curtains; on top there were two flying apsaras; and in front of the door there was a mechanism on the ground. When stepped on, it would cause the apsaras to descend and the double-door leaves and bookcase doors to open.

Even after the ravages of war, the ornate ornaments and the luxurious architectural designs still stunned Li Shimin.

"This was how Emperor Yang (Yang Guang) gratified his insatiable desire for luxury," he observed. "It would have been a miracle if he did not stumble and fall."

On leaving the Palace City, the Prince issued an order that the gatetower of the End Gate, the watchtowers of the Zetian Gate, and the Qianyang Basilica itself be dismantled. The destruction of these prominent structures—whether it was an expression of his personal aversion or a symbolic act carried out on behalf of his father—showed the determination of the Tang to distinguish themselves from the decadent Sui.

ON THE NEXT DAY, Prince Li Shimin paid a visit incognito to the Yuqing Abbey in the west of the city, bringing with him a small group of associates and adjutants. Leaving his men at the Abbey's gate, Li went in with only one person, Fang Xuanling. Twenty-years older than the Prince, Fang had been awarded the prestigious *jinshi* (advanced scholar) degree at age 17 under Emperor Wen (Yang Jian) and was one of its earliest recipients in history.

It was in the west room of the main basilica that Master Wang Yuanzhi received them. In spite of his advanced age, Wang remained remarkably healthy. As soon as Li and Fang entered the room, he said,

"I can feel it: one of you is a Prince."

"Master, Prince of Qin is here to pay homage," said Fang Xuanling.

The Prince made a courtesy and said, "The Emperor would like to extend His gratitude. Now we honor Lord Lao as the divine ancestor of the Li clan thanks to you."

"Excellent. In fact, under the divine protection of Lord Lao, the Tang dynasty will bring peace and prosperity to all under Heaven, and will enjoy longevity."

After spending some time examining the physiognomy of the Prince, Wang said to him, "Now I have a secret message. But it is for your ears only."

Pointing to Fang Xuanling, the Prince said, "He is a trusted one. You can tell me what you want to say."

"All right. The message is this: Prince of Qin, sooner or later, you will become the Son of Heaven. And your reign will be long and peaceful."

The Prince was so taken aback that he remained speechless as Fang Xuanling said sharply, "Such talk will get the Prince into serious trouble."

"I know," said Wang. "I just want the Prince to know what lies in his future."

"From this day onward," resumed Wang, addressing the Prince, "every act of yours has to be carefully planned. If things do not go as planned, the consequences will be unthinkable."

For days after the miraculous meeting with the Master, Prince Li Shimin kept thinking about the implications of his message. He was tempted by the prospect of becoming the next sovereign, but could not convince himself of its viability. Although his father was already in His 50s, He was still going strong—*just look at the women He has slept with since Mother's death*—and Jiancheng's position as Crown Prince was as secure as ever. If a long and peaceful reign was in his future, how could he possibly attain the throne in the first place? Eventually, he had to let the thought be buried in the back of his mind.

IN COMPLIANCE WITH A Tang policy, only a small number of Wang Shichong's men—16 top military officers and civil officials—would be executed for war crime. They were condemned for a variety of different reasons. One of them was Du Yan, who had caused the death of his own nephew, in addition to being an influential official under Wang Shichong. One of the victim's brothers, Du Ruhui, happened to be on the staff of Prince Li Shimin. Even though of relatively low rank, Du Ruhui had ready access to the Prince as one of his favorite staffers. Overcoming his own aversion to Du Yan and urged by his relatives, Du Ruhui made a request for leniency on his uncle's behalf. The Prince then spared Yan's life, and the list of top criminals was shortened to 15.

To General Li Shiji, the fact that his friend Shan Xiongxin also made the death list was a surprise. He and Shan had become sworn brothers when serving in Li Mi's Wagang Army and were bound by an oath to die together. Feeling duty-bound to help his friend, Li brought up his case with the Prince.

"As a Tang subject," said Li Shiji, "I would give up all my titles and official posts in exchange for Shan's life."

"But he was the main reason that Wang Shichong held out for so long," said the Prince, unmoved by Li Shiji's plea.

"That may be true. But his loyalty and his unsurpassed fighting skills should make him a great Tang general."

"His hands are dripping with the blood of Tang soldiers. You saw how he killed the two Carriage-and-Horse Generals the other day. Shan Xiongxin must die."

After a further attempt to change the Prince's mind failed, Li Shiji left with tears in his eyes.

AS THE EXECUTION DATE drew near, Li Shiji paid a visit to Shan Xiongxin in prison.

"I know you won't be able to save me," Shan Xiongxin said ruefully.

"My apologies for failing to get you out. We took an oath, promising to die together as true sworn brothers. I wouldn't mind dying with you at all. But..."

"No, no. I didn't mean that."

"Now that I pledged allegiance to the state of Tang, I can no longer live up to our oath. However, if I die, who will take care of your wife and sons?"

"Shiji, you should not blame yourself for…" Before Shan Xiongxin could finish, Li Shiji pulled out a dagger from his boot, and sliced off a piece of flesh from his left thigh and offered it to Shan, saying, "For the sake of our friendship, eat it. Let my flesh accompany you to the Underworld."

"With a friend like you, I will die content," said a teary-eyed Shan as he picked up the blood-dripping flesh and swallowed it.

On the following morning, the 15 condemned men were trussed up and paraded in the markets and residential Wards before they were brought to the south side of the Heavenly Ford (Tianjin) Bridge. They were then dragged onto a makeshift scaffold and forced to kneel down in a line. As the slaughterers lopped off their heads, boisterous cheers issued forth from the multitude of spectators. Among them was Li Shiji, who was quietly bidding goodbye to his best friend Shan Xiongxin.

23. Li Shimin's Return

ON AUGUST 1, WUDE 4 (621), Chang'an opened its arms to welcome Prince of Qin Li Shimin as the great hero of the civil war. Both sides of Zhuquemen Avenue, the north-south thoroughfare, were lined with people, dressed in their holiday best. They cheered energetically as the Prince, clad in gold-plated armor and riding a tall, white war-horse, emerged from the Mingde Gate—the southern main entrance of the city. A long procession followed, marching amidst the roll of drums, the blare of trumpets, and the fluttering of banners. Riding closely behind the Prince were 25 mounted generals, Li Yuanji and Li Shiji among them, followed by 10,000 cavalry in iron armor, and 30,000 armored warriors on foot. At the end of the procession were the spoils of war, including dozens of Sui Imperial carriages, and the most famous prisoners of war, Dou Jiande and Wang Shichong.

The Emperor, dressed in ritual vestments, led three dozen top civil and military leaders to greet the Prince outside the Zhuque Gate at the northern terminus of Zhuquemen Avenue. Father and son then proceeded to the Ancestral Temple (in the southeast corner of the Imperial City), where they made sacrifices to the ancestral spirits and where the spoils of war were presented.

THE NEXT MORNING, WHEN the Emperor was sitting in the audience hall of the Liangyi Basilica, Dou Jiande was brought into His presence. The Emperor almost felt sorry for this great hero of the age, the archrival of the Tang. All his arrogance gone, Dou stood there trussed up, with his head bowed low, and his face pale and wan. The Emperor went up to him, untied his hands, and asked him to sit down.

"Dou Jiande," the Emperor began, "do you admit your crimes?"

"Not really, Your Majesty. When the immoral Sui lost the Mandate of Heaven, power became fair game. All the heroes under Heaven chased after it."

"Fair enough. But you had no business in trying to prevent us from taking Luoyang."

"Perhaps. But I hope Your Majesty could see things from my perspective. The fall of Luoyang and the Central Plain would bring grave danger to the Kingdom of Xia."

"So you launched a massive invasion with a force of 300,000?"

"Well, I cited that number in my letter. But that was a bit of an exaggeration. It was closer to 200,000."

"What happened next?"

"It was worsted by Your Majesty's army under Prince of Qin Li Shimin."

"How was it possible, considering Shimin's army was grossly outnumbered?"

"I have to admit that the Prince was either a military genius or was extremely lucky. Anyway, he chose the right moment to strike at my headquarters before I had time to array my troops in battle order."

The Emperor paused for a while before He resumed, as if with a heavy heart, "Speaking of Prince of Qin, I am sorry to inform you, that he has recommended capital punishment. Unless you can change My mind, I will have to support his recommendation and make an example of those who defy us. Do you have anything to say in your defense?"

After a long silence, Dou said calmly, "No, Your Majesty. But if I may, I would like to request a favor."

"Say it."

"I take full responsibility for what I have done. But my wife has all along opposed my move to rescue Luoyang. Could Your Majesty spare her life?"

After a brief pause, the Emperor said, "Your request is granted." The Emperor then motioned to have Dou Jiande taken out of the hall. A few moments later, Wang Shichong was brought in.

"Why did you repeatedly ignore Prince of Qin's request for surrender?" the Emperor asked sharply.

"It was a bad decision, Your Majesty."

"Your 'decision' had cost thousands of Tang soldiers' lives."

"What I did clearly deserves the most severe punishment. But the Prince has promised to spare my life."

"We'll keep our promise. But you still have to be punished. You shall spend the rest of your life in exile in Shu (in the southwest), and never be allowed to return to the capital."

"I am sincerely grateful for Your Majesty's leniency."

The Emperor waved His right hand, and Wang was marched out of the room.

As Wang was getting ready to leave for his place of banishment, his past caught up with him. One of his personal enemies stabbed him to death in his Chang'an home.

24. Du Ruhui and Li Shentong

THANKS TO HIS VICTORIES over Dou Jiande and Wang Shichong, Prince Li Shimin's power base was greatly enhanced. Among his most loyal supporters were Zhangsun Wuji (his brother-in-law), Gao Shilian (Zhangsun's uncle and stepfather), Fang Xuanling (a great strategist), Hou Junji (a rising star in the military), and the fearless Yuchi Jingde who had joined the Tang after the defeat of Song Jingang. More recently, Du Ruhui, an able administrator, and Li Shentong, a cousin of the Emperor and a powerful general, had also come under Li Shimin's wing.

Soon, however, Du Ruhui and Li Shentong would get Prince Li Shimin into serious trouble with the Emperor in an unexpected way.

One morning, as Du Ruhui was riding past a private residence with palatial houses in a Ward near the Eastern Market, he was accosted by three manservants hurling insults. Before Du could react, he was dragged off his horse, and given a thrashing that left him with a broken little finger.

"Next time, we'll not let you get off so easy!" howled one of them.

"What have I done?" Du asked, puzzled at the reason for his mistreatment.

"Don't you see? This is the Yin Residence."

"The Yin Residence?"

"The Residence of Yin Ashu! You have to dismount to show respect each time you ride past."

"I see," Du said as he bit his swollen lips, got on his horse, and rode away at a slow trot.

Prince Li Shimin was livid with anger when he found out how his adviser's little finger had been broken. Under normal circumstances, he would have lodged a complaint with the Metropolitan Prefect, the leading Magistrate of the capital. However, the case was complicated by the fact that the perpetrators all worked for Yin Ashu, the father of Consort Yin. The consort not only ranked the highest among the 121 titled Imperial concubines, but was also one of the Emperor's favorites. Unofficially, she filled the role of Ms. Dou, who had died in 613. Because she was not named Empress, the son she had with the Emperor, Li Yuanheng, was not in line for the throne. Nevertheless, she was the most trusted of those women whom the Emperor often shared bed with. Her power gave her father an air of arrogance that rubbed off on his minions. The local authorities virtually had no jurisdiction over him and his men. So the Prince reported the case directly to his own father, the Emperor. But no sooner had he finished his account of the unhappy incident than he was upbraided by the Emperor for unjustly protecting Du who had acted "aggressive" towards Yin Ashu and his servants. Apparently, the Emperor had already been fed a version of the incident by the consort. In the end, not only did the Prince fail to have the injustice done to his adviser rectified, he had to apologize on his behalf to soothe the ire of the Emperor.

Li Shentong's trouble was of a different kind, but had a similar outcome. Because of his military merit, Prince of Qin Li Shimin rewarded him, with the court's approval, with a large swath of land in Shandong. But the property also attracted the attention of a certain Mr. Zhang, a local upstart, whose interest would have meant little, had it not been for his daughter, Fair Lady (*jieyu*) Zhang, another one of the Emperor's women. Much younger than Consort Yin, Lady Zhang never enjoyed the same status at court. But she managed to win the favor of the Emperor with charm, youth, and beauty. However, by the time she was admitted into the Harem, the Emperor had passed His prime, and she was not able to give birth to a single child for Him. And yet her ability to have the ear of the Emperor made her powerful. It was at her request that the same piece of land in Shandong was granted to her father by an Imperial edict. When Mr. Zhang went to take possession of the land, and got rejected, he reported it through his daughter to the Emperor, who immediately summoned the Prince of Qin for questioning.

"How come a Prince's order is worth much more than an Imperial edict?" the Emperor asked sharply.

"I am awfully sorry, Your Majesty," said Prince Li Shimin. "I was completely unaware of Li Shentong's rejection." He sounded obsequious, since he understood that suspicion of defying Imperial authority could prove disastrous. After the meeting, Li Shimin lost no time in forcing Li Shentong to issue an apology to Mr. Zhang and yield the disputed land to him.

25. The Crown Prince and His Little Brother

BY THE END OF Wude 4 (621), most of the realm had been brought under Tang rule. With the crushing of Dou Jiande and Wang Shichong, the entire North China Plain, including the Central Plain, became a Tang domain. The separatist state in the Middle Yangzi headed by Xiao Xian was annexed, thanks to the brilliant campaign launched by General Li Jing, a great strategist, and General Li Xiaogong, a royal. The rebel leader Du Fuwei in the Lower Yangzi was co-opted. In the far north, it was true that the Tujue still conducted cross-border raids, but they had virtually run out of Han Chinese proxies to wreak havoc with the Tang farming communities, and their relations with the Tang were actually on the mend.

The only serious trouble spot south of the Great Wall was the rebel regime recently founded by a middle-aged man called Liu Heita. Based in Zhangnan (near Wucheng,

Shandong), Liu had served as Dou Jiande's general. After the fall of Dou's Kingdom of Xia, he returned to farming. The execution of Dou Jiande, who had treated high-profile Tang captives (including Li Shiji's father) well, was widely considered unfair, and the relentless campaign to hunt down Dou's erstwhile supporters was extremely unpopular among ex-officers of Dou's army. Some of them subsequently staged an open rebellion against the Tang. Liu Heita joined them and soon became their leader.

The explosive growth of Liu Heita's rebel army took everyone concerned by surprise. Xu Yuanlang, who had been Li Mi's general, responded by starting his own rebellion in Shandong, taking over Yan Prefecture and declaring himself King of Lu.

The Emperor appointed Li Shentong to head the suppression effort. But Li Shentong's army was soon worsted. Li Shimin and his brother Li Yuanji were called upon to fight Liu Heita, who had captured much of Dou Jiande's lands in Hebei and emerged as the biggest threat to the Tang after the fall of Wang Shichong.

By early Wude 5 (622), Prince Li Shimin had positioned himself on the south bank of the Ming River (somewhere north of Xingtai in south Hebei), and entrenched himself. In spite of the enemy's repeated provocations, the Prince refused to engage them. Instead, he secretly sent small detachments to cut off Liu's land and water transport routes and dam the upper reaches of the Ming. As the Prince bided his time the enemies became starved and anxious. Then, on May 16, without any warning, the Prince started a general assault at noon and had the dam breached in the late afternoon. Having been forewarned of the flooding, the Tang troops managed to move to higher ground and were essentially unharmed. Liu's army, however, was all but destroyed by a torrent of water that inundated the battlefield.

Liu Heita somehow survived the Ming River debacle, and went north to join the Tujue. After Prince Li Shimin's return to Chang'an, Liu made a comeback, backed by tens of thousands of Tujue cavalry. By the end of the year, he had won a number of victories and penetrated as far as south Henan and west Shandong.

THE BADMOUTHING BY THE Imperial concubines notwithstanding, Prince of Qin Li Shimin remained in good graces with his father. As Premier of the Department of State Affairs, he was by default the most powerful leader of the bureaucracy. The Department with its Six Boards—those of Personnel, Revenue, Rites, Works, Justice, and War—held executive powers at the highest level. As Commander-in-chief of the Tang armies in a series of victorious campaigns, he had forged close bonds with some of the best Tang generals. After his return from Shandong, the Emperor rewarded him with even more titles and privileges. A special military post was created just for him, that of "Superior General of Celestial Strategy," with a rank higher than all the Princes but Crown Prince Li Jiancheng. An administration was set up for this post, complete with its own generals, adjutants, and staffers. Crowning it all, Li Shimin was granted the privilege to found the Institute for Literature (Wenxue *guan*), a think-tank of sorts, housed in the west part of the Palace. The Institute had 18 academicians, all Shimin's followers.

For the first time, Crown Prince Li Jiancheng felt seriously threatened. It was true that he had been made heir not only because of his age and maturity but also because of his proven administrative and military abilities. It was also true that he had played an important role in the founding of the Tang dynasty. However, after the court had been set up in Chang'an and he had taken up residence in the Eastern Palace, he had not been given a single opportunity to lead a military operation. Since the founding of the Tang, it was his younger brother Li Shimin who had covered himself with military glory. With these reflections in mind, he called in Wei Zheng, his top adviser, for consultation in the Cheng'en Basilica.

"Your Highness is in trouble," Wei said frankly.

"Why?"

"You are now living in the Eastern Palace only because you are the eldest son of the Emperor. But your brother Li Shimin is the one who has won all the victories on the battlefield. To all under Heaven, you haven't done anything important in recent years to deserve the post of Crown Prince at all. Neither do you hold much real power. By contrast, Li Shimin controls both the bureaucracy and the military. He even has his own think-tank."

"The Institute for Literature?"

"Yes."

"But that is an institution of learning, isn't it?"

"At the Institute there are scholars such as Kong Yingda and Lu Deming among the academicians. However, people like Fang Xuanling and Du Ruhui—they are no scholars, but advisers on strategy. In my view, the 'Institute' is just a front. You don't know what they are planning under the guise of promoting literature."

"What should I do?" Li Jiancheng asked, alarmed.

"Your Highness has to acquire military merit before it is too late."

"How?"

"Relatively speaking, Liu Heita is an easy target. True, he has regained some of his lands since Li Shimin's campaign. But his armed force is small, barely 10,000. Without massive Tujue support, he can be defeated in short order. Such a victory will allow you to garner support among the magnates in Shandong and help you build up your power base at court."

"All right," Jiancheng said in agreement.

A few days later, with a special approval from the Emperor, Li Jiancheng was put in charge of the military operations in Hebei, Henan, and Shandong. In January of Wude 6 (623), he launched a campaign against Liu Heita. But the main force of his army came to a halt at Nanle (Changle, Henan), where the enemies offered stubborn resistance.

"We should release the enemy's prisoners-of-war," Wei Zheng proposed.

"Why?" asked Li Jiancheng.

"Liu Heita's generals are loyal to him because of their fear of us. Previously, whenever the Tang army won a victory, it released a list of Liu's officers condemned to death in absentia while holding their captured wives and children in bondage. That is why recent announcements by the court to pardon them are not convincing. By releasing the prisoners-of-war, we can not only prove our sincerity, but also help destroy the cohesiveness of Liu's army."

"Excellent!" exclaimed Li Jiancheng. "Without cohesiveness, Liu's army will fall apart."

So on Li Jiancheng's orders, all the enemy captives under his control were set free. Initially, what Wei Zheng predicted did not happen. However, when Liu Heita's grain reserves were nearly exhausted, many deserted him. Some even went over to the Tang camp, taking their officers in bonds with them. Under attack by Li Jiancheng and Li Yuanji, Liu Heita retreated north as his followers dwindled to a few hundreds. His luck finally ran out when one of his subordinate officers kidnapped him before delivering him to the Tang. Li Jiancheng then had his head cut off and delivered to Chang'an.

Soon, the other rebel leader in Shandong Xu Yuanlang, his army destroyed by Li Shentong and Li Shiji, was on the run and killed in the field by peasants.

AN UNEXPECTED OUTCOME OF the war against Liu Heita was the strengthened bond between the Crown Prince Li Jiancheng and his little brother Li Yuanji. Not long after his return to the Eastern Palace, Li Jiancheng paid a visit to Yuanji one evening, to express his gratitude for the latter's help.

"At least I don't have to worry too much about being outshone by Shimin any more," said Jiancheng.

"But," said Yuanji, apparently unconvinced, "you still have a long way to go."

"Do you really think so?"

"Yes. I know Shimin very well. During the war against Liu Wuzhou I was with him day and night. He is an extremely ambitious man."

"In what way?"

"It is obvious he wants the throne."

"No, he doesn't!"

"Believe me, he does. The Superior General's Administration and the Institute for Literature are actually the military and civil arms of his shadow government. They will take over power as soon as he seizes the throne."

"Suppose what you just said is true," said Jiancheng, surprised at his little brother's tone of hostility, "what has to be done to curb his ambitions?"

"Get rid of him," Yuanji said tersely.

"Fratricide?"

"Brother, if you don't do it, you will live to regret it."

"I think I can contain him."

"All right, if that's what you want. But you have to act soon. By the way, I may be able to help."

The two brothers continued to talk well into the night.

ABOUT TWO WEEKS LATER, Li Yuanji made a surprise visit to the Eastern Palace apparently with a secret message. Having dismissed his attendants, Crown Prince Li Jiancheng asked, "What brings you here, Brother?"

"Well, I was told that the Emperor will visit my residence the day after tomorrow."
"So?"
"Both you and Shimin will come with Him."
"So what?"
"The party will spend a night in my place and leave next morning." Lowering his voice, Li Yuanji continued, "I can hide a killer inside Shimin's bedroom and ask him to do the job at night."

Suppressing his disbelief, the Crown Prince asked, "Who is the killer?"

"Yuwen Bao, a brave warrior. He owes his life to me, and will die for me without blinking. But if we plan it well, the chance of his getting caught is none."

"I think it is too rash."

"Hey, Brother. It is for you, not for myself."

"Whatever you say, I am not going to allow it to happen."

The meeting broke up unpleasantly. But it alerted Li Jiancheng to the potential threat Shimin posted to him as heir and started him thinking about plans for eventualities. The first measure he took was to strengthen his guard force. Through his former guard officer Yang Wengan, more than 2,000 cavalry from Qing Prefecture (in northeast Gansu), were transferred to the Eastern Palace. They were all selected for bravery and excellent fighting skills, and quartered in barracks near the Right and Left Long Wood Gates of the Eastern Palace. With the help of another associate 300 assault cavalry were transferred from You Prefecture (in north Hebei). Billeted in the residential Wards east of the Eastern Palace, they served as a backup force to the Long Wood Gate guard units.

26. Lady Zhang

ABOUT 300 *LI* NORTH of Chang'an, the sprawling Renzhi (Benevolence and Wisdom) Palace (in Tongchuan, Shaanxi) was under construction. Most of its structures were situated in the Yuhua Mountains. Known for its cool temperatures and scenic vistas, the Renzhi was an ideal summer resort.

In June of Wude 7 (624), the Palace was completed, and the Emperor Li Yuan, who could hardly tolerate the oppressive summer months in the Palace City, made His first visit. His stay was thoroughly enjoyable until He received a disturbing report that an officer in Qing Prefecture (seat: Qingyang, Gansu) called Yang Wengan was suspected of a secret plot against the throne. One of his backers was allegedly the Crown Prince! In a fit of fury the Emperor threatened to depose him. But, eventually, after His temper cooled, He decided to call him to account first.

In the Imperial entourage, there were two Princes, Li Shimin and Li Yuanji. The Crown Prince was left in Chang'an to take care of government business as Vicegerent.

In fairness to Crown Prince Li Jiancheng, he was not privy to the secret plot at all. Although he had been involved in some secret activities of his own, they were of an entirely different nature. His official residence, the Eastern Palace, was linked to the Taiji Palace through the Right Long Wood Gate. As the primary resident of the Eastern Palace, he was physically close to the Taiji, including its Harem, which housed the Emperor's women. One of them was Lady Zhang, who had been able to keep company with the Emperor (which was not necessarily sexually unsatisfying) more often than most, but nonetheless felt frustrated because He was constantly distracted by other women. Besides, she was in her early 20s and He was getting old.

Because of her ability to charm the Emperor, she was considered one of the most powerful women at court. When the Crown Prince started looking for possible political allies around the throne, Lady Zhang was at the top of his list. He sent her expensive gifts—jade bracelets, gold and silver hairpins, pouncet boxes, diamond necklaces, jeweled brooches, and such like.

When he received a thank-you note from her, he was pleased. It took the form of an enigmatic poem. And the Prince did not think much of it until he read it acrostically from left to right at night and discovered a hidden message: "Thinking of Jiancheng." The Crown Prince was thrilled. Still, he wanted to make sure he did not misread her. So he had a red silk love-knot placed in a silver cosmetic box, and had it sent over with other gifts to Lady Zhang. It lit up an unquenchable fire in her. She sent him a secret reply to indicate her appreciation of his gesture.

After several more exchanges, they decided to meet in private. Dressed as an unranked court lady and accompanied by two trusted maids, she arrived in a small basilica of the Yiqiu Palace in the northwest part of the Eastern Palace. She was led to a secluded chamber on the second floor, where she and the Prince consummated their amorous passion.

After the first rendezvous, they met frequently; the Emperor's preoccupation with other women gave them the opportunities. However, when the Emperor departed for the Renzhi Palace, He took Lady Zhang with Him.

RESIDENT IN CHANG'AN, THE Prince had expected to receive the Lady's secret love letters from the Renzhi. But none was forthcoming. Instead, one day, an Imperial envoy arrived with an urgent summons that left the Prince frozen with terror. Even though the summons did not specify the reason, he feared for the worst. For his sin—making a cuckold out of the Emperor—he would surely lose his chance for the throne and probably his own life for good measure.

One adviser urged open rebellion using Chang'an as his base. Another disagreed—the risk was too great—and argued that he should instead make the visit to the Renzhi, riding in a plainly decorated carriage, without his usual entourage, and dressed in simple attire. After some hesitation, he set off with a small suite of men. When they reached Maohongbin Castle 60 *li* from the Renzhi, he left most of his staff in a local inn and completed the rest of the journey with only a dozen cavalry.

BY THE TIME THE Crown Prince was brought face-to-face with the Emperor, the latter was still in a foul mood.

"Your guilty son is here to pay homage to Your Majesty," the Prince said, sounding very remorseful.

"What are you guilty of?"

"I don't know exactly, Your Majesty."

"But why declare yourself guilty?"

"Your Majesty looks unhappy. I must have done something wrong to cause it."

"Well then, how well do you know Yang Wengan?"

"He was a middle-ranking officer in an Eastern Palace guard unit," the Prince answered, relieved that the Old Man made no mention of his illicit affair. "He was posted to Qing Prefecture a while ago. I know him personally, but not very well."

"He is suspected of plotting against the throne with *your* support!"

His face turning pale, the Prince dropped down on his knees and started hitting his forehead against the marble floor repeatedly, shouting, "Spare my life, Father. I swear on the honor of my ancestors I don't know anything about the plot."

"How do you explain the 2,000 cavalry?"

"They were recruited from Qing Prefecture. But their job is to guard the Eastern Palace. They have nothing to do with Yang Wengan's evil intentions."

An intense interrogation followed until the Emperor felt tired and ordered Li Jiancheng taken into custody.

Two days later, the Emperor received more bad news. Yang Wengan, defying the Imperial summons, openly rebelled in Qing Prefecture. Yuwen Ying (Director of the Court for Agriculture), the Imperial envoy appointed to summon him, had betrayed the court and joined the rebel.

A frustrated Emperor called in Prince of Qin Li Shimin for consultation.

"Since the rebellion probably involves Jiancheng as well," the Emperor said gravely, "it may have much support at court. We have to send a most powerful person. In fact, Shimin, I think you should go. I've made up My mind. Once you return, I will make you Crown Prince, and demote Jiancheng to Prince of Shu. This is as much as I can do. I just can't follow Emperor Wen's example, condemning His first Crown Prince. On the other hand, the Shu area is weak militarily. After you come to power, if Jiancheng is willing to serve you, you should tolerate him. If not, you can take him down easily."

Prince Li Shimin left the Renzhi and went quietly on his mission, pleased with his father's promise. Master Wang Yuanzhi's prediction was coming true after all.

When Li Shimin arrived in Qing Prefecture, the anti-government rebellion was over. Yang Wengan had been killed, and his main accomplice captured.

By the time Li Shimin returned to the Renzhi, his prospects of becoming Crown Prince had vanished. During his absence, both Consort Yin and Lady Zhang had made several attempts to persuade the Emperor to withdraw His decision against Crown Prince Li Jiancheng. At court, Li Yuanji and Feng Deyi, now a Chief Minister, had taken turns to remonstrate with Him for the same purpose.

Since his involvement in the rebellious plot could not be proven, Li Jiancheng was pardoned and allowed to return to Chang'an to continue to serve as Vicegerent. Nonetheless, two of his advisers were sent into exile as a token punishment. Anxious not to look biased in favor of Li Shimin, the Emperor exiled one of his advisers as well.

27. The Debate on the Capital

IN MID-AUGUST, THE EMPEROR Li Yuan and His entourage returned to Chang'an and there was a renewed fear of the Tujue. Their leader Xieli Khan, egged on by his wife, a Sui Princess, had intruded deep inside Tang territory, posing a serious threat to the capital. At the Emperor's request, the court advisers proposed a long-term solution for the Tujue problem:

The reason that the Tujue have raided Guanzhong repeatedly is the presence of wealth—jades, silks, and gold and silver—and beautiful women in Chang'an. If we burn down the city and move the capital elsewhere, the Tujue raids will stop by themselves.

The proposal had won the support of Crown Prince Li Jiancheng, Prince of Qi Li Yuanji, Pei Ji, and other key figures at court. Finally, the Emperor gave His nod, and asked Yuwen Shiji to look for a possible site for a new capital south of the South Mountains (Nanshan).

"However," said Li Shimin contentiously to Xiao Yu, "the move of the capital will be horrendously costly and can only be achieved on the backs of corvée labor drafted from the fields. Haven't we learned any lessons from Emperor Yang's Luoyang? The Tang is still young, and a reckless move like this could bring about serious social unrest and perhaps even the ruin of the dynasty."

"You are absolutely right, Prince of Qin," Xiao Yu said with sympathy. "But it has been decided by the Emperor with the support of much of the court."

"We have to stop it."

"But how?"

The Prince did not answer. That night, he wrote a memorial, and submitted it in person to the throne the following morning. It read:

Barbarians have conducted raids into China since antiquity. But Your Majesty with His elite army of a million strong has proven invincible against them. There is no reason to move the capital simply because of recent barbarian raids. The move will make us a laughing stock to all within the Four Seas for a hundred generations. In the past, General Huo Qubing of Han spoke courageously of vanquishing the Xiongnu single-handedly. Today, our frontier garrisons are in a much better position than those of the Han; and we can surely confront the Tujue. Please give me a few years, I will capture Xieli Khan and bring him to the court. If I fail, the court can move the capital then.

"This proposal," responded Crown Prince Li Jiancheng, "reminds me of the obstreperous Fan Kuai of Han. He once bragged about leading an army of 100,000 to crush the Xiongnu, for whom the Han were clearly no match."

Fan Kuai was the Han general who insisted on killing the Xiongnu emissary who had delivered a disrespectful letter to the ruling Empress, and starting a Xiongnu war in 192 BCE. Eventually, cooler heads prevailed and the war the Han could not win was avoided.

Angry with the comparison, Li Shimin retorted, "Now the situation is quite different. It is simply inappropriate to bring up Fan Kuai, a lightweight. In all seriousness, the Tujue lands north of the Gobi Dessert can be conquered in less than a decade."

A ragged debate followed until the two brothers started exchanging insults. The Emperor had to issue an order to stop them.

Although Li Shimin's memorial did not impress his elder brother, it caused the Emperor to have second thoughts on the plan to move the capital, which He eventually put on hold indefinitely. But Li Jiancheng and his supporters in the Harem, Consort Yin, Lady Zhang, and others, did not give up. "The Tujue have caused a lot of trouble on the frontier," they said, "and it is much cheaper to buy them off than to contain them. The Prince of Qin says he wants to fight the barbarians, but what he really wants is to dominate the army."

Such backbiting did not change the Emperor's view of Li Shimin. However, it made Him painfully aware of the acrimonious tension between Shimin and his elder brother.

28. The Li Brothers

SOUTH OF CHANG'AN WAS the Shaoling Plain, a vast wilderness, which was home to a rich variety of wild animals: boars, feral horses, moose, deer, foxes, hares, and different types of water fowls: herons, kingfishers, swans, cormorants, cranes. Because of its convenient location, it was a favorite hunting ground for the royal.

Early one morning, Prince of Qin Li Shimin went hunting there. As he chased after a herd of deer on horseback with his bow drawn, he shot at and hit two of them, a doe and a fawn. Several hounds rushed forward to drag the carcasses from the bushes. The hunt continued until noontime. He rode to the royal hunting lodge and dismounted while his attendants took the wild game he had killed into a storage room: five deer, a dozen hares, and two boars.

Ascending a flight of steps, Li Shimin went inside the lodge and saw the Emperor sitting at a long table with goblets and flagons. Opposite the Emperor on a long bench sat His two sons, Jiancheng and Yuanji. They were drinking and talking jovially. Responding to his father's beckoning hand, Li Shimin sat down on the bench beside Jiancheng and joined the merriment. Several goblets of wine later, the Emperor stood up to propose that the three brothers bury the hatchet. At His urging they hugged one another, and took turns to drink from the same goblet of wine, pledging eternal brotherly love.

After father and sons consumed a repast prepared with wild game, the three brothers, at the instance of their father, walked together towards the woods, where they would take part in friendly contests in archery and equestrian skills like in the good old days. As the Emperor watched their backs fade into the distance, He shed tears of joy for the first time in a long time.

In a gesture of friendship, Jiancheng brought up a stout Tujue bay horse with black mane and tail.

"Shimin," said Jiancheng, "this is a great horse. It can jump over ditches 10 paces wide. Why don't you give him a try?"

Li Shimin accepted the offer and mounted the steed. Immediately, he began to curvet violently. Shimin pressed his legs firmly against the silky sides of the horse, his hands tightly clutching his mane. Refusing to be tamed, the horse struggled desperately to throw off his rider in a series of sudden leaps and bounds until Li Shimin jumped into the air to land on his feet several paces away. Having made two more attempts to break the horse, Li Shimin gave up.

Obviously upset, Shimin said to his companion Yuwen Shiji, "Life and death is determined by the will of Heaven. What is the use of trying to harm me?"

A few days later, Li Shimin appeared on an Imperial summons before the Emperor in the Ganlu Basilica where Jiancheng and Yuanji were also present.

"You are being too arrogant, Shimin," said He, flushed with anger. "How can you say something like, 'Following Heaven's will, I will become the sovereign of all under Heaven.'"

"Your Majesty, I did not…"

"Don't you deny it, Shimin," yelled the Emperor. Having been informed by Lady Zhang of the equestrian incident, He was not interested in Shimin's self-defense.

After Jiancheng and Yuanji had left, the Emperor said in a reproachful voice: "Shimin, succession to the throne is determined by Heaven's will, not something you can get through wishful thinking!"

Falling on his knees, Li Shimin took off his cap, kowtowed, and said, "Your Majesty, these words were not exactly what I said."

"Put on your cap and sit down."

Li Shimin did as his father ordered.

"Tell Me what you did say," said the Emperor.

"What I said is, 'Life and death is determined by the will of Heaven. What is the use of trying to harm me?'"

"But what I heard is different."

"If Your Majesty finds it hard to believe, I would like to subject myself to an investigation by the Board of Justice."

"That won't be necessary," said the Emperor, waving His hand dismissively. "Perhaps I can give you the benefit of the doubt this time. But, I want you to remember this: if you covet something that is not rightfully yours, there will be serious consequences."

29. Fu Yi

THE TUJUE SCARE SOON dissipated. The period of relative peace that followed allowed the Emperor to devote more attention to domestic issues. One of them was religion. From the beginning of the Tang, He had adhered to a policy of religious toleration. However, after being on the throne for almost eight years, He began to doubt its wisdom. While He did not necessarily have any enmity toward Buddhism itself, He was worried about its dynamic growth and negative impact on the economy, and wanted to rein it in. It was then that He received a memorial from Grand Astrologer

Fu Yi calling for the abolition of Buddhism. In many ways a successor to An Qieluo, Fu was in charge of divination, astrology, and predicting disasters for the court. Fu took as his model in life Zhangqiu Zituo, a thaumaturge of the Northern Qi, who had blasted the wastefulness of the Buddhist clergy and sangha. Thrown into jail for his audacious remarks, Zhangqiu, remaining true to his belief, was executed in the market of the Qi capital Ye for blasphemy.

For His part, the Emperor would never approve of outright abolition. Nonetheless, He held a special court session in the assembly hall of the Lizheng Basilica to discuss ways to curb the growth of the religion. But, of the hundred or so officials and officers present, only one was supportive of Fu Yi's proposal. Xiao Yu expressed the majority view when he said, "The Buddha is a great sage. Fu Yi criticizes the Sage and defies the Law, and should thus be prosecuted."

Undaunted, Fu Yi rejoined, "Of human relations, none are greater than those between us and our fathers and between us and our sovereigns. The Buddha was the heir of his father, but he betrayed him by renouncing the mundane world. The Buddhists are commoners, but they refuse to reverence their fathers and sovereigns. Thus Buddhism is a religion that belittles fathers and sovereigns. Yet Xiao Yu believes in it. The *Classic of Filial Piety* says, 'Those who are not filial do not have parents.' That must apply to him."

Not knowing how to refute Fu Yi, Xiao Yu brought his two palms together in front, and uttered softly, "Hell is set up just for people like him."

"I am not terribly interested in these issues," interjected the Emperor. "However, it is a fact that the Buddhist monks and Daoist adepts avoid corvée duties and taxation, and disobey laws and regulations. Just like what Fu Yi has said. Furthermore, Buddhist monasteries and Daoist abbeys are often located close to bazaars and hostels, and their clerics rub shoulders with lowly slaughterers and traders. Something must be done about it."

Using Fu Yi's memorial as an excuse and ignoring widespread opposition at court and beyond, the Emperor issued an edict on April 22, Wude 9 (626) to greatly reduce the size of the Buddhist and Daoist clergies, and the number of Buddhist monasteries and Daoist abbeys. In Chang'an there were more than 100 Buddhist monasteries and convents and about a dozen or so Daoist abbeys and nunneries. Of these, only three Buddhist institutions and two Daoist ones would be allowed to survive. All others were slated for destruction or secularization. Most of the clerics were to be laicized and returned to their native communities.

Members of the officialdom, overwhelmingly Buddhist, accepted the policy with resignation, but they dragged their feet on its implementation.

30. The Wine Party at the Eastern Palace

IN MIDSUMMER, CROWN PRINCE Li Jiancheng hosted a wine party in the Eastern Palace to celebrate his birthday. Among his guests were the Imperial Princes including Li Shimin, with whom he had been reconciled thanks to efforts by their father.

The party started in the late afternoon and continued well into the night. When Jiancheng challenged Shimin to a drinking contest, Shimin took him on. After Shimin had quaffed down his second jug of wine, he felt a twinge in his solar plexus and collapsed onto the floor. Li Shentong helped him to his feet and two servants carried him to his palanquin, which conveyed him to his residence, the Hongyi Palace (built by the Emperor in 622) west of the Palace City.

IN HER BEDROOM AT the Hongyi, Ms. Zhangsun was looking at herself in a bronze mirror and saw a plain-looking woman in her mid-20s. *I just don't understand what Shimin sees in me*, she thought. After her father's death, when she was still a toddler, her uncle, Gao Shilian, took in her mother (his younger sister) and her children. It was Uncle Gao, as her stepfather, who married her to Li Shimin when she was 12. Although her uncle's friends and colleagues never failed to call her a "pretty girl," she always considered herself average and counted herself extremely lucky to have been married to such a caring husband.

That night, when Shimin returned, she went out to greet him and was horrified to see him lie listlessly in the palanquin, his face completely drained of blood.

With the help of several servants, Shimin was settled in his bed. Feeling a bout of nausea, he threw up. The vomit was dark and mixed with streaks of blood. The palace physician, whom Li Shentong had sent for, came rushing in. Bending over, he felt Shimin's pulse and examined his tongue. He took out two herbal boluses from a silver medicine box and gave them to the patient, who, propped in bed with pillows, took them with a gulp of water. The physician handed over the medicine box to Ms. Zhangsun, and said, "Make sure he takes two per night before sleep until they are gone."

The physician then took leave of Ms. Zhangsun, and walked out, escorted by Li Shentong. At the gate, he stopped to whisper into Li Shentong's ear, "The Prince of Qin has been poisoned!" and went on his way.

On the following morning, Li Shimin woke up to the bright light of midsummer and was delighted to find Li Shentong by his side.

"You looked scary last night," said Li Shentong.
"I got a funny feeling when I finished the first jug."
"Someone had actually put a poison potion in your drink."

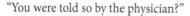

"You were told so by the physician?"

" Yes."

"Bastard," Li Shimin snarled.

"Please don't, Prince of Qin. This is not the time to get angry. Anger is the enemy of recovery."

Li Shimin nodded in agreement. He was too weak to think of how to get back at his adversary.

AFTER THE DRINKING INCIDENT, the Emperor heard rumors about Jiancheng's attempt to poison Shimin, but could not bring Himself to believe them. Still, He was deeply worried. *They are already at each other's throats when I am alive and well. What's going to happen when I am gone?*

When the Emperor visited Li Shimin in the Hongyi Palace, the sight of His second son too feeble to even sit up reduced Him to tears. He forthwith issued a rescript to Jiancheng, "Since Shimin cannot drink, you shall never invite him to drinking parties! Never!"

A few days later, the Emperor visited Shimin again with a solution.

"You and Jiancheng don't get along," said He. "If you live in the same city, you just can't help fighting each other. Now I have decided: after you are fully recovered, you shall move to another city, Luoyang, and reside there permanently."

With tears in his eyes, Shimin begged imploringly, "Please let me stay, Your Majesty. I can't bear being separated from Daddy."

"What's the matter with you, Shimin?" said the Emperor, in an attempt to comfort him. "Our royal house rules over all under Heaven, including Luoyang. Besides, Luoyang is not that different from Chang'an. Nor is it far away from the Western Capital. Whenever I miss you, I will pay you a visit. Don't be sad."

Not long after the Emperor's visit, Li Shimin began to make preparations for the move. He gradually got over his initial reluctance and came to accept his fate: Luoyang was not such a bad choice after all. A few years before, when the clash with Jiancheng became obvious, he had two of his close followers, Wen Daya and Zhang Liang, sent to Luoyang. Wen Daya served as the city's top civil-military leader. Zhang Liang was the head of a special task force comprised of 1,000-plus officers and men with a mission to use gold and silk to cultivate ties with local magnates and build up a strong support network in and around the city. Alarmed, Prince of Qi Li Yuanji requested an investigation. Zhang Liang was thrown into jail on conspiracy charges. But he refused to talk. Eventually, the authorities failed to prove his guilt and had to release him. Since then, Luoyang had grown into Li Shimin's power base in the east.

On hearing of the Emperor's plan for Li Shimin, Li Yuanji went rushing to the Eastern Palace.

"What do you think of Shimin's transfer to Luoyang?" Li Yuanji asked on seeing Jiancheng.

"Good riddance," answered the Crown Prince.

"However, the area has a formidable military force and a large population. Once he's there, it'll be impossible to subdue him."

"In your opinion, it is better to keep him in Chang'an?"

"Absolutely. In Chang'an, his hands are tied. He can't cause too much trouble, can he? Besides, we'll have other opportunities to get rid of him."

"But how can we make the Emperor change His mind?"

"Don't worry. I'll do it," Yuanji said with confidence.

A few days later the Emperor received a secret report that on hearing of the decision to transfer the Prince of Qin to Luoyang, his associates were overjoyed. Judging by their reaction, the Prince of Qin and his followers probably would never return to Chang'an again. That suggested the nightmarish scenario of splitting Tang China into two realms upon the Emperor's death. Meanwhile Li Jiancheng's allies at court, Consort Yin and Lady Zhang, took turns to persuade the Emperor to withdraw His decision, which He was reluctant to do. Still, the doubts they planted in His mind gave Him pause. As tension between the two rival camps escalated, He felt increasingly frustrated.

For his part, Li Jiancheng, egged on by his adviser Wei Zheng, started a campaign to weaken his rival. One important step was to isolate Li Shimin from his supporters by buying them off or by transferring them out of the capital. At the same time, Li Jiancheng and Li Yuanji started making serious accusations against Li Shimin to the throne. Shimin, they alleged, had engaged in underhanded activities that threatened the Crown Prince and the throne. For a while the Emperor was even seriously thinking of penalizing Li Shimin, but He stopped short when He heard the counterarguments presented by Shimin's sympathizers. However, the Emperor did not strongly protest His second son's innocence. Emboldened by the Emperor's apparent indecision, Li Yuanji made the most damning allegation: Li Shimin had been plotting sedition ever since the conquest of Luoyang, bribing officials and local magnates with money and silk and defying Imperial edicts. "He should be eliminated immediately," urged Li Yuanji. But that was going too far.

"Your wild accusation is not convincing at all," said the Emperor, His face crimson with anger. "What is the world going to say about Me if I kill him on these flimsy charges? Shimin is not only My second son, but also My top general. His role in founding and consolidating the Tang was absolutely essential."

31. The Xuanwu Gate

FOR DAYS PRINCE OF Qin Li Shimin had been agonizing over his choices. Was he going to lie supine while his enemies did everything in their power to destroy him? Of course not. But to defeat them, he had to replace Jiancheng as Crown Prince, something his father would never allow to happen unless someone forced His hand. The only way to force His hand, however, was to kill Jiancheng, and to present it as a *fait accompli* to the court, which could be considered a most atrocious act of lèse-majesté.

While the Prince was between two minds, he was surprised to hear Fang Xuanling—one of his most amenable advisers—speak to him in a forceful voice, "No doubt, the die is cast. If the Crown Prince gang were allowed to have its way, you and all those working for you would lose their lives, and the Great Tang would crumble from within. The time for discussion has passed. Great Prince, you must act now following the example of the Duke of Zhou. This is a life-and-death struggle, and you don't have a moment to lose."

The Prince clearly understood the message. In antiquity, the Duke of Zhou of the Western Zhou was challenged by two of his brothers in an open rebellion. After he squashed the rebellion, the Duke executed one of them and exiled the other.

"This is what I wanted to say but didn't have the guts to," concurred Zhangsun Wuji, the brother of the Prince's wife. "Xuanling speaks for me."

"Jiancheng and Yuanji have been trying to woo away officers in the Administration of the Superior General," said Du Ruhui. "I, too, agree with Xuanling. If we don't act now, our military support will be seriously eroded. By then, it will be too late."

By now, the contentious arguments of his supporters had left the Prince favorably inclined towards Fang Xuanling's position. Still, he wanted to secure the support of the military. Secretly, he consulted Li Jing and Li Shiji, the two most prominent military figures. To his chagrin, both declined to get involved in what they considered the "family matter of the Li house." That left uncertain how the other top military leaders would react to a preemptive action except for those directly under his command.

Unfortunately for him, it was then that the Tujue launched a massive invasion in Wuwei (in Gansu). At the instance of Li Jiancheng, Li Yuanji was to lead an expedition against it. Using that as an excuse, Li Yuanji requested the transfer of some of the Prince's most trusted generals to his command, including Yuchi Jingde, Cheng Zhijie, Duan Zhixuan, and Qin Shubao, together with their elite troops. As Li Shimin was desperately looking for ways to stop Yuanji from carrying out his request, the latter's farewell party was announced. Just days before the party, Li Shimin received an urgent secret report from one of his spies: an assassination plot had been hatched. At the farewell party, Li Jiancheng would have Li Shimin killed in a tent by braves and then report it as an accidental death.

"WHAT IS TO BE done?" Prince Li Shimin asked his supporters whom he had just gathered for an emergency meeting. All urged him to take immediate action.

"However, since antiquity, fratricide has been condemned as a major crime," the Prince responded. "I want to wait until they make the first move."

"We can't just wait without putting up a fight," Yuchi Jingde rejoined impatiently. "If we wait, we'll be butchered. Who doesn't treasure life? Still, all of us are willing to lay down our lives for you, Great Prince. But if you can't make up your mind, I'll have to leave."

"Jingde is right," said Zhangsun Wuji. "Great Prince, if you can't do what Jingde said, you are finished. I will have to follow Jingde and leave you too."

All the others now sided with Yuchi and Zhangsun.

After mulling the matter over for a few moments, the Prince said with determination, "You leave me no choice. Let's do it."

To better his chance of success, the Prince wanted to have an optimum day selected by divination. He contacted one of his associates, Zhang Gongjin, an expert in divination. Zhang picked up a tortoise for the occasion, only to drop it onto the floor, saying, "We don't need this, do we?"

The Prince looked at him in puzzlement.

"Divination is for resolving doubt," Zhang Gongjin continued. "Today there is no doubt to resolve. So we don't need divination. Besides, if the results are inauspicious, are you going to stop?"

"I suppose not," said the Prince, throwing the last shred of caution to the wind.

ON JULY 1, WUDE 9 (626), Venus was seen traversing the sky in broad daylight. In response, Grand Astrologer Fu Yi submitted a secret memorial, which said,

Venus appeared in the [Lodges corresponding to the] Allotted Field of Qin. The Prince of Qin will have the throne.

Extremely upset, the Emperor Li Yuan summoned the Prince.

"What do you say to this, Prince of Qin?" the Emperor asked, pointing to Fu's memorial.

"It is ridiculous! How am I going to attain the throne?"

"Presumably by replacing Jiancheng as heir?"

"If Your Majesty believes in this divination and wants to revenge the death of Wang Shichong and Dou Jiande, go ahead and kill me."

The Emperor was taken aback by Prince Li Shimin's apparent asperity.

"When my soul descends into the Underworld, I wonder if it will be too ashamed to meet those bandit leaders," the Prince continued chokingly. "Concerning Elder Brother,

I always have a clear conscience; and to Your Majesty I have always been a loyal subject and a dutiful son. But Your Majesty simply cannot stop suspecting me of threatening the throne. The real threat is not me, but Jiancheng himself."

"That is a very serious charge," said the Emperor. "You have to back it up with evidence."

"I have irrefutable evidence that Jiancheng and Yuanji have illicit relations with members of the Imperial Harem."

"Enough!" said the Emperor, beyond belief. "Early tomorrow morning, you and your brothers shall come to the Linhu Basilica for an interrogation."

The Prince took off in a huff.

ON THE MORNING OF the following day, July 2, a crowd of armed men on horseback was seen gathering at the Xuanwu (Dark Warrior) Gate, the main northern entrance of the Taiji Palace. Among them was Li Shimin, surrounded by his most loyal followers: his brother-in-law Zhangsun Wuji in his 20s, the even younger Hou Junji who had cut his teeth as Li's adjutant, Zhangsun's 50-year-old stepfather Gao Shilian, and the daredevil general Yuchi Jingde.

Lady Zhang noticed the flurry of activity, and suspected something sinister. She sent one of her maids to alert Li Jiancheng in the Eastern Palace, and Li Jiancheng immediately summoned Li Yuanji.

"Shimin and his gang are at the Xuanwu Gate now," Crown Prince Jiancheng said to his younger brother.

"Are they? This means war. We have to call our troops to arms right now, Elder Brother."

"We will certainly do that. But we'd better see the Emperor first. He is expecting us in the Linhu Basilica."

"We have to report ourselves sick."

"That probably won't sit well with the Emperor."

"It's our lives that are at stake. Why are Shimin and his gang at the Xuanwu Gate? The Gate holds the key to the security of the Palace."

"Don't worry. Commandant Chang He is in charge of the Gate. And he is a loyal subordinate."

"Is he?"

"Yes, I can assure you."

"What should we do, now?"

"Go and see the Emperor at the Linhu Basilica. We are already late for the meeting."

Begrudgingly, Yuanji accepted his brother's request. Under the escort of a small group of attendants, the two brothers mounted their horses and started trotting towards the Taiji Palace to the west.

By this time, the Emperor had been holding court with Pei Ji, Xiao Yu, and other important court officials in the Linhu Basilica. Annoyed that none of His three sons had appeared as expected, the Emperor, at Pei Ji's suggestion, suspended the court meeting and went to the adjacent Sea Pond for a boat ride.

AS LI JIANCHENG AND Li Yuanji were approaching the Linhu from the west, they saw in the distance a group of riders in black moving towards them. Suddenly, Yuanji turned south and rode at full speed towards the Wude Basilica with Jiancheng following closely behind.

Then, a thunderous "Stop!" boomed out as Li Shimin on his white Tujue horse galloped towards them, bow drawn. Hit in the head by an arrow, Jiancheng instantly slumped off his horse. Yuanji frantically pulled out his bow. But before he could open it, he was unhorsed by a volley of arrows, as Yuchi Jingde leading 70 mounted warriors came after him. Weakened by arrow wounds, Li Yuanji staggered desperately towards the Wude for a few steps before he fell to a fatal shot by Yuchi Jingde. Yuchi Jingde then rushed to the two fallen Princes and lopped off their heads.

Meanwhile, as his steed bolted towards the woods nearby, Li Shimin was struck by a low-hanging tree bough and thrown onto the ground. Unable to get up, he was carried by his troops to safety.

The officers loyal to the two Princes mounted a counterattack against Li Shimin's men, but it melted away the moment they saw the severed heads of their masters held up by Yuchi's men.

All this while, the Emperor was unaware what had exactly happened. After the boat ride in the Sea Pond, He returned to the Linhu, and was taken completely by surprise when He saw a fully armored towering figure standing at the gate, spear in hand.

"What is going on?" the Emperor asked, fearing for His own life.

"The Crown Prince and the Prince of Qi," answered Yuchi Jingde, "started a riot, and it has already been crushed by the Prince of Qin with his troops."

"That was unexpected," said the Emperor. Turning to His advisers Pei Ji and others, He asked, "What should we do?"

"When Your Majesty started the Righteous Uprising, Jiancheng and Yuanji were not there," said Xiao Yu. "After they joined us later, they did not accrue much merit at all. Out of jealousy, they schemed against the Prince of Qin. Now that the Prince of Qin has crushed them, Your Majesty should appoint him Crown Prince. All under Heaven will welcome this decision."

"It is fine with Me," the Emperor said, looking askance at Yuchi Jingde as if to tell him to leave.

"Among Jiancheng's and Yuanji's followers," Yuchi Jingde said, not budging, "there are still officers and men resisting change. Would Your Majesty issue a rescript to transfer them to the command of the Prince of Qin?"

"All right. I will have it written now."

With the rescript in hand, Yuchi Jingde took leave of the Emperor.

A few moments later, Li Shimin appeared in the presence of his father, threw himself into His embrace, and started sucking on His nipples while crying like a baby.

"It is all right, it is all right," said the Emperor.

Father and son finally patched things up, or so it seemed.

32. Crown Prince Li Shimin

THE JULY 2 COUP, known in history as the "Xuanwu Gate Incident," was a brilliant victory for Crown Prince Li Shimin. At one stroke he eliminated his challengers, effectively sidelined his father, and emerged as the true power-holder at court.

On the following morning, sitting in his study in the Cheng'en Basilica, the Eastern Palace, the Crown Prince was musing on various issues that claimed his attention.

Yuchi Jingde, the hero of the coup, has to be rewarded handsomely. So have Zhangsun Wuji, Fang Xuanling, Gao Shilian, Du Ruhui, Hou Junji, and other staunch supporters. Don't forget Chang He, Commandant of the Xuanwu Gate. His switch of allegiance was crucial for preventing the Imperial guard units in the Forbidden Park from intervening. How about Lady Zhang and Consort Yin? They badmouthed me all the time. But, for Father's sake, it is better to leave them alone. The followers of Jiancheng and Yuanji? There are more than a hundred of them. Several of my advisers have suggested severe punishment. But I am inclined to agree with Yuchi Jingde that they should not face prosecution. Actually, I kind of like them. If they could risk their lives for their masters, they could do the same for me too! And the sons? Jiancheng and Yuanji have five boys each. They are my nephews and some of them are only babies. My heart goes out to them. But I am awfully sorry, they have to go. Succession is a deadly business. How about religion? Father's restrictive measures against Daoism and especially Buddhism are nominally still in force, although nobody has bothered to enact them yet. Xiao Yu has urged me to revoke them, which I think I should do.

With these reflections in mind, he started dictating decrees to his aides until an attendant came in to inform him of the arrival of Grand Astrologer Fu Yi.

"Are you all right?" asked Li Shimin, who was startled to see the dead white pallor of this old man in his early 70s.

"I am fine," answered Fu Yi. "Except..."

"Except what?"

"Except that I have not had anything to eat for days."

The Prince instantly ordered an attendant to bring a full-course meal. Sitting Fu Yi down, the Prince started a casual chat with him. A few moments later the attendant returned with flatbread, three dishes of pork, green vegetables, and tofu, a bowl of potage, and a flagon of wine—all on a lacquer serving tray. The attendant set the food on the table, and poured out two goblets of wine.

As Fu Yi devoured the meal with relish, Li Shimin sipped his wine quietly.

The meal was over and Li Shimin resumed the conversation, saying, "One of your earlier memorials almost cost me my life."

"I am guilty as charged," answered Fu.

"But don't get me wrong. To observe and report the Way of the heavens is your duty. You should continue to work as Grand Astrologer and not be bothered by what happened before."

"Thank you, Crown Prince. I am grateful for your magnanimity and greatly honored to be of service to you."

"I have taken notice of your memorials on Buddhism," said Li Shimin, switching to a new subject. "The religion of the Buddha is both mysterious and wondrous, and has a lot to offer. Why can't you understand it?"

"The Buddha was a crafty and cruel barbarian. He bewitched his own people. In our land, some wicked men mixed his teaching with the words of Master Lao and Master Zhuang, and embellished it with magic language to deceive the people. The truth is, this religion is of no benefit to the people, and is harmful to the country. It is not that I don't understand it, Your Highness, but that I don't believe it."

Obviously, Fu Yi was not going to change his mind any time soon. Li Shimin gave up trying to persuade him.

THE TRANSFER OF POWER from the Taiji Palace to the Eastern Palace went smoothly. It was aided by Crown Prince Li Shimin's decision to pardon Jiancheng's supporters. There had been a few small-scale rebellions since the Xuanwu Gate Incident. For example, the one by Commander of Youzhou Command Li Yuàn, Shimin's second uncle, who had had close ties with Li Jiancheng. But all of them had been promptly squashed and their leaders executed, usually on the spot. In dealing with the associates of these recent rebels, Li Shimin, as before, followed a policy of leniency.

However, there was one staunch Jiancheng supporter the Crown Prince was not ready to forgive—Wei Zheng. Among Jiancheng's advisers, Wei Zheng was known for his vision and strategic thinking. He was the one who had repeatedly warned of the growing threat of Li Shimin.

One morning, Wei Zheng was brought into Li Shimin's study in the Cheng'en Basilica.

"Why did you," the Prince asked reproachfully, "stir up bad blood between my brother and me?"

"Crown Prince," Wei Zheng answered, with respect but not servility, "I was Jiancheng's adviser. It was my duty to serve him loyally, making sure that he would succeed."

"Did he take your advice to heart?"

"Not really. If he did, he would not have ended so disastrously." There was a hint of regret in Wei Zheng's voice.

The Prince was surprised by the sharp answers of this ordinary-looking man of medium-build in his late 40s. One could easily mistake him for one of the round-of-the-mill bureaucrats at court. But there was a firmness in his voice and a frankness in his face, extremely rare for a high ranking official who had survived the vicissitudes of court life.

"Well, it is no crime to be a loyal servant of the ex-Crown Prince," said the Prince. "Prior to Jiancheng, you served Li Mi. What, in your honest opinion, caused his downfall?"

"Li Mi was a visionary leader and a magnetic character, and commanded the largest military force in the realm. But he made a fatal mistake. He failed to live up to the ideal of the enlightened sovereign."

"Enlightened sovereign?"

"An enlightened sovereign," Wei Zheng continued without hesitation, "listens to the opinion of everyone around him. By contrast, the vacuous sovereign only listens to the opinion of his favorites."

"I agree! How about the relations between the sovereign and his subjects?"

"They are comparable to those between a boat and the water that carries it. The water can carry the boat, but it can also overturn it!"

"Excellent! What, then, is the best style of rulership?"

"To lead by moral example. Moral leadership is like wind and the people are like grass. When the wind of moral leadership blows strong, the grass has no choice but to bend."

"Confucian *Analects*?"

"Yes, Your Highness. This I call the 'rule of benevolence.'"

"How about law and discipline?"

"No doubt, they are important tools for government, Your Highness. But if you become too dependent on these tools, you command no respect, and instead inspire fear from your people. If the people have no respect for you, and obey you only out of fear, they will rise against you when driven to desperation. Emperor Yang is a case in point."

"Who, then, would you consider 'benevolent' rulers?"

"The familiar ones include Yao and Shun in far antiquity and King Wen of the Western Zhou. A more recent example is Emperor Wen of the Han dynasty."

"What do you like about Emperor Wen?"

"His policy of 'give the people a break.' Light taxes, light penal punishments, and rewards for voicing criticisms of the throne."

The conversation went on for hours. In the end, the Prince asked his guardsmen to take Wei Zheng into the waiting area. After a brief consultation with his advisers, the Prince called Wei Zheng in, and said,

"Wei Zheng, I have decided to appoint you as Left Counselor of Remonstrance. You will be affiliated with the Chancellery."

After thanking the Prince, Wei asked, "What are my responsibilities?"

"You will be responsible for making candid suggestions, suggestions aimed at rectifying the errors of senior court officials and the throne."

"Including errors committed by Your Highness?"

"Absolutely."

"Excellent!" said Wei Zheng. "I am deeply grateful for your trust. You won't be disappointed." With these words, he took leave of the Prince.

INSPIRED BY THE IDEA of the "rule of benevolence," and in consultation with several advisers, the Crown Prince issued the following public decree from the Eastern Palace:

All the hawks and hunting dogs kept in the Forbidden Park shall be released; royal hunting activities in the same Park shall be suspended in perpetuity; the flow of tributary goods to the capital from the Four Quarters and tributary states shall stop; the Hundred Officials are encouraged to present their views on how to run the government.

For his part, Wei Zheng was exhilarated by the prospect of working for a truly enlightened sovereign. Of his own accord, he went on his first provincial mission as the Crown Prince's man with the task of pacifying Shandong, where there were still many former followers of Li Jiancheng's gang.

En route, Wei stopped in Ci Prefecture (seat: Cixian, Hebei) for the night and saw a party of prisoners in transit to the capital. He recognized among them a bodyguard of Li Jiancheng who had been a member of the elite Swordsman Guard and an officer who had served directly under Li Yuanji. The prisoners wore fetters and cangues and were strung together by rope. Wei Zheng was so disturbed by the humiliating scene that he wanted to stop the transit altogether.

"Probably, it is better not to intervene, considering your past ties to Jiancheng," an attendant warned him.

"It is true that I was Jiancheng's main adviser," said Wei Zheng. "But I can't remain silent simply for fear of arousing suspicion."

He went up to the Commandant in charge of the transit, and said, "I am the Shandong Commissioner on behalf of Crown Prince Li Shimin," and showed him the decree.

The officer bowed reverently, and said, "Mr. Wei, it is a great honor to meet you. What can I do for you?"

"Crown Prince Li Shimin," Wei replied, "has pardoned all the associates of the former Crown Prince and the Prince of Qi. If you send these men as criminals to the capital, all those who worked for the two fallen Princes in the past will be in fear of the authorities, and the government will lose trust."

"What do you want me to do with them?"

"Release them."

"Yes, Commissioner."

Thereupon, all the prisoners were unshackled and set free.

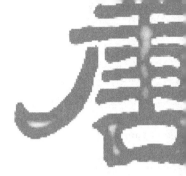

Part II.

The Good Government of Zhenguan (627–643)

33. The Emperor Li Shimin

ON SEPTEMBER 4, WUDE 9 (626), a *jiazi* day, Crown Prince Li Shimin (known posthumously by his temple name "Taizong") ascended the throne as "the Emperor" in the Xiande (Jiade) Basilica of the Eastern Palace without much pomp and circumstance. His father who had just abdicated now assumed the title of "Honorary Emperor." A new reign period, that of Zhenguan, "Honorable Outlook," would be declared next year. The Ten Circles (*dao*) were set up as the local governments at the highest level. In accord with tradition, the newly enthroned Emperor announced a general amnesty. Except for those who had committed the Ten Abominations (ten unpardonable crimes such as plotting rebellion, treason, extreme unfilial behavior, and incest), all prisoners were set free. Residents in Guanzhong and a few neighboring Prefectures were granted a two-year reprieve on land and cloth taxes and one-year reprieve on corvée duties. Commiserating with the fate of the older court ladies, who would remain unmarriageable for years, the Emperor issued an edict to allow them to return to their parents so that they could be married off.

At the end of the day, the Emperor found time to be alone for a few moments as He began to reminisce about His long and winding path to the throne. The emperorship gave Him an entirely new perspective on the Palace and on Chang'an, the Imperial capital, which would have been abandoned and torched had it not been for His effort to save it. Picking up a writing-brush, He gave expression to His thoughts in poetry:

The Qin Plains give grandeur to the Emperor's mansion,
The Han Valley gives might to the regal residence.
Ornate basilicas rise to a height of a thousand yards,
Touring palaces span more than a hundred perches.
Rooftops, linked together, remotely touch the Milky Way,
Soaring belvederes rise up to the void in the distance.
Clouds and Sun hide behind multi-storied watchtowers,
Vapor and mist flow from florid traceries.

[The Qin Plains: Guanzhong]

TWO WEEKS AFTER THE coronation, while Chang'an was still in a festive mood, it was hit by the most serious existential crisis since the founding of the dynasty: the Tujue were advancing on the city in the largest invasion ever against the Tang.

"The Tujue may reach Chang'an soon," the Emperor warned at an emergency conference with his top advisers and generals.

"What has happened to General Yuchi Jingde's army, Your Majesty?" asked Zhangsun Wuji.

"It scored a brilliant victory in Jingyang (Jingyang, Shaanxi; 70 *li* north of Chang'an)," answered the Emperor. "But the main Tujue force is coming from the west."

Turning to Du Ruhui, the Emperor asked, "President of the Board of War, how many troops do we have in Chang'an and its environs?"

"About 50,000, Your Majesty," answered Du.

"If I am not mistaken," the Emperor said, looking somewhat troubled, "the Twelve Armies alone have 300,000."

"Yes, Your Majesty," answered Du Ruhui. "But they are spread out in Guannei Circle."

The Emperor's heart sank. Guannei Circle was the super-region that encompassed Guanzhong and the vast area to the north as far as the Ordos.

"I suppose most of them are too far away for deployment?" asked the Emperor.

"Yes, Your Majesty."

"The Tujue have come with a numerous army," said the Emperor, addressing the entire audience. "We are likely to be outnumbered five to one. We must mobilize the military and civilian populace for the defense of the city."

"Your Majesty should move south to Hanzhong," suggested Hou Junji, General-in-chief of the Left Guard. "We can keep the Tujue at bay in the western suburb while waiting for reinforcements."

For a fleeting moment, the Emperor was tempted to say yes. *Maybe Father is right after all*, He thought. But immediately He thought of the high cost associated with abandoning the city and the threat it posed to the dynasty. That was very reason why He had opposed His father's plan to move the capital in the first place.

"No," the Emperor said, "I am not going anywhere."

In spite of strong opposition from His senior advisers, the Emperor was to play a central part in defending the city.

ON SEPTEMBER 23, THE Tujue halted their advance just west of the Wei River, about 80 *li* west of Chang'an. Their leader, Xieli Khan, sent his emissary Zhishi Sili to parley with the Emperor. Xieli had become Khan after the death of his brother Chuluo Khan (successor to Shibi Khan).

On arrival in the Palace City, Zhishi presented a list of demands, including annual tribute of silver, silk, grain, oxen, and sheep.

Without addressing the demands, the Emperor asked, "How many troops has Xieli brought with him?"

"About one million, Your Majesty."

"That's a hell of an army. But if you think you can take advantage of My lack of experience as Emperor, you are gravely mistaken. The Honorary Emperor graciously abdicated and the transfer of power took place seamlessly. There is not a hint of disharmony."

"I can assure Your Majesty that has not crossed the mind of Xieli Khan. He only wants to negotiate a deal."

"I am not against negotiation. But don't you think you are awfully close to My Palace?"

"But the troops are not advancing, Your Majesty," Zhishi said, and went on to assure Him that under no circumstances would they attack the capital. Then he added, "Unless the Tang refuse to pay the tribute."

"Then what?"

"Then, I can no longer guarantee that the situation will last."

In a fit of annoyance, the Emperor asked sharply, "Are you trying to bully us?"

"No. I just want Your Majesty to be sensible."

"Frankly, we don't owe you anything," said the Emperor, in a rising voice. "We have concluded marriage alliances with your Khans, and given you a countless amount of cash and silk. Still, Xieli has time and again broken his promises and invaded our lands. You are barbarians all right, but barbarians have conscience as well. Where is your conscience?"

After stopping for a brief moment, the Emperor continued in an agitated voice, "I have to send the Khan a clear message—by cutting off your head!"

"Please don't, Your Majesty," pleaded Zhishi.

Both Xiao Yu and Feng Deyi rushed to stop the Emperor from acting out His threat. Killing the enemy's emissary would not only tarnish the Tang's reputation but would almost guarantee an assault on Chang'an. Instead, they asked the Emperor to send Zhishi back to his master in keeping with common decencies.

After regaining His composure, the Emperor softened his stand. Still, He did not want to look soft. So He said, "If I let him return today, the barbarians will think I am afraid of them. They will be even more brazen."

"What are we going to do with him, Your Majesty?" asked Xiao Yu.

"Incarcerate him in the Chancellery," the Emperor answered curtly. The Tujue emissary and his suite were then taken into custody.

CLAD IN ARMOR AND helmet, the Emperor trotted on His white horse to the east side of the Bian Bridge on the Wei River, under the escort of six light cavalry and a few senior advisers including Fang Xuanling and Gao Shilian. Surprised by the unexpected appearance of the Emperor, Xieli rode hastily to the Bridge to meet Him. Meanwhile the Tang forces started to arrive in disciplined formation with banners flapping in the wind and warrior armors glinting under the sun until they positioned themselves near the river. The Emperor then ordered the various units to retreat for some distance.

As the Emperor was about to move closer to the Bridge, Xiao Yu hurriedly rode up to Him to caution against it, fearing for His safety. But the Emperor was firm, saying, "The Tujue have invaded because they believe that this Emperor can't fight them. The last thing you want is to show any sign of weakness or fear."

After the Emperor came face to face with His Tujue adversary, a dialog ensued. Eventually, nothing substantive came out of it. But it created the impression that Tang would put up a serious resistance should the Tujue cross the Wei River.

Later that day, the Khan's messenger arrived with an offer to conclude a peaceful alliance. The Emperor jumped at the chance.

Two days later, the Tang Emperor and the Tujue Khan, both with their entourages, reappeared on either side of the Bian Bridge. Xieli then crossed over to the east side to join the Emperor. A sacrificial white horse was butchered near the bridgehead, carved into sections, and then offered to the Lord on High on a makeshift altar set up for the occasion. Both sovereigns took part in a solemn oath-taking ceremony. It was followed by the release of Zhishi Sili to the west side and of Wen Yanbo—a Tang senior official retained by the Tujue—to the east side. Soon afterwards, the Tujue withdrew to the north.

34. Empress and Crown Prince

FOR THE SAKE OF continuity, the Emperor Li Shimin had kept most of the officials of the previous administration on the job including those with close ties to Li Jiancheng and Li Yuanji. But He did introduce drastic personnel changes at the highest level, bringing into power a cadre of talented leaders who had been His close associates. He also rewarded His meritorious supporters with noble ranks and fiefs.

Anticipating that not all would be satisfied with these decisions, He provided a channel for airing grievances. "In case you consider the rewards of ranks and wealth inappropriate, you are encouraged to speak out," said He in an edict.

Prince of Huai'an Li Shentong was the first to respond, saying, "I, your subject, raised an army in Guanzhong in the earliest days of the Righteous Uprising. People like Fang Xuanling and Du Ruhui have done nothing but engage in the exercise of writing and rhetoric. How come they rank higher than I? I find it hard to understand."

"Well," answered the Emperor, "indeed, you were among the earliest to raise an army. But you also suffered disastrous defeats. When Dou Jiande was encroaching upon Shandong, you lost an entire army sent to suppress him. When Liu Heita rose in arms, you were worsted by him. Fang Xuanling, Du Ruhui, and other top civil officials—they are strategists and leading administrators whose service the country absolutely depends upon. On the other hand, I realize that you are My uncle. But that's no reason to increase your rank."

That quieted Li Shentong. But there were still other military officers with grudges against leading civil officials who outranked them. Among the staffers of the old administration of the Prince of Qin, quite a few were unhappy. "Now we are even falling behind those who worked for the ex-Crown Prince and the Prince of Qi!" they complained vociferously.

To this, the Emperor responded, "A good sovereign should work in the interest of the public, not himself. That is the only way to get himself accepted by all under Heaven.

How can I promote people only for old time's sake? What if the new-comers are good, and the old-timers are not so good?" Clearly, for now, the Emperor would not consider seniority as a reason for promotion. The disgruntled officers grudgingly withdrew their complaint.

AS THE XUANWU GATE Incident receded into memory, the Emperor was able to look upon His two fallen brothers with more impartiality, and partially rehabilitated them. Princely titles were restored, and posthumous titles were granted: Yin (Reclusive) for Crown Prince Li Jiancheng and La (Ruthless) for Prince of Qi Li Yuanji. Neither was flattering. Nonetheless, they were an indication of status. Their remains were exhumed and given a proper reburial in accord with ritual. A special permission was granted to their former associates, Wei Zheng, Wang Gui, and others, to participate in the burial rites. The Emperor Himself attended a memorial service in their honor in the gatetower of the Yiqiu Gate, in the northwest of the Eastern Palace, and sobbed sorrowfully for His lost brothers.

The Emperor then made two announcements concerning His spouse and eldest son.

First, His wife, Ms. Zhangsun, was officially appointed Empress. A grand coronation ceremony would follow. Although it was just a matter of formality (virtually every Emperor made His wife Empress), the court officials were delighted, because Zhangsun was widely considered as an exemplary political wife. Not only did she refrain from meddling in her husband's business, she often cautioned her kinsmen, for example, her brother Zhangsun Wuji, against presuming upon their privileges as her close relatives.

Ms. Zhangsun was of Xianbei descent. Either proto-Mongol or proto-Turkic, the Xianbei had moved from the Greater Xing'an Mountains in north Manchuria and northeast Inner Mongolia to south Manchuria and central Inner Mongolia in the second century. In the subsequent centuries, they became empire-builders in North China. That the Emperor took a Xianbei wife was hardly surprising, since He Himself was half-Xianbei through His mother, Ms. Dou. But it is impossible to know how "pure" the Xianbei heritage of these women was. Their ancestors had lived in North China for generations and had intermarried with Han Chinese and become more or less Sinicized.

Second, Li Chengqian, the eldest son of the Emperor and Empress, was named Crown Prince. There was no telling how this Crown Prince, now aged seven, would turn out. But the Emperor was taking no chances. To make sure that the Prince would be equal to his task when he took over the reins, the Emperor carefully selected a small group of top court officials known for their erudition and probity to serve as the his mentors and advisers.

35. Balance Between *Wen* and *Wu*

ON WEI ZHENG'S ADVICE of "benevolence," the Emperor greatly alleviated the financial burden of the multitude, and time and again urged the court officials and private subjects to criticize the government. Before these new measures came to fruition, however, a calamity befell Tang China that threatened to take the wind out of His sails. A prolonged summer drought was affecting much of the North, especially Hedong (Shanxi), Henan, Longyou (mainly Gansu), and Guanzhong. It resulted in a grain shortage so severe that one peck of rice could now fetch a bolt of silk in the capital. The Emperor's response was to encourage farming by suspending or lowering taxes, and to slash government expenditure by fostering frugality, shrinking the number of fiefdoms granted to the Princes, and reducing the size of the bureaucracy.

"The key to good government is the quality of its recruits, not the size of its bureaucracy," the Emperor once said. Taking their cues from Him, Fang Xuanling and others went to work to radically reduce the number of civil officials and military officers working for the central government, eventually to 643.

In the face of rising food prices, and the declining purchasing power of money, the task to keep government officials free of corruption was becoming increasingly challenging. The Emperor instructed some of His close advisers to test the probity of these officials by offering false bribes. A low-ranking official in the Board of Justice took the bait, accepting a bolt of silk. The Emperor handed down the death sentence.

Alarmed by this arbitrary decision, Pei Ju, President of the Board of Revenue, submitted a memorial, which read,

…*Taking bribe as a court official, this person certainly deserves to die. But Your Majesty trapped him into committing the crime. This runs counter to the Confucian principle of "Guide him with virtue, and make him behave in accord with ritual."*

Upon reading the memorial, the Emperor summoned the President of the Board of Justice.

"That bribe-taker of your Board—have you carried out his sentence yet?" asked the Emperor.

"Not yet, Your Majesty."

"Good," said the Emperor, with a sigh of relief.

"Should I put it on hold?"

"Well, just read this first," said the Emperor, handing him Pei Ju's memorial.

Quickly scanning through the lines, the Board President observed, "Pei seems to have a point there. Entrapping its subjects was a notorious practice of the despotic state of Qin, especially when Shang Yang was Chancellor. It has been condemned by good sovereigns ever since."

"What do you think we should do?"

"Commuting the sentence to banishment."

"All right," said the Emperor, "go ahead."

In the evening, the Emperor reread Pei's memorial, and wrote down the following comment on it:

If I can have honest opinions like this on every government affair, I am confident that we will achieve good government!

On the following morning, the Emperor had the memorial circulated among high-ranking officials (rank 5 and above) at court, in the hope of encouraging them to make candid suggestions.

ASPIRING TO RULE LIKE a fair-minded sage-king of the past, the Emperor strove to keep a proper balance between the two complementary essential aspects of government, *wen* (civil or literary) and *wu* (military or martial). To enhance the *wen* element He expanded the existing Institute for the Cultivation of Literature (Xiuwen *guan*), now renamed the "Institute for the Advancement of Literature" (Hongwen *guan*). (Note: it was different from the Institute for Literature, which was by now defunct.) Housed in the compound of the inner branch of the Chancellery (southeast of the Taiji Basilica), the Institute boasted the largest collection of books in the capital, more than 200,000 *juan* (scrolls). The enlarged Institute trained its own students, recruited from male royal relatives, consort relatives, and sons of high-ranking officials. Its academicians—senior officials of distinct literary achievement—were often invited into His inner basilica to discuss political matters, and to discourse on the words and deeds of the early sages.

Apart from the civil aspect of government, *wen* also referred to a government style that stressed leniency over cruelty, and edification over punishment, which could be characterized as "civilized" or "humane." This concept was particularly relevant to law and law enforcement. Acutely aware of the harshness of the existing laws, the Emperor appointed a panel of top officials and experts, headed by President of the Board of Personnel Zhangsun Wuji and Chief Minister Fang Xuanling, to revise the existing law code to make it more *wen* or civilized. One notable result was the reduction of 50 types of death penalty to a lighter punishment: the amputation of the toes. It immediately caught the Emperor's attention.

"It doesn't look right," the Emperor commented. "Mutilating punishment has been abandoned for a long time. One should be able to replace it with something else."

"Your Majesty," said a member of the panel, "mutilating punishment in the past was not related to capital punishment. The revised law code replaces capital punishment with the amputation of the toes. That already shows leniency by replacing death with life."

"Leniency is the reason why I wanted to do it in the first place," said the Emperor. "Amputation seems too cruel."

Lending support to the Emperor's view, Fang Xuanling and his associates submitted a report, which said, "After the abolition of mutilating punishment, there are five types of punishment on the books: capital punishment, banishment, penal servitude, punishment with the heavy stick, and punishment with the light stick. If amputation is introduced, it will be the sixth type of punishment, which will make the Tang penal system unnecessarily harsh."

On reading the report, the Emperor wrote down His comment, *It clearly suggests that there is no place for amputation in the Tang Code*, and sent both report and comment to the Eight Chairs for further deliberation—the eight top leaders of the executive branch of the central government: the two Vice Premiers of the Department of State Affairs, and the Presidents of the Six Boards under the Department. Their subsequent proposal was that amputation should be changed to banishment to a distance of 3,000 *li* and three years of penal servitude. It won the Emperor's instant approval.

As for the *wu* aspect of government, despite efforts by some advisers, particularly Wei Zheng, to minimize its influence, the Emperor still found it important especially because of the threat posed by the Tujue. As the most accomplished general of His time, the Emperor took great pride in His martial achievement. As reflected in the talks He held with General Li Jing on the arts of war, He had a keen sense of military strategy. Above all, He was profoundly aware of the indispensible part the military played in defending the regime and the country.

One morning in October, hundreds of officers and men of the various Guard Commands were gathered in the courtyard of the Xiande Basilica, the main structure of the Eastern Palace. The Emperor, clad in His general's armor, made the following address to them,

...Barbarian invasions have occurred since antiquity. And here is the problem: oftentimes before the frontier is pacified, the sovereign has already become lax, and forgotten his military responsibility. Consequently, he won't be able to defend himself when the enemy strikes. That is why today I am not going to use you to dig ponds and build gardens. Instead, I will ask you to take part in archery practice. When there is peace, I will be your archery teacher. When the Tujue invade, I will lead you into battle.

The Emperor watched on as the Guard officers and soldiers plunged into archery practice. Whenever He saw someone hit a bull's-eye, He would shout words of encouragement. When winners of archery contests were declared, He would personally bestow prizes—bows, silks, or swords—on them. Obviously, the purpose of this exercise was to accentuate the *wu* aspect of government and to improve His Guard troops' combat readiness. But some of His attendants became worried, arguing, "To allow those lowly soldiers to pull bows and shoot arrows in Your Majesty's presence is dangerous. What if one of the archers is a madman and aims secretly at Your Majesty? Should something happen, the whole country will be in danger. Your Majesty must stop attending the archery practice."

"No, I won't," the Emperor responded. "I regard all within the Four Seas as belonging to the same family—My family. All young men living inside the borders are My loyal sons. I trust every one of them. Why doubt the intentions of those loyal sons of Mine serving in My Guard units?"

So the Emperor spent the whole morning rubbing shoulders with the officers and soldiers. From that point on, the Xiande archery practice was established as a periodic military exercise for the Guards.

NOT LONG AFTERWARDS, THE Emperor went to another Xiande archery session, accompanied by Chief Minister Feng Deyi. In their conversation, the Emperor talked about the growing threat of the north and the need to increase the size of the military. "Without disrupting farming, that is," the Emperor hastened to add.

"Yes, Your Majesty," said Feng. "I have got an idea that might work."
"What is it?"
"As Your Majesty knows, young people categorized as 'striplings' (*zhongnan*; those be-tween 15 and 17) are exempt from military service. In my opinion, they should be drafted as well if they are tall enough."
"That may do," the Emperor said contemplatively. "Let Me touch base with other ad-visers first."

After the archery practice was over, the Emperor conferred with some of His advisers at court, who all agreed with Feng, and had an edict written to draft tall striplings. Following an established procedure, the edict had to be approved by Wei Zheng to go into effect. However, Wei Zheng refused to affix his seal. In fact, he rejected the same edict on four occasions.

The Emperor, now furious, called Wei Zheng in, and reproached him, "What's the harm in getting those tall striplings? They are probably cheaters, anyway, who want to avoid conscription."

"Your Majesty, I have to respectfully disagree," replied Wei Zheng. "The strength of an army does not necessarily depend on the number of its soldiers but on the way it treats them. If Your Majesty recruits the strong and treats them in the right way, the army will be invincible all over the world. Is it necessary to draft the weak so as to make up the numbers? And there is something else. Your Majesty often says, 'I govern all under Heaven with honesty in the hope that My subjects will follow My example and not engage in fraud.' But, not long after enthronement, that promise was broken."

"Really?" the Emperor asked, sounding incredulous.

"Your Majesty promised 'a two-year reprieve on land and cloth taxes and one-year reprieve on corvée duties.' Your Majesty also said, 'For those who already paid their taxes and performed corvée labor this year, the reprieve will take effect next year.' Still, before the year was out, Your Majesty started drafting people again. Can it be called 'rule with honesty?' "

As the Emperor listened His face became flushed with shame and embarrassment. In the end, he said, "I am so delighted that you pointed it out, Wei Zheng. It is all My fault." After pausing to mull over Wei's words, He resumed, with a sigh, "Previously, I thought you were stubborn because you were inexperienced in government affairs. Now I realize you have a perfect understanding of the fundamental principles of the state. Indeed, if My orders are not credible, the people won't be able to follow them. If My orders are not followed, no matter how numerous My army might be, I would not be able to govern all under Heaven."

The Emperor immediately cancelled Feng Deyi's conscription plan and rewarded Wei Zheng with a golden jar for giving candid advice.

36. Master Xuanzang

AMONG THE 100-ODD BUDDHIST institutions in urban Chang'an, the Zhuangyan Monastery was one of the two largest, taking up the entire space of a large Ward. Located in the southwest corner of the city, it was especially famous for the richness of its architecture, which was considered superior to that of any Buddhist monasteries in the nation. Of its 20 courtyards, the largest one, located in the center of the premises, was host to the Grand Basilica, an imposing structure topped with a hipped roof of yellow glazed tiles that glistened majestically under the sun. The interior of the Basilica and other tall buildings, as well as much of the surface of the courtyard walls, was painted with intricately executed murals depicting Buddhist themes. Towering over the Monastery was its seven-story wooden pagoda, soaring to a height of 70 meters, which served as the apotropaic anchor of the city's southwest corner. The grounds of the Monastery were dotted with ornamental plants, luxuriant bamboos, and towering dark pines. Because of its architectural, artistic, and scenic splendors the Monastery had earned itself the sobriquet of "Paradise on Earth."

With the help of Vice Premier Xiao Yu, Master Xuanzang took up residence in the Monastery. In spite of his young age of 25, the Master, a good-looking tall man with bright eyes and slightly arched eyebrows, had already established his reputation as a learned Buddhist scholar. Having found Buddhist scholarship in China contradictory and unsatisfying, he decided to travel to the Western Regions in quest of the true Law of the Buddha. He was particularly interested in seeing the all-important Sanskrit treatise called the *Yogācārabhūmi-śāstra* (*Discourse on the Stages of Yogic Practice*).

Inspired by an auspicious dream, he set off on an epic pilgrimage to India in September, Zhenguan 1 (627). More than a month later, he arrived in Liangzhou (Wuwei, Gansu), the seat of Liang Prefecture. It was the major urban center of the northwest, with a constant flow of merchants with deep-set eyes and tall noses from all over the Western Regions. By popular demand, Xuanzang gave several lectures on Buddhism. His audience, impressed with his scholarship and talent, loaded him with gifts—gold, silver, and even horses—which he mostly donated to local monasteries.

Before he resumed his westward journey, Xuanzang was tipped off by an admirer that Li Daliang, Commander of Liangzhou Area Command, had issued his arrest warrant—unauthorized travel abroad by Tang subjects was forbidden on pain of banishment. Law-enforcement officers would detain him the next day. Accompanied by two novice monks, Xuanzang departed into the dark night in a hurry.

Having passed through neighboring Gan and Su Prefectures, Xuanzang entered Gua Prefecture, where he was given a safe haven by the Prefect, a declared fan of his.

One night, just as Xuanzang was about to retire, a middle-aged man called Li Chang showed up at his door, claiming to be an officer of Liang Prefecture.

At Li's insistence, Xuanzang acknowledged who he was. To Xuanzang's surprise, the officer, bringing his two palms together in front to show reverence, said, "Please accept the deepest respects from your disciple."

"Look," Li continued, taking out a piece of paper. "This is your arrest warrant. For your sake, I am tearing it up." As he said so, he ripped the writ into pieces.

"Thank you so much," Xuanzang said with gratitude. "I wonder why you came all the way here only to tear up the warrant."

"I long wanted to see you, because I was a great fan of yours."

Xuanzang made a deep bow to show his appreciation.

"I also must tell you," Li resumed, "it is not safe here in Gua Prefecture. The authorities are still after you. You must leave as soon as possible."

After bidding Mr. Li good-bye, Xuanzang set off immediately.

XUANZANG WENT THROUGH THE Jade Gate (Yumen) Pass, where, surprisingly, he did not experience official harassment. The Pass was the last heavily garrisoned outpost, beyond which the Tang's influence declined markedly.

About 80 *li* to the west, he saw in the distance the First Beacon Tower manned by Tang border troops. He waited until dark and moved quietly past the Tower without being detected. A few moments later, he was thrilled to find a greensward and a body of water nearby. He squatted down to fill up his leather canteen. Suddenly, two arrows flew by. And one of them nearly hit his left knee.

"Don't shoot," shouted Xuanzang. "I am just a monk from the capital."

Two soldiers went up to him and took him into the Tower, where, by the dim light of a firebrand, Sergeant Wang Xiang, a middle-aged man with a weather-worn face, was waiting.

"Your travel document, shaveling?" asked Wang.

Xuanzang fumbled in his saddle-sack, and produced his certificate of ordination.

"I am talking about a special pass to travel in the frontier zone, not the certificate," said Wang Xiang as he gave a casual glance at the paper.

"My goodness!" exclaimed Wang. "You are Master Xuanzang! Please accept my respects and apologies, Master. I am a great fan of yours. May I ask what the purpose of your travel is?"

"I am traveling to the land of the Brahmins in the West in search of the Law."

"But the road to the West is long and full of danger, Master. You will never make it. However, I am not going to fault you for trying. I'll tell you what. I, your disciple, am going to send you to my hometown Dunhuang instead. I am sure you will be pleased to meet Master Zhang there, a sagely and virtuous Buddhist."

"Thank you, officer," replied Xuanzang. "But I have made up my mind to go west. I want to resolve many of the contradictions in the sutras. Not that I make light of Dunhuang, but I have studied Buddhism in the Two Capitals, and in Wu and Shu (the lower Yangzi valley and Sichuan), and realized that only a trip to the West can solve my problems. If you want to retain me, it is in your power. But I would rather end up in jail than go back one step."

"Don't get me wrong," said Wang Xiang. "It is a great honor to see the Master in person. I do want to offer my help."

After a brief silence, Wang said, "It is getting late and you look very tired. Let me put you up in the barracks for the night. I will see you off tomorrow."

Early the next morning, true to his words, Wang Xiang came, bringing with him two soldiers carrying a large leather bag of water and a sack of parched flour.

Having ridden with Xuanzang for more than 10 *li*, Wang Xiang stopped at a fork in the road. Pointing to one direction, he said, "Take this path, and you can reach the Fourth Beacon Tower. The officer in charge there belongs to my clan. He is a kind-hearted man. Just tell him I send you. He will take care of you."

Tearfully, they bid goodbye to each other, and Xuanzang went on his way.

At the Fourth Beacon Tower, Xuanzang was pointed to a path to bypass the unfriendly Fifth Tower altogether and go in the direction of the Wild Horse Spring about 100 *li* away.

No sooner than Xuanzang resumed his journey than he got lost in a sea of sand. After four nights and five days without a drop of water, he went into a dizzy spin. His mount meandered aimlessly until a greensward and a small pond came into view. An ecstatic Xuanzang struggled off his horse and clambered to the edge of the pond, where he quenched his thirst and filled up his water canteen.

After traveling for two more days Xuanzang reached the oasis state of Yiwu. Upon entering Yiwu City (Hami), he felt he was positively in a foreign land. The people looked different, and dressed different. And there were no more Tang officials attempting to stop him. It was here that he accepted an invitation from a Gaochang emissary to visit Gaochang City.

37. King Qu Wentai

AFTER SIX MORE DAYS' journey, Xuanzang, accompanied by the emissary and his suite, reached Gaochang City, the capital of the largest oasis state in Eastern Turkistan, Gaochang.

It was well past midnight when Xuanzang entered the city through its eastern gate. At the entrance to the Palace, he was met by a welcoming party comprised of King Qu Wentai himself and dozens of his attendants, holding candles in their hands. He was led into a jeweled tent in a two-storied pavilion. Momentarily, the King and the Queen with their entourages came to pay homage and to converse with him.

After the distinguished visitors left about an hour later, Xuanzang was escorted to a dorm room in the State Monastery nearby. Thoroughly exhausted he threw himself into bed and fell asleep immediately. Outside, the dawn was breaking.

Late in the next morning, an elderly man in his 80s came. He was the State Master, the most respected Buddhist cleric of Gaochang. It was clear that his mission was to persuade Xuanzang to stay. But Xuanzang politely refused him.

Having spent a pleasant two weeks with the royal and clergy in and around Gaochang City, Xuanzang was ready to leave. He went to the Palace to bid farewell to King Qu Wentai.

"When I toured the Sui Empire with my father," said the King, "I visited the Two Capitals, Hedong (Shanxi), and Hebei. I have seen numerous famous monks. But none has impressed me. None but you. I have enjoyed your company so much that I don't know how to describe it. Please stay. I entreat you. The entire people of my state will be your disciples. We don't have many monks. Still, there are a few thousands. They can hold the sutras for you and be the audience of your sermon at a moment's notice."

"I, a poor monk," replied Xuanzang, "thank you profusely for your incredible generosity. But I do not deserve it. I set off on this journey because of the lacunae in the Buddhist teachings in my country. Like a Sadāpralāpa Bodhisattva in quest of the truth, or a Sudhanakumāra seeking friends, I am determined to complete the journey."

"As your greatest fan," the King said, in a raised voice, "I insist that you stay."

An argument back and forth ensued for hours. Eventually, King Qu Wentai was beginning to lose his composure, saying, "The Pamirs may be removed, my will is immovable. Either you stay, or I send you back to your country."

"I have come so far, because I am on a quest for the Great Law. You can keep my physical shell here, but you cannot keep my spirit." As Xuanzang uttered these words he broke down with sobs.

Sitting cross-legged in a lotus position, the Master started refusing food and water. After three days, life was obviously ebbing out of him. When King Qu Wentai saw him that morning, he was overcome with horror and shame. "Master, do accept my apologies," said he. "If you insist on continuing with your journey to the West, I will not stand in the way. But do have some breakfast first."

"Your Majesty," said Xuanzang in a faint voice, "if you are really sincere, please swear by the sun."

"Of course I can do that. But instead of swearing by the sun, how about taking an oath in front of the Buddha."

"That is even better."

"But I want you and me to take the oath together and enter into a sworn brotherhood."

After a brief moment of hesitation, Xuanzang gave his assent.

The King and his esteemed guest then entered the main basilica of the Monastery, where they paid homage to the Buddha and took part in the sworn brotherhood ritual with Queen Dowager Zhang as witness. Thereupon, the King gave Xuanzang official permission to continue his journey. It was hoped that, upon his return, Xuanzang would spend three years in Gaochang. For now, at the King's request, Xuanzang would stay for one more month, to lecture on the *Benevolent King's Prajnaparamita Sutra*, a Buddhist scripture addressed to sovereigns.

With the ceremony over, Xuanzang sat down to have his first meal since the start of his hunger and water strike.

Two days later, a gigantic tent was set up for Xuanzang's lectures with a capacity for three hundred people. Before the start of the first lecture, the King holding an incense burner led Xuanzang to a tall chair inside the tent. The Queen, the government ministers, and the top army commanders were all in the audience. The King then prostrated himself as Xuanzang stepped on his back to climb into the chair.

For the following month, the process was repeated each time Xuanzang gave a lecture.

At the end of the lecture series, the King showered Xuanzang with gifts that could support his trip for 20 years, including 25 porters and 30 horses. In addition, the King wrote 24 letters addressed to the Kings of various oasis states, asking them to render assistance to the Master. The Commander of the Palace was to escort him to the khanate (qaghanate) of Tong Yehu, the leader of the Western Tujue, together with generous gifts, and a personal letter from the King to the Khan that said,

Please have compassion for the Master in the same way you have compassion for me, your slave.

Overwhelmed, Xuanzang penned a long tear-stained letter to express his boundless gratitude.

The King responded, "Xuanzang is my sworn brother, and I am perfectly willing to share the wealth of my state with him."

Then the day of departure inevitably arrived. The King, the Queen, the monks, the government ministers, and commoner subjects all came out to see him off. When they were passing through the western suburb, the King and Xuanzang rode to a halt, dismounted, fell into each other's embrace, and sobbed hysterically together for a long while. Most of those present, clergy and lay alike, broke out crying. Having ordered the reluctant crowd to stop following the Master, the King himself, joined by the State Master and a few clerics, continued to accompany Xuanzang for several dozen *li*, before they finally parted company.

38. The Office of Vice Premier

IN CHANG'AN, THE MIRACULOUS escape of a Buddhist monk to the West incurred the Emperor's displeasure. However, although not a believer in Buddhism, the Emperor was always sympathetic to its cause, so He decided not to launch an investigation, much to the relief of Xiao Yu and Li Daliang. For Him, there were far more pressing affairs to attend to. Most notably, for example, was the appointment of another Vice Premier. For that purpose, He held a special meeting of the Chief Ministers' Council with Yuwen Shiji, Fang Xuanling, Xiao Yu, and Gao Shilian in the Liangyi Basilica in August, 627.

"The recent death of Feng Deyi has left Xuanling alone in charge of the Department of State Affairs," the Emperor began. "Deyi's post as Vice Premier is so important that I cannot afford to leave it unfilled for long."

"Indeed, Your Majesty," said Fang Xuanling.

"There is a very qualified candidate I want you to consider," resumed the Emperor.

"Who does Your Majesty want for the job?" asked Yuwen Shiji.

"Zhangsun Wuji."

"It seems to me, Your Majesty," said Xiao Yu, "Zhangsun is a bit too young and inexperienced."

"I think he can do it," rejoined Fang Xuanling. "He has proven to be a great administrator either as General-in-chief of the Militant Reserve Guard Command or as President of the Board of Personnel."

Turning to Gao Shilian, the Emperor asked, "What's your opinion?"

"Wuji is my stepson, Your Majesty," answered Gao. "I should probably refrain from giving my opinion."

"Nonsense," said the Emperor emphatically. " 'When recommending worthies, one should *not* avoid blood relations.' "

"All right. If Your Majesty wants my honest opinion, it is this: he has a natural ability for leadership and organization."

"And you?" the Emperor asked Yuwen Shiji.

"I am with Shilian, Your Majesty," answered Yuwen.

"Great!" said the Emperor. "I will then appoint him."

THAT NIGHT, AS THE Emperor sat in His study in the Ganlu Basilica, reading His favorite history, the *Book of the Han* (*Hanshu*) by the first-century historian Ban Gu, Empress Zhangsun came in.

"Your Majesty, I hear that Wuji has been appointed Vice Premier," the Empress said inquiringly.

"Isn't that wonderful?" asked the Emperor. "You should be happy for your brother."

"Isn't it true that the Vice Premier is actually the co-leader of the Department of State Affairs and the entire officialdom?" asked Empress Zhangsun.

"Of course, the position of Premier exists only in name," said the Emperor. "The two Vice Premiers are the two most important 'Chief Ministers.' "

"Your Majesty," continued the Empress, "because of his blood ties with me, Wuji is already enjoying many privileges. If he is allowed to hold such a key position, I am afraid, he won't know how to handle it."

"My dear wife, but I've got good reasons to pick Wuji. Not only was he a staunch supporter at the time of the Xuanwu Gate Incident, he is also a relative by marriage, an old friend, and most importantly, someone who is possessed of excellent leadership and organizational abilities."

"I am worried precisely for these reasons, Your Majesty. As Vice Premier, my brother will surely overshadow the other Vice Premier before long and become the dominant court leader. There are many cautionary tales in the past about consort relatives (male relatives of Imperial consorts) who became dominant court leaders. I am sure Your Majesty remembers the Lüs, the Huos, and the Shangguans. All are given detailed coverage in the *Book of the Han*. At any rate, these were the most powerful consort families in the Western Han. What happened after they reached the zenith of their power? They were all executed, and their clans were exterminated. I entreat Your Majesty to take this into consideration!"

"Of course, I'm familiar with Ban Gu's accounts of the Lüs, the Huos, and the Shangguans. I greatly appreciate your concerns. But the country is urgently in need of talents like Wuji. I think he can handle his job well and won't fall victim to power. So long as I am alive, I will make sure that he does not overstep his bounds. He *will* be all right."

The Emperor liked the self-effacing humility of His wife. But the need to place a reliable and capable person in the Vice Premier's post was overwhelming. So He went ahead with His decision.

AS WAS FEARED BY his sister, Zhangsun Wuji as Vice Premier soon became de facto the most powerful person at court under the Emperor. Because of this, each time he visited Empress Zhangsun, he would receive an earful. She would warn of a pending disaster for the Zhangsun clan if he were not careful. So at court he acted as if he "walked on the edge of a deep abyss or trod on thin ice." As both consort relative and Chief Minister, he received greater scrutiny than most. Nonetheless, after several months on the job, he was beginning to get the hang of it and establish a reputation as a highly efficient and fair-minded court leader.

One day in February of Zhenguan 2 (628), Zhangsun Wuji had a routine meeting with the Emperor to discuss government affairs in the Liangyi Basilica. At the end of the meeting, the Emperor showed him a top-secret memorial with the author's name blotted out. It reported how Zhangsun had acted arbitrarily, and attributed it to too much power and favor concentrated in a single person. *Sister is right*, Zhangsun Wuji thought. *One can never be too careful with this job.*

"Don't worry," said the Emperor. "You have My confidence. I've treated you like a son, and I'll always do so. But reports like this are important. They are filed by My censorial officers, who, as you know, are gentlemen of rectitude and probity. Furthermore, if My subjects couldn't tell Me what is on their minds, I would be out of touch with them."

"I understand that perfectly, Your Majesty."

"Remember, Wuji, whatever happens, you will always be My most trusted court official."

The meeting left Zhangsun Wuji nervous for the rest of the day. After consulting with his sister Empress Zhangsun, he submitted a written request for resignation in the following morning, which was promptly rejected by the Emperor.

In that evening, when the Emperor was ready to retire into the residential basilica, He was shocked to find the Empress kneeling at the gate. He went up to her and made an attempt to help her to her feet. But she refused to stand up. Raising her head, she said beseechingly, "Would Your Majesty leave Wuji alone?"

"All right, all right," said the Emperor as He looked at the two streaks of tears on her face. "But do get up please."

On the following day, the Emperor issued an edict to relieve Wuji of his post as Vice Premier, while conferring upon him the title of "Equal in Honor to the Three Dukes with the Power to Open His own Administration" (*kaifu yitong sansi*)—the highest prestige title in the Empire.

39. An Old Foe on the Northern Frontier

AFTER THE CRUSHING OF Liu Heita and Xu Yuanlang, the North was essentially "pacified." True, there had been sporadic minor revolts. But all of them blew over as soon as they started. None managed to establish a viable regime that could post a serious threat to the Tang. The only holdout was Liang Shidu. Having spent most of his life in north Shaanxi, he struck out on his own in 617 at a time when Li Yuan was launching his Righteous Uprising. Because of the Tujue's backing, he had successfully resisted the Tang's efforts to subdue him and declared himself Emperor of Liang. He had received a Khan's title from the Tujue and prevailed upon them to invade the lands of the Tang.

In 627, a devastating civil war broke out among different Tujue tribal confederations on the steppes. In a few months' time, the Tujue became fragmented, no longer able to give much assistance to their client regime to the south. The Emperor seized the opportunity to send Liang Shidu a letter in early 628, requesting submission. Liang refused the request. The Emperor gave orders to Xia Prefecture bordering on Liang's territory to undermine his power. Tang light cavalry were sent to the Liang area to trample on crops in the fields, and Tang spies went to work to suborn Liang's officers. One Liang general even tried to overthrow Liang Shidu from within. But the plan was aborted, and the conspirator fled south to the Tang. The incident made Liang Shidu edgy and suspicious of his associates. The Emperor chose this moment to launch a general assault, and the state of Liang soon collapsed. Eventually, only one city remained: Shuofang. As Liang and his men huddled behind the city walls, waiting for the arrival of the Tujue rescue forces (which had been repulsed), one of his cousins killed him and surrendered the city.

THE STATE OF LIANG was by no means a major power. Nevertheless, the annexation of it was of great importance to the Tang. It marked her total victory against the last Tujue-backed regime and the complete pacification of the northern frontier. Now that external peace in the North was assured, the Emperor was able to focus attention on His domestic policy of low taxes, small government, and overall frugality. But so far it had not been effective, chiefly because of something beyond His control: Nature. In the past winter, there had been little snow in the North, especially in Guanzhong. It was followed by a drought that started in the early spring and dragged on for three months.

On a bright early summer morning, the Emperor was made painfully aware of the wrath of Nature when He was riding in the Forbidden Park north of the Xuanwu Gate as the sun was beating down from the cloudless sky. Looking east, He noticed a dark mass on the horizon. As it moved swiftly westward, a barely audible humming noise it emitted became louder. All of a sudden, a swarm of locusts like a huge black cloud flew by, blocking the sun from view, before they descended on a wheat field. The brazenness with which they ignored His presence made the Emperor angry. He got off His horse and snatched one of them. Holding it up in His right hand, He stared intensely at it—its tentacles, strong hind legs, protruding belly, brown eyes. He then said loudly, "Crops are the life of the people. How dare you eat them in the fields? I would rather let you eat up My lungs and bowels."

As He was about to consume the locust, an attendant made an attempt to stop Him, saying, "Don't, Your Majesty. The evil insect may cause disease!"

"I would rather suffer the disastrous effects of a disease for My people." As He said so, He put the locust in His mouth, and munched it noisily before swallowing it.

A few moments later the horde of insects took off to continue their flight to the west, leaving nothing green in their wake.

But the problem was much more serious. Because of the poor winter crops of millet, wheat, and barley in the capital region, starving peasants thronged the streets of Chang'an, begging for food. Some of them openly offered to sell their sons and daughters in exchange for grain.

The Emperor stopped His routine work to pay homage to the Gods of the Soil and Grain at their Altars, and perform expiatory ceremonies at the Ancestral Temple. He understood that it was His moral failures that had incurred the displeasure of Heaven, which had manifested itself in the form of natural disaster. Although the legitimacy of His rule was not threatened, He nonetheless felt mortified. So He ordered His underlings to use cash and silk from the Imperial storehouses to ransom those unfortunate youngsters sold in exchange for food and return them to their parents. He even issued a general amnesty in hopes of bringing down rain to alleviate the suffering of His poor subjects in the country.

In the days that followed, a few good rains descended on Chang'an and its environs. It was believed that Heaven had been moved by the widespread gratitude among the recipients of government generosity. The Emperor's wishes had been answered, or so it would seem.

40. Lu Zushang

IN SPITE OF HER early growing pains, Tang China, under the Emperor Li Shimin, was becoming an Empire with a vast area that extended from the Great Wall in the north to north Vietnam in the south. As the natural disaster in the North was beginning to abate, a new challenge emerged in Jiaozhou Area Command in the far south. Luckily for the Tang, the problem did not involve a rebellion (even though many of the local residents were Viets known for their ferocious struggle for independence in the past). The Commander of the Command, Duke of Sui'an Li Shou, had been convicted of embezzling a large sum of public funds, and dismissed from office. Encompassing Guangdong, Guangxi, and north Vietnam, the Area Command was the southernmost Tang territory. For months, the court had not been able to find a suitable replacement. Then someone recommended Lu Zushang, currently Prefect of Ying Prefecture. After perusing his dossier and recommendation letters, the Emperor concluded that Lu was the ideal choice for the job. At least on paper, Mr. Lu was an embodiment of the civil and martial virtues with a perfect track record. The Emperor called him in to offer him Li Shou's job. Lu accepted it with gratitude, much to the delight of the Emperor.

After returning home, Lu learned more about the Jiao area, especially the prefectural capital Jiaozhou (Hanoi, Vietnam), and became worried. Eventually, he changed his mind and turned down the job offer after all. The Emperor sweetened the deal by promising to recall him in three years, and sent Du Ruhui and Lu's own brother-in-law to persuade him. Politely but firmly Lu rejected them.

"The humid and rainy weather will be dreadful for my rheumatism," argued Lu. "The area is infested with miasma. One has to drink wine all day long to survive. The problem is, I cannot drink. If I go, I will never be able to come back."

Infuriated, the Emperor said to His aides, "If I can't ask him to take up this post, how can I govern all under Heaven?" So He ordered decapitation as Lu's punishment, which was carried out summarily in front of the Audience Hall at the Chengtian Gate (the southern main entrance of the Taiji Palace).

SOON THE DEATH OF Lu Zushang began to weigh on the Emperor's conscience. He talked about it with Du Ruhui, but Du argued that for the sake of Imperial authority Lu had to be made an example of. That was no great consolation, for the Emperor now came to believe that He had acted too hastily. Only with the passage of time did the unpleasant episode fade into memory.

One morning, the Emperor held an informal meeting with His advisers. This was the occasion where a whole range of issues were discussed: politics, the economy, the military, and culture, among others. At that meeting, the topic of the conversation drifted to key historical figures. Someone mentioned Gao Yang, the founding sovereign of the Northern Qi. The Emperor asked Wei Zheng, "What sort of person was he?"

"Generally speaking, he was a despot," answered Wei Zheng. "However, when he got involved in an argument, he would always give in if his opinion was proven wrong. Take, for example, Chief Administrator of Qing Prefecture (in Shandong) Wei Kai. After a visit to the Liang in the South, Wei refused to accept an appointment as Chief Administrator of Guāng Prefecture. Chief Minister Yang Yin reported the case to Gao Yang. In a fit of rage, Gao called in Wei Kai, and berated him. 'Previously,' Wei replied,'I was in a large Prefecture (Qing), and during my recent mission to the South, I worked diligently and did not commit a single misstep. So I do not think I deserve to be assigned to a small Prefecture (Guāng).' Gao Yang accepted the argument and left Wei alone. This was his strong point."

"Well, I am not even as good as this despot," said the Emperor.

"I did not mean to suggest that, Your Majesty," Wei Zheng answered in apparent astonishment.

"I know," said the Emperor. "But My decision to kill Lu Zushang was obviously too rash. Lu shouldn't refuse to follow an Emperor's order. But what I did was terrible; it made Me an even worse sovereign than Gao Yang."

Addressing Fang Xuanling, the Emperor asked, "What happened to Lu Zushang's family?"

"Based on the law code of the Great Tang, his family was banished to a distance of 3,000 li; all his family assets were confiscated. Since Lu was also disenrolled, his family lost all its hereditary-protective (yin) privileges."

The Emperor then said to Secretariat Drafter Li Baiyao, "Write up a rescript that includes the following:

Rehabilitate Lu Zushang completely;
Allow him to receive a posthumous title;
Recall his family members to the capital;
Return all the confiscated assets to the family;
Restore all the hereditary-protective privileges to his next of kin."

41. Pei Ji

AFTER THE MEETING WAS adjourned, all the advisers left except for Wei Zheng.

"Yes?" asked the Emperor.

"There is something I need to discuss with Your Majesty in private."

"What is it?"

"The Palace recently admitted Ms. Zheng as an Imperial concubine."

"Yes, the daughter of Zheng Renji. She is a handsome 16-year-old of good birth recommended by My wife. I have just granted her the title of 'Lady of Wholesome Beauty' (*chonghua*)."

"The edict has already been written?"

"Yes, but the envoy hasn't been sent yet, why?"

"I have heard that Ms. Zheng has already been betrothed."

"To whom?" the Emperor asked, sounding displeased.

"To Mr. Lu Shuang, Your Majesty."

"What should I do, in your opinion?"

"Your Majesty is the father of all the people, and cares for the masses. He should feel worried when they are worried; and should feel joyful when they are joyful. Ms. Zheng has been betrothed for quite some time. Still, Your Majesty took her into His Palace without so much as asking a question. If this story gets out and spreads to the Four Seas, what will the people think of Your Majesty?"

"My goodness," said the Emperor, alarmed. "I have to say *mea culpa*."

As the Emperor was about to return Ms. Zheng to her family, He received two memorials. The first one was from Fang Xuanling, which offered a different view, "Concerning Ms. Zheng's betrothal to Mr. Lu Shuang, it was never finalized. But her admission into the Palace was consummated in accord with grand ritual. So it is too late to be reversed."

The second one was from Mr. Lu Shuang himself. It claimed, "While my father was alive, he did give a fair amount of money to the Zheng family, but no betrothal ever took place."

The Emperor, confused, called Wei Zheng in for clarification.

"Fang Xuanling may have tried to please Me, how about Mr. Lu?" asked the Emperor. "Why did he deny the betrothal?"

"Well, has Your Majesty heard the story of Mr. Xin Chujian?"

"No. What about him?"

"When the Honorary Emperor (that is, Li Yuan) first entered Chang'an, He inadvertently took in a married woman, Xin Chujian's wife, as His concubine. Later when He found out about it, He was very upset. So He ordered to have poor Chujian transferred from the Administration of Crown Prince Affairs to Wannian County. For a long time after that, Xin Chujian lived in fear of getting beheaded by the Honorary Emperor. Mr. Lu Shuang realizes that although Your Majesty tolerates him now, Your Majesty may go after him any time in the future. That is why he denies ever having betrothal ties with Ms. Zheng at all!"

"I see," said the Emperor. "I have to give her back after all."

A strongly worded edict followed. It blamed Himself and the court officials concerned for the error and demanded in unequivocal language that Ms. Zheng be returned.

ON THE MORNING OF the 21st day of the first month, Zhenguan 3 (February 19, 629), the Emperor Li Shimin took part in the annual Spring Plowing ceremony in the ritual field of Chang'an's eastern suburb. He felt invigorated by the cool morning breeze and the suburban fresh air.

Arriving back in the Taiji Palace, He was told by an attendant that Pei Ji had been waiting for two hours. He immediately granted him an audience.

The Emperor had felt indebted to Pei Ji for his role in starting the Righteous Uprising. He used to have fond memories of how Pei had convinced His father to break away from the Sui. But His feeling of gratitude disappeared when Pei's malicious attack caused the death of Liu Wenjing. After He assumed the throne, the Emperor quietly took away Pei's chief ministerial power.

Recently, Pei Ji was implicated in the case of Faya, a favorite monk of Li Yuan, who had been condemned for spreading libelous rumors about the throne. Allegedly, Pei Ji was in the know but failed to file a report. His punishment was dismissal from office and banishment to his home village. For months, however, Pei Ji had refused to move, and the Magistrate of Chang'an County, who had jurisdiction over Pei Ji's Ward in the city, had turned a blind eye. When the Emperor had been told what had happened, He had issued an edict to banish Pei immediately.

"Your Majesty," said Pei Ji, "please have mercy on me, for old time's sake."

The Emperor was on the verge of taking pity on this man of small build approaching 60. Then He recalled how much grief Pei had caused during the previous reign, and His face turned crimson with anger.

"How can you have the cheek to make such a request?" the Emperor asked. "You were a trouble-maker in the first reign. Because of you, Liu Wenjing was executed on dubious charges. Now I allow you to spend your old age guarding your ancestral tombs—you should consider yourself lucky."

"Yes, Your Majesty," said Pei Ji, his eyes averting the Emperor's gaze.

"I want you to move out of the city as soon as possible. Can you do it by the end of this month?"

Pei Ji nodded his head and left, completely disheartened.

The Emperor then ordered to have the Magistrate of Chang'an County punished with 30 strokes by the light stick, and called in His senior court advisers to discuss the issue of Liu Wenjing's rehabilitation. They unanimously supported the idea. The Emperor issued an edict that reversed the verdict he had received; posthumously restored his official titles; and granted one of his sons the privileges to inherit his noble title as the Duke of Lu and to receive the hand of an Imperial Princess in marriage.

42. The Histories of the Five Dynasties

IN HIS TWO AND a half years on the throne, the Emperor spent most of His time in Chang'an, poring over memorials submitted by officials and occasionally by ordinary subjects, presiding over court sessions, holding meetings with the Chief Ministers, adjudicating important cases, formulating political and economic policy, making top civil and military appointments, attending state ritual ceremonies, receiving foreign visitors, and making foreign policy decisions. As peace began to settle over the country, the Emperor's work became increasingly routine. To stimulate his mind, He engaged in a number of past-time pursuits, including poetry, calligraphy, hunting, and, the reading of histories. Not only was He an avid reader of such great historical works as the *Grand Scribe's Records* by Sima Qian and the *Book of the Han* by Ban Gu, He also aspired to becoming the sponsor of the largest history-writing project ever.

To get it off the ground, the Emperor summoned a special conference in the Wude Basilica with a small group of senior officials including His close advisers such as Wei Zheng and Fang Xuanling, and those with a reputation for learning.

"Because of war and chaos," the Emperor began, "official history has been neglected for a long time. It is time that a history project was launched under the aegis of this court."

Turning to Wei Zheng, He continued, "Can you explain in detail the rationale and objective of the project?"

"Yes, Your Majesty," answered Wei Zheng. "The writing of veritable history has been a glorious tradition since antiquity. One of the earliest classics *Shangshu* (*Venerated Documents*) is a history. History is a mirror that reflects the accomplishments and errors of sovereigns and subjects, and acts as a guide for our future course of action. The project in question will essentially deal with the hundred years prior to the rise of the Tang."

"Now, who else wants to comment on that?" asked the Emperor.

"Your Majesty," said Fang Xuanling, "I would like to add that some people have proposed the establishment of the Institute of Historiography (*shiguan*). It will gather the best historical talents and provide them with the best resources and environment in which to work. It seems like a wonderful idea."

"Where will it be housed?" asked the Emperor.

"Inside the Chancellery."

"Good. We will support the history project *and* set up the Institute. Now then, isn't that true that the Honorary Emperor started an ambitious history project? And it covers the Five Dynasties of Liang, Chen, Northern Qi, Northern Zhou, and Sui?"

"Yes, Your Majesty," replied Wei Zheng.

"What happened to that project?"

"Your Majesty, it was abandoned halfway," answered Yan Shigu, one of the most learned officials.

"The new project will cover the same Five Dynasties," said the Emperor. "But you can do better, can't you?"

It was greeted by a chorus of affirmatives. A discussion followed on each of the five histories planned and who was best equipped to write them.

At the end of the meeting, the Emperor announced the inauguration of the new History of the Five Dynasties project. Wei Zheng, Chief of the Directorate for the Palace Library, would assume overall responsibility as its Editor-in-chief, and Vice Premier Fang Xuanling would serve as its Supervising Director. The Institute of Historiography—headed by one Director and two Deputy Directors—would be set up immediately inside the Taiji Palace as an affiliate to the Chancellery. A Chief Minister would be appointed as Supervising Director of the Institute to provide overall guidance.

"One more point, Xuanling," said the Emperor. "The *Book of the Han* (*Hanshu*) and the *Book of the Later Han* (*Hou Han shu*) have recorded verbatim a number of rhapsody pieces, such as 'Sweet Springs' (Ganquan) and 'Plume Hunt' (Yulie) by Yang Xiong, 'Sir Vacuous' (Zixu) and 'Upper Forest' (Shanglin) by Sima Xiangru, and the 'Two Capitals' by Ban Gu. They are all written in an ornate style, with little substance to offer. Pieces like these should not be included in the histories."

"Yes, Your Majesty," Fang Xuanling said, nodding his head.

"On the other hand," the Emperor said, after a brief pause, "there are candid memorials that rulers may read with benefit—they should be recorded, regardless whether I have adopted them or not."

"Yes, Your Majesty," Fang Xuanling said approvingly.

43. Heavenly Khan

AS ZHENGUAN 3 (629) WORE on, the mighty Tujue Empire under Xieli began to unravel. Although Xieli was the nominal overlord of the vast Tujue realm stretching from Manchuria across the Mongolian Plateau to the Altai Mountains and the oasis states of Central Asia, a rival regime—the Western Tujue Empire—had been in existence for decades. Xieli could only lay claim to the Eastern or Northern Tujue Empire, which nonetheless was much larger and more populous than its Western counterpart.

Chafing under Xieli's domination, such tribal confederations as Xueyantuo (Syr Tardush), Uighur, and Bayegu (Bayïrqu) broke away. An exasperated Xieli sent his nephew Tuli Khan on a punitive campaign against them. To his dismay, Tuli was soon worsted by Xueyantuo.

In a fit of fury, Xieli had Tuli whipped and thrown into prison for two weeks. After Tuli got out, he secretly contacted the Tang, offering his help against his uncle.

The Tang court watched these developments on the steppes with growing interest. Frontier officers periodically sent intelligence reports on Xieli. One submitted by Zhang Gongjin, Commander of Daizhou Command, captured the Emperor's attention. Zhang was the officer who had refused to perform the tortoise divination requested by then Prince Li Shimin on the eve of the Xuanwu Gate Incident. Had he not done so, the preemptive action would have been delayed with unthinkable consequences. It was Zhang's report, which provided a detailed analysis of Xieli's military, logistical, and political weaknesses, that prompted the Emperor into action.

Two brilliant Tang generals, Li Jing and Li Shiji, leading an expeditionary force of more than 100,000, launched the Eastern Tujue War. Over a six-month period, they dislodged Xieli from Dingxiang (northwest of Horinger, Inner Mongolia) and routed his main force at Baidao in the Yin Mountains and at Qikou beyond. Having lost his army, Xieli with a small retinue fled south in an attempt to join Tuyuhun in Gansu and Qinghai, and was caught while still in central Inner Mongolia.

His Tujue Empire crumbled.

UNDER PRESSURE FROM XUEYANTUO, more than 100,000 semi-starved Tujue nomads, Xieli's former subjects, moved into Tang territory for protection. The Tang frontier commanding officers, who had no experience in dealing with the influx of refugees on such a massive scale, sent urgent requests to the court for provisions.

An emergency meeting of the Chief Ministers' Council was held to discuss the issue. Wei Zheng was the first to speak: "The Tujue are our enemies and have raided our communities for generations. They should be returned to their homeland, and not be allowed to remain inside China."

"I disagree," said Wen Yanbo, President of the Secretariat.

"Why?" the Emperor asked, clearly surprised. Of all the senior court officials of His inner circle, Wen was the only one who had an intimate knowledge of the Tujue way of life.

"Your Majesty," Wen answered, "the Tujue have already come to us, and I don't see any reason in turning them away. Doesn't Confucius say, 'In education there is no distinction whatsoever?' If we save them from the brink of extinction, show them how to make a living, and teach them ritual and righteousness, several years later they will become *our* people."

"Yanbo," Hou Junji said, with a puzzled look on his face, "you were detained and mistreated by the Tujue. Why do you still want to welcome them?"

"It is true that I spent a long time in captivity under the Tujue. But my experience with them told me that they, too, are human beings, not that different from us."

"I think Yanbo's got a point," the Emperor weighed in. "The fact that Yanbo lived among the Tujue for so long makes his argument all the more convincing. If the Tujue submit to our authority, they are our subjects. We should welcome them and give them assistance as we would Han people under similar circumstances."

Subsequently, a number of key decisions were made to deal with Tujue refugees and related issues. Those who were already inside the border were to be settled locally and provided with food assistance; the vast territory that had been under Xieli's dominance was to be divided into six Area Commands; and the Tujue elite and their dependents were encouraged to move to Chang'an. Eventually, about 10,000 Tujue households permanently settled in that city. Many former Tujue tribal chiefs were appointed Commandants (*zhonglang jiang*). More than 100 of them received appointments of rank 5 and above. Soon, they were seen rubbing shoulders with Tang senior officials at court.

To really appreciate the importance of these appointments, it is necessary to know something about the Tang official ranking system. The Tang bureaucracy was organized into a hierarchy of 30 rungs and nine ranks. Ranks 1 through 3 had two classes each (upper and lower or *zheng* and *cong*). Ranks 4 through 9 also had two classes each, but each class was further divided into two grades (upper and lower or *shang* and *xia*). Generally, anyone with a post of rank 5 or above could be regarded as a senior official. At the top, the Vice Premiers of the Department of State Affairs and the President of the Chancellery were in the second rank; and the President of the Secretariat was in the third rank. There were very few rank 1 positions, and they were rarely filled.

ON THE MORNING OF May 20 (3rd day of the fourth month), Zhenguan 4 (630), a most spectacular ceremony took place in the gatetower of the Shuntian (Chengtian) Gate. For all practical purposes, this gatetower was a tall basilica with its own spacious assembly hall on the second floor. Located at the southern terminus of the Taiji Palace's central axis, it served as the venue for some of the grandest ritual ceremonies each year, including those of the Winter Solstice and the New Year. The ceremony on this particular day, however, was not intended to mark a recurrent event, but to celebrate the Tang's final victory over the [Eastern] Tujue.

Inside the hall, the main floor was filled with key civil officials, military officers, and foreign dignitaries in two sections separated by a wide central path that extended from the main door all the way to the dais at the northern end. As the distinguished guests were standing at attention, a faint sound of music wafted in from afar. As it became louder it began to fill the air with the militant tune of "Breaking through the Enemy Array" (*Pozhen yue*). Then through the main door the band of the Court of State Sacrifices entered. Led by the Court's Director, two dozen court musicians marched in, playing bamboo flutes (*di*), bamboo oboes (*bili*), vertical bamboo flutes (*xiao*), reed pipes (*jia*), bronze bells (*nao*), and drums.

Falling in behind the band was a parade of Tujue weaponry and military paraphernalia and Xieli Khan himself, who was marched into the presence of the Emperor seated on the dais.

The music stopped. The Emperor stood up and ceremoniously chastised Xieli for his breach of the oath taken at the Bian Bridge and for the numerous raids he had conducted against the Tang subjects. The once proud overlord of the Mongolian steppes broke down in tears and was subsequently marched out of the hall.

Just as the ceremony was about to end, several leaders of the nomadic and oasis states submitted a joint petition that took the Emperor by surprise. They requested that the Emperor accept the title of *tian kehan* or "Heavenly Khan" (Qaghan).

"I am already the Son of Heaven," the Emperor responded. "Am I expected to demote Myself and become a Khan?"

"No, Your Majesty," a foreign state leader answered. "The Heavenly Khan is the 'khan of khans,' the 'king of kings,' the overlord of various states on the steppes."

"Has anyone received this title before?"

"No. This is created for Your Majesty."

"Well then, there seems no reason to reject it," said the Emperor as He looked at His senior advisers in the audience. Hearing no objection, He resumed, "From this day forward, I will use the title 'Heavenly Khan' in dealing with foreign leaders."

The foreign dignitaries broke into chants of "Long live the Heavenly Khan!"

With this title came the expectation that its bearer would act as the arbiter in disagreements and differences among the various states and as the keeper of peace on the steppes. There would be future Heavenly Khans, but this one was the first, and was the only one not self-proclaimed. Instead, it was created by the foreign state leaders in acknowledgement of the preeminence of the Tang sovereign in the wake of Xieli's fall.

AT THE CELEBRATION, ONE key person, Li Yuan, was conspicuously absent. In fact, in the last few years, the Honorary Emperor had been unhappy. Under the reign of his son, his own religious policy had been reversed; his favorite monk Faya, executed; and his best friend Pei Ji, banished. He had moved out of the Taiji Palace to settle in the Hongyi Palace (west of the Palace City) at the Emperor's request when relations between father and son had reached a nadir. However, the Emperor's decision not to invite Li Yuan to the Shuntian Gate event was purely based on a concern for his declining health, or so it seemed. Li Yuan did not seem to mind. In fact, when he heard of Xieli's capture, he felt genuinely happy for and proud of his son for the first time since the Xuanwu Gate Incident.

In the evening, to celebrate the occasion, Li Yuan threw a small drinking party at the Mist-transcending (Lingyan) Pavilion, northeast of the Liangyi Basilica. Apart from the Emperor Himself, only a small number of guests were invited, including a dozen or so senior advisers, the Princes and their consorts, and the Princesses.

When the soirée was halfway through and most guests had dropped their guard under the influence of wine, Li Yuan started dancing to *pipa* music played by the Emperor. As soon as the performance was over, the senior advisers, obviously inebriated, lurched to their feet one after another to stammer out words of felicitation to the former and current Emperors. The festivities did not end until the wee hours.

AS THE REPUTATION OF the Tang rose in East Asia, a delegation from the southern country of Linyi (south Vietnam) arrived to pay tribute with a fire orb (*huozhu*), a crystalline precious stone the size of a hen's egg. But a Tang official in charge found the language in the Letter of State presented by the emissary impertinent. The official retained the emissary and his entourage, and proposed a punitive campaign against the distant country.

"Well," responded the Emperor, "war-mongers are doomed to destruction. Emperor Yang (Yang Guang) of Sui and Xieli Khan are two cases in point. Moreover, there is nothing martial about defeating a small state, let alone fighting a war that is not necessary. As for the language problem, you don't have to mind it at all!"

Thus no action was taken against Linyi. The emissary and his suite were let out of detention and admitted into the Court for Tributaries where they received royal treatment as distinguished foreign guests from a tributary state.

44. The Renovation of the Luoyang Palace

IT HAD BEEN ALMOST ten years since the Emperor had sacked Luoyang. Although He had condemned Luoyang as a decadent city and ordered the destruction of some of its landmark structures, He had maintained close ties with it. Before His ascension to the throne, Luoyang, under the management of His protégé Zhang Liang and others, had become His power center in the east. By now memories of its evil past had faded, and that gave the Emperor confidence to issue an edict on August 5, Zhenguan 4 (630), to openly discuss construction projects in the city. It said:

The Palace in Luoyang was founded by the Sui. I, the Emperor, have not renovated it. Today, some of the structures have sustained water damage. Repairs should be made to render them inhabitable.

In view of My need for a place of rest while on hunting trips in the east, the Qianyuan Basilica (Qianyang under the Sui) *shall be revived. An appropriate number of foot soldiers shall be mobilized for that purpose.*

Chief of the Directorate for the Palace Buildings (jiangzuo jian) *Dou Jin shall be in charge of the project.*

In fact, the renovation of the Luoyang Palace had been going on for months. This innocuous-looking edict simply gave it an air of Imperial sanction. It elicited praise from some leading members of the bureaucracy, who argued that not only did the Emperor show reason but also sympathy with the multitude. However, it kept one official in the Chancellery awake at night. Supervising Secretary Zhang Xuansu was so alarmed that he submitted a long, scathing memorial, which excoriated the Emperor for surpassing even Emperor Yang (Yang Guang) of the Sui in profligacy.

The Emperor was not amused. *Why can't this straitlaced prig mind his own business?* He thought, and called him to account.

"To you," said the Emperor, "I am not even as good as Emperor Yang. How about King Jie of Xia and King Zhòu of Shang?" Needless to say, Jie and Zhòu, the embodiments of evil, were two notorious despots who had lost their dynastic fortunes through wanton abuse of power in antiquity.

"If this Basilica is eventually revived, you Majesty," answered Zhang, "it will lead down the road of Jie and Zhòu."

"What? Are you accusing Me of being the most pathetic ruler in history?"

"No. I just wanted to alert Your Majesty to the danger."

"What are you? Supervising Secretary (jishi zhong) in the Chancellery?"

"Yes, Your Majesty."

"And your rank is?"

"Rank 5, upper class, upper grade."

"You sound like a Vice Premier," said the Emperor mockingly.

"I am awfully sorry to have offended…"

"Not at all, not at all. I will see what I can do with your memorial."

After Zhang Xuansu left, the Emperor spent a long time mulling over the memorial before calling in His close adviser Fang Xuanling for a discussion.

"Frankly," Emperor began, "I was not too happy with the memorial at all. But after My meeting with him I became more sympathetic to his view. One has to admire his courage. A rank-5 official has the pluck to confront the Emperor! This sort of thing has never been easy since antiquity. Come to think of it, the Luoyang Palace probably does not have to be renovated after all. Don't you agree?"

Fang Xuanling, who had been watching the Emperor's mood carefully, responded, "As a matter of fact, I do, Your Majesty."

The Emperor forthwith dismissed Chief Architect Dou Jin, ordered the destruction of those extravagant structures he had revived and renovated, called a complete stop to the Luoyang project, and had 200 bolts of silk sent to Zhang Xuansu as a reward for his candor.

45. The Good Reign of Zhenguan

BY THE END OF Zhenguan 4 (630), finally, widespread prosperity had arrived. In all the key regions of the country, the year had seen the best harvests of rice, wheat, barley, and millet in decades. Many poor peasants who had drifted away from their villages in search of food returned home to engage in farming. Rice was selling for 3 cash (bronze coins) per peck at the capital. As a result of a precipitous decline in serious crime, the total number of death sentences for the entire year was 29, a record low. Empire-wide travel was not only safe, but becoming a bit comfortable. Post houses, roadside inns, and hostels were numerous, and well provisioned. Gone were the days when travellers had to carry their own food. There was even talk that "people now leave their doors unlatched at night." That was, of course, a bit of an exaggeration. But there was no denying that an era of *Pax Sinica* or "Chinese peace" was dawning.

"Xuanling," the Emperor said, "you remember the crop failures we had in Guanzhong and elsewhere?"

"Yes, Your Majesty," replied Fang Xuanling. "Because of the crop failures, in the first year of Zhenguan (627), a peck of rice could fetch a bolt of silk! There was widespread starvation. In the second year, the entire country was hit by the locust plague. In the third year, there was flooding everywhere."

"We have come a long way, haven't we?"

"Yes, Your Majesty. The policy of light taxation and small government has worked wonderfully."

"In the early Zhenguan years, everybody advised Me, 'The sovereign must hold a tight grip on power, and must never share it with His subordinate ministers'; 'Your Majesty must heighten the martial spirit and conquer the neighboring barbarians.' In fact, Wei Zheng was the only one who proposed a shift of focus from the military to the civil. I followed his advice. See what happened? Not only was Xieli captured, his tribal chiefs are now sword-carrying officers in My Palace Guard."

"On the other hand," said Fang Xuanling, "armors and weapons in our arsenals have far surpassed those of the Sui."

"No doubt, we can't do without armors and weapons," said the Emperor. "But was Emperor Yang's weaponry ever in short supply? No. Still, He lost. In the last analysis, people are far more important than weapons. It is with the help of people like you that I have pacified all under Heaven. These people are My best weapons!"

THE FIFTH YEAR OF Zhenguan (631) can be best described as an *annus normalis*. With the Tujue subdued and Tang China at peace with her neighbors, more attention was devoted to diplomacy.

"We have accomplished a great deal in dealing with neighboring states, haven't we?" the Emperor asked rhetorically at a banquet for the Chief Ministers at the end of the year.

The top decision-making officials all nodded their agreement.

Addressing Fang Xuanling, the Emperor asked, "You are responsible for external relations, aren't you?"

"Yes, Your Majesty. I was recently appointed, concurrently, as Supervising President of the Board of Rites."

"That is right," said the Emperor. "The Board of Rites is in charge of the Court for Tributaries (*honglu si*). There has been much contact with neighboring states in the past year, hasn't there?"

"Yes, Your Majesty," said Fang Xuanling. "We received Qu Wentai, King of Gaochang, as our first distinguished guest of the year. In fact, he came in the last week of Zhenguan 4, but most of the functions took place in Zhenguan 5."

"Of course," said the Emperor. "I remember. He was the guest of honor at our first banquet of the year for foreign dignitaries. Qu Wentai used to be a vassal of Western Tujue's Yehu Khan. Now he is more interested in paying tribute to us."

"When Master Xuanzang was on his way to India," said Fang Xuanling, "Qu Wentai gave him a royal treatment."

"It was really kind of him," said the Emperor. "When he was on visit here, at least ten more states wanted to send their tributary missions."

"That did not materialize," said Fang Xuanling.

"Why?" asked Li Jing.

"Well, Wei Zheng, can you speak to that?" asked the Emperor.

"Yes, Your Majesty," Wei Zheng said, looking a bit uneasy. Wei was attending the banquet as a de facto Chief Minister, someone who was appointed to hold chief ministerial power without receiving the full appointment. "I had misgivings about allowing ten more oasis states to pay tribute, because of the cost. Accommodating Qu Wentai and his huge party was already very expensive. Ten additional tributary missions would probably bring an additional 1,000 people to Chang'an."

"Wei Zheng, you did the right thing," said the Emperor.

"Thanks, Your Majesty," said Wei Zheng.

"Quite a few tribal chiefs were already residing in Chang'an," said Fang Xuanling.

"Indeed," said the Emperor. "When I hunted near Lake Kunming (west of Chang'an) in early spring, I had several of them in My entourage. And we had a great time."

"In the eighth month, we sent a delegation to Koguryŏ," said Fang Xuanling. "With the help of the Koguryŏ, we were able to have the remains of the Sui fallen officers and soldiers buried in accord with ritual."

"The Sui Emperors," said the Emperor, "launched four expeditions to subdue this small kingdom. Once under Emperor Wen (Yang Jian), and three times under Emperor Yang (Yang Guang). And they all failed. We did not fight Koguryŏ, but she nonetheless became a tributary state to us."

"In the 11th month, two tributary missions came, one from Linyi, and the other from Silla," said Fang Xuanling.

"They brought exotic gifts," said the Emperor.

"The Linyi (in south Vietnam) sent a five-colored talking parrot," said Fang Xuanling. "The Silla (in southeast Korea) sent two beauties."

"They were here only briefly before we returned them, again because of Wei Zheng," said the Emperor.

"Yes," said Wei Zheng. "Your Majesty commiserated with the talking parrot which felt lonely, and with the young Silla girls who were homesick."

"I took My cue from you," said the Emperor. "We also received a tributary delegation from Yamato. Xuanling, are you familiar with that?"

"Yes, Your Majesty," said Fang Xuanling. "In response, we sent our Imperial mission headed by Gao Biaoren."

"Yes, the son-in-law of Yang Yong, the first Sui heir apparent. The mission to Yamato did not go very well. What happened?"

"There was a controversy over ritual. Gao insisted that the *tenno* (Japanese Emperor) get off his throne and face north while listening to the pronouncement of the Tang Letter of State. The Yamato people refused, and the Letter was not even delivered."

"What a shame!" exclaimed the Emperor. "The north-facing position is for subjects, not sovereigns."

"Other than this unpleasant event," said Fang Xuanling, "the Yamato treated Gao Biaoren and his party well. They escorted them back as far as Tsushima."

"What happened to Gao Biaoren after his return?" asked the Emperor.

"Gao failed to pacify a distant state and was punished with the suspension of salary for two years," said Fang Xuanling.

"But he was allowed to hold on to his post as Prefect, wasn't he?" asked the Emperor.

"Yes, Your Majesty," answered Fang Xuanling.

"Good," said the Emperor. "Now then, what is the most distant country you had to deal with?"

"Kangju in Samarkand," answered Fang Xuanling.

"Of course, the Sogdians," said the Emperor. "They wanted to submit to the Tang. But we had to turn them down. Unlike previous Emperors, I am not interested in the vainglory of conquering distant places. If they are really in trouble, we will come to their rescue. But we are not going to dispatch an army to a place twice as far as Dunhuang simply for the sake of an empty name."

"I wonder," said Wei Zheng, "where Your Majesty obtained such wisdom."

"I don't know if you can call it wisdom," said the Emperor, "but I do know that running a country is like taking care of a patient. Even if the patient is cured, one still has to constantly watch out for his health. If not, he is sure to suffer relapses, which may even be fatal."

"This is," said Wei Zheng, "what is really great about Your Majesty: to be able to constantly think of potential danger in times of peace."

"Well, it is so because I have advisers like you to guide Me," said the Emperor. Raising His goblet, He continued, "Let us toast to the past year, a year of peace for all under Heaven."

As the Emperor drank up His goblet of wine, the Chief Ministers did the same.

AS WHAT LATER HISTORIANS termed the "Good Reign of Zhenguan" was in full swing, a petition campaign picked up momentum in early Zhenguan 6 (632). Hundreds of memorials from top civil officials and military officers and even tribal chiefs flooded the court, imploring the Emperor to conduct the *fengshan* ceremony. As the crown jewel of thanks-giving rites, the *fengshan* ceremony had to be performed on Mount Tai in Shandong, the most sacred mountain in China. It was the occasion where the Emperor would personally communicate to Heaven and Earth the accomplishments of His reign and His gratitude.

"You all argue that *fengshan* is the highest ritual for a sovereign," said the Emperor to His advisers. "But I don't think so. If all under Heaven are at peace and every household is well provided with food and clothing, we can do without a *fengshan* trip, can't we? The First Emperor of Qin made a *fengshan* trip and Emperor Wen of Han did not. Can one say that Emperor Wen was not nearly as worthy as the First Emperor? Why do we have to go to Mount Tai to express our gratitude to Heaven and Earth?"

"I highly appreciate Your Majesty's sagacious observation," said Zhangsun Wuji. "However, under Your Majesty's wise reign, the Six Accomplishments are achieved together. That is unprecedented and makes the trip very deserving."

"Enlighten Me on the 'Six Accomplishments'—I have never heard of them before," requested the Emperor.

"First, the accrual of extraordinary merit, both civil and military; second, the accumulation of great virtue; third, peace within the Four Seas; fourth, submission of the barbarians; fifth, great harvests all over the country; and sixth, the appearance of auspicious portents."

"No wonder all of you are so insistent on My making the *fengshan* trip. I probably should consider taking it after all."

All the advisers present were pleased with the Emperor's change of heart. All except one—Wei Zheng.

Noticing Wei Zheng's lugubrious countenance, the Emperor asked, "Something is bothering you?"

"Yes, Your Majesty," answered Wei Zheng, "I don't think the *fengshan* trip is a good idea."

"But haven't you heard about the Six Accomplishments?"

"Yes, I have."

"Aren't they true?"

"Absolutely."

"But why do you still oppose the trip?"

"Well," said Wei Zheng, "the population was decimated during the late Sui war. By now, in spite of the prosperity, it is still below the pre-war level, and the granaries are not quite full. If Your Majesty makes this long trip east, thousands of carriages and horses will follow. Countries far and near will send their delegations. They all have to be accommodated and entertained. The cost will be enormous. Does Your Majesty really want to spend so much in pursuit of an empty name regardless of the consequences?"

"I haven't made up My mind yet," answered the Emperor. Certainly, He was not pleased with Wei Zheng's irreverent remarks on something that had won almost the unanimous support of the court, but was nonetheless involuntarily impressed with his well-reasoned argument.

A few days later, news of flooding in the lower Yellow River valley arrived, and the issue of *fengshan* was dropped from His agenda. Still later, when petitions for *fengshan* resurfaced, the Emperor turned them down on account of His "recently developed acrophobia."

46. The Harrier Chick

AS THE PRINCESS OF Changle (Li Lizhi), the first daughter born to the Emperor Li Shimin and Empress Zhangsun, entered the 12th year of her life in early Zhenguan 6 (632), she was considered ripe for marriage. Changle was the apple of her parents' eyes. Pretty, smart, kind-hearted, and well-schooled in the arts of brush painting and calligraphy, she would make an excellent wife to a high-ranking scholar-official. Through the good offices of Empress Zhangsun, finally, Zhangsun Zhong, Zhangsun Wuji's son, was chosen as her bridegroom. Changle was too precious to be married off to some prefectural governor.

Concerning her trousseau, the Emperor suggested that its value should be double that of His own sister's, the Princess of Yongjia, and was pleasantly surprised when the suggestion was readily endorsed by the frugal Empress. But soon His mood was dampened by a memorial submitted by Wei Zheng. It cited the case of Emperor Ming of the Eastern Han. Despite His reputation as a spendthrift, Emperor Ming insisted that the fiefs of His sons should only be half the size of those granted by His father (Guangwu) to His sons. He did so out of filial reverence. By the same token, the dowry of Changle should by no means surpass that of her aunt in value.

The Emperor overcame His own reluctance and accepted Wei Zheng's suggestion. But He was concerned that to persuade His wife to do the same would not be so easy. When He brought up the matter with the Empress, the latter sighed, with a serious look on her face.

"If you don't like it..."

"No, Your Majesty. Not that I don't like it, but I am overwhelmed. I, your servant, heard Your Majesty praise Wei Zheng many times. I didn't know why until today. Although I am Your Majesty's wife, each time I am about to speak to You about something, I always closely watch Your mood first, for fear I should choose a wrong moment and incur Your wrath. Wei Zheng, however, seems to have no such fear at all. Changle is our favorite daughter; her dowry is our family business. Still, Wei Zheng had the courage to remonstrate against it, citing a historical case, which is quite convincing. This is something very hard even for me to do. And that makes Wei Zheng truly remarkable. There is no doubt in my mind that Your Majesty should follow his advice."

"My dear wife," said the Emperor affectionately, "that's exactly what I have in mind."

The next morning, the Emperor felt as if a load of anxiety had been taken off His mind. He called in a eunuch officer and issued a rescript, "Award Wei Zheng with 400 strings of cash and 400 bolts of silk."

"WHEN WILL MY VISITOR arrive?" the Emperor asked a eunuch officer in the Ganlu Basilica, one morning a few days later.

"Your Majesty, Wei Zheng will be here on the *si* double-hour (9 o'clock)."

"I've still got plenty of time," murmured the Emperor. "Bring Me the bird. I'll wait outside."

"Yes, Your Majesty," the eunuch responded and left.

The Emperor strolled into the courtyard. A few moments later, the eunuch came into sight with a harrier chick. It was a gift from a northern tribal leader. With a beaming grin, the Emperor perched it on His palm and set it off carefully. Still learning how to fly, the chick flapped its wings energetically to keep itself air-borne for a few minutes, only to land on the Emperor's forearm. He repeated the process again and again until the bird peeped in protest. He raised His arm to appreciate the beauty of this majestic-looking creature with its enormous black eyes and its hooked beak. Then the corner of His eye caught sight of a medium-build man with a gray beard moving towards Him. Intuitively, the Emperor grabbed the chick and hid it inside His outer garment.

Wei Zheng believed that he had seen at a distance the Emperor playing with something like a bird, but he was not sure. When he came close, the bird was nowhere to be found. He then launched into a long discourse on past sovereigns who had become decadent because of their obsession with trivial playthings. He proceeded to address what he came for that day: the confirmation of a provincial official's appointment as Director of the Court of Judicial Review (*dali si*). Immediately, the Emperor nodded His approval and sent Wei Zheng away.

The Emperor gingerly pulled the little harrier from inside His garment. It had already expired from suffocation. He was raging mad.

Returning to the Ganlu Basilica, He muttered angrily, "I have to kill this country bumpkin."

"Who is this, Your Majesty?" asked Empress Zhangsun.

"Who else? Wei Zheng!" The Emperor went on to relate how His beloved bird had perished.

A few moments later, He was surprised to see His wife dressed in her best court attire standing in the middle of the courtyard. The Emperor went up to her and asked, "What is going on?"

"I want to congratulate Your Majesty," said Empress Zhangsun.

"What for?"

"I, Your servant, heard that a sovereign who has candid subjects is a wise sovereign. Because Your Majesty is wise, Your subject Wei Zheng is candid. So I have to congratulate Your Majesty."

"Thanks, Wife," said the Emperor, His ire beginning to abate.

47. The Qingshan Palace

ON THE COOL MORNING of October 6, Deputy Chief of the Directorate of the Palace Library Yu Shinan, in spite of his advanced age of 74, walked swiftly up three flights of steps to enter the Ganlu Basilica. A southerner and a brother of Yu Shiji (the notorious power-broker at Emperor Yang's court), he had been recruited by Li Shimin immediately after the fall of the Sui. Thanks to his reputation as a highly accomplished literatus, he was frequently called into the Palace, not to deal with matters of state and military significance, but to discuss literature and art. Having studied calligraphy with Zhiyong—a direct descendant of Wang Xizhi (the greatest calligrapher of all times), Yu Shinan was acknowledged as the foremost calligrapher of China then; and his poetry and prose were widely considered first class.

"I read your piece called 'On the Virtue of His Majesty,' " said the Emperor on seeing Yu. "I feel really flattered. How can I be compared with those ancient sages?"

"Your Majesty is being modest," answered Yu Shinan. "It may sound a bit flattering, but itexpresses my true feelings."

"In fact, you have set very high standards," said the Emperor. "I will be content if I can say, 'I have lived up to them,' at the end of My life!"

Yu responded with a smile, and the Emperor continued, "Well, I recently wrote a poem. I want you to write a poetic response to it if you don't mind."

"It will be a great honor indeed," replied Yu Shinan as the Emperor handed him His recent composition. It read,

The Palace is infused with the scent of orchid,
The shrubs are faintly decked out with budding flowers.
The colors are light whereas the fog is heavy,
Wind arrives as fragrance is departing.

YU SHINAN REMAINED QUIET for a while before he commented, "Your Majesty, this is undoubtedly a great Palace Style poem. I became familiar with the style when growing up under the Chen dynasty. But I have never liked the style because it is too ornate, too effeminate, and too enamored of trivialities. The decline and fall of the Chen dynasty was not entirely unassociated with this type of poetry. I am afraid that if Your Majesty professes His preference for it, it will probably become all the rage with the literati. I am awfully sorry, but I cannot endorse it, nor can I comply with Your Majesty's request."

"Are you suggesting," the Emperor asked, "one should avoid the Palace Style because it is too ornate and too trivial?"

"Yes, Your Majesty."

"All right. Let Me show you another one."

Thus the discussion continued.

After Yu Shinan left, the Emperor had 50 bolts of silk delivered to Yu's home as a token of thanks for his candid opinion on poetry.

IN WINTER, THE EMPEROR made a long overdue visit to the Qingshan Palace, about 140 *li* west of Chang'an, where He had been born and raised. As the old saying went, "If, after becoming rich and noble, you don't pay a visit to your hometown, you are no different from someone clad in a brocade garb walking at night."

Throughout the visit the Emperor was in a magnanimous mood as He recalled fond memories of His childhood. On His orders, generous presents were distributed among the dwellers of the Palace.

On November 16, He held a lavish banquet in the main courtyard of the Palace to entertain the court nobles and senior officials and officers. As the guests were beginning to arrive, a scuffle broke out at one of the front row tables. Yuchi Jingde, now Prefect of Tong Prefecture, was incensed when he saw Prince of Rencheng Li Daozong (nephew of Li Yuan) sitting at a table closer to the front than his.

"What have you done to deserve that place?" rasped Yuchi Jingde.

Li Daozong rose to explain, "The seating has been arranged by the Board of Rites."

"To hell with you!" Yuchi Jingde snarled as he punched Li in the face so hard that it almost blinded him.

The Emperor rushed to pull Yuchi aside, and objurgated him. After a profusion of apologies, Yuchi returned to his assigned seat. Initially, he was one of the Emperor's most meritorious generals. But, because of his explosive temper, he was unable to get along with other high-level advisers and had to be transferred to a provincial post.

The unpleasant incident, however, was not enough to dampen the Emperor's spirits. Inspired by the visit, He composed a poem extempore, the first part of which read,

Of Shouqiu only a ruin remained,
Of Fengyi there was still the foundation.
As I inherited the sagacity of the past ages,
The hanging bow was ever present.
Encountering dynastic turmoil at a young age,
Sword in hand, I threw Myself into setting things aright.
Under My command, the Eight Wild Domains were secured,
The myriad states were pacified.

[Shouqiu: the birthplace of the Yellow Emperor in Shandong.

Fengyi: the birthplace of Liu Bang (the founder of the Han) in Peixian, Jiangsu.

Hanging bow: in reference to an ancient custom that required a bow be hung on the left side of the door when a boy was born. Here: aspiration to leave home and realize one's ambitions.

Eight Wild Domains: remote areas that lie farthest from the capital.]

COURT DIARIST LÜ CAI set the poem to music under the title "Music for Celebrating Accomplishments at the Qingshan." The Palace entertainers, after minimal rehearsal, put on a performance set to it. They consisted of 64 boys and girls dancing in eight rows. The boys wore *jinde* (advancing virtue) caps and pantaloons with tight-fitting legs; and the girls wore buns fastened with dark-colored combs, gowns with long sleeves, and wooden clogs. The music purported to sing praise to the *Pax Sinica* that prevailed under Heaven.

Among the audience sitting close to the stage was Wei Zheng. The music and the dance set him thinking. *I am certainly no fan of pageantry or extravagance, but the Emperor deserves to celebrate His success in His birthplace. One point bothers me though. In the poem, the merit of the Honorary Emperor is completely ignored.*

Then, the familiar tune of "Breaking through the Enemy Array," the Emperor's signature music, started playing. Wei stared aimlessly into the dark space beyond the stage, with a look of boredom on his face. The music was jingoistic with too much *wu* in it, although it paid well-deserved tribute to the Emperor's martial virtue. The Emperor took notice of Wei's expression, but remained calm, unruffled by what He considered one of Wei's idiosyncrasies.

Later when Xiao Yu requested that the dance of "Breaking through the Enemy Array" be revised to depict the fall or capture of Liu Wuzhou, Xue Rengao, Dou Jiande, and Wang Shichong, the Emperor turned him down unequivocally. *If that happens, how much more is it going to irk Wei Zheng?* But He replied adroitly, "These were all great heroes for a time. Many of their followers are serving the court right now. They are sure to feel hurt when they see their former masters insulted on the stage!"

About two weeks later, the Emperor began to head back for Chang'an. On December 2, He broke journey at the Hongyi Palace to pay homage to His father, the Honorary Emperor. The Emperor and His Empress took turns to serve drinks and foods and to present ornamental pieces set with precious stones to the Honorary Emperor. When the reunion broke up after midnight, the Emperor offered to take the place of one of the eight bearers of His father's palanquin and carry him to his residential basilica. But He stopped short when His father strenuously opposed the idea. Eventually, Crown Prince Li Chengqian, now a teenager, was called upon to do the carrying instead. This was perhaps the Emperor's way to make up for His failure to acknowledge His father's past merit during His recent trip to the Qingshan Palace.

48. Huangfu Decan

UPON RETURN TO CHANG'AN, the Emperor plunged into work. In fact, He was so busy that He did not find time for leisure until the 11th of the 12th month, Zhenguan 7 (January 15, 634). On that day, He paid a visit to the Hibiscus Garden—the largest public park in Chang'an—situated in the southeast corner of the city. The centerpiece of the Garden was the Serpentine River Pond taking up much of the space. Its shores were covered with meadows, bamboos, and evergreen trees. After spending two days there roaming the gravel paths and enjoying the scenery, the Emperor journeyed further south to the suburban Shaoling Plain for winter hunting.

Two more days later He returned to the Taiji Palace, only to depart for the old Weiyang Palace in the northwestern suburb. The Weiyang had been the largest palace enclosure of the Han city (also called Chang'an). It was abandoned by Emperor Wen (Yang Jian) of Sui together with the old city itself when Daxing City (Tang Chang'an) took its place as the capital.

The Emperor's aging father Li Yuan was hosting a drinking party at the Anterior Basilica of the Weiyang. Professional entertainers—musicians, dancers, and singers—enlivened the occasion with performances. But two amateur performers stole the show. At the request of Li Yuan, Xieli and Feng Zhidai, a tribal chief of the Southern Mán, performed their numbers. Xieli put on Tujue dances, pirouetting and capering passionately to authentic Tujue music; and Feng recited poetry in elegant Chinese. Both drew thunderous applause. Excited by the spectacle, Li Yuan proclaimed, "The Hu (northern barbarians) and the Viets now belong to the same family! Never before has it happened since antiquity."

Touched by His father's excitement, the Emperor said, "The barbarians from the Four Quarters have all submitted themselves. And I credit it to the teaching of My father. In the past, when Gaozu of Han, Liu Bang, held a party for His father, He got carried away with His megalomaniac remarks. This I will never do. Father, I will always be your faithful servant!"

The Emperor then proposed a toast to His father, and everyone drank heartily to his longevity, while shouting, "Ten thousands years!"

While the festivities proceeded apace, the Emperor went up to Xieli and offered him a toast. Xieli reciprocated. "I am delighted to see you," said the Emperor. "How have you been these days?"

Ever since he settled down in Chang'an, this former Tujue overlord had been miserable. Still, out of politeness, he answered, "I am very well, Your Majesty."

"Have you considered My suggestion: take up position as Prefect of Guo Prefecture? It has large herds of moose. You can go moose hunting any time."

"Thanks, Your Majesty, but I have decided not to go," Xieli answered, somewhat defensively.

"That is perfectly fine. So long as you stay here, you are General-in-chief of the Right Guard. If there is anything I can do to make you feel better, let Me know. I will do it."

"I don't know how to thank Your Majesty enough," Xieli answered, looking genuinely grateful.

In early Zhenguan 8 (634), about a month after the Weiyang party, the Emperor received the news of Xieli's passing at the age of 55. In Chang'an, the entire Tujue community was plunged into mourning. It also filled the Emperor with a sense of loss. For all the trouble he had caused as the lord of the steppes, Xieli had proven to be a worthy adversary. The Emperor composed and brushed His message of condolence, which was then delivered to Xieli's close relatives. As the Board of Rites was planning his funeral and burial in accord with ritual (Xieli was, at any rate, a rank-3 officer of the Tang army), the Emperor received a request from the leader of the Tujue community that Xieli be afforded a Tujue burial. The Emperor gave His approval. On the day of his burial, after the funeral rites, his remains were cremated and his ashes entombed in a suburban tomb.

IN AUTUMN, AGE AND declining health finally caught up with Li Yuan. He had a stroke and was incapacitated. The Emperor suggested that he move to the Jiucheng Palace (previously the Renshou Palace), a summer resort 300 *li* west of Chang'an. Nestled in the Tiantai Mountains, the Palace was known for its mild temperatures during the summer months. But it was far from perfect. First, it was too far away from Chang'an. A prolonged stay might make one feel isolated. Second, it was the scene of the infamous murder of Emperor Wen in 604, and was thus considered unlucky. So Li Yuan rejected it.

Convinced that a cooler, less humid place would have a salutary effect on His father's health, the Emperor ordered the construction of a new palace immediately northeast of Chang'an on much higher ground. This palace would be called "Daming" or "Great Brilliance." About the same time, the Emperor lifted the ban on the renovation of the much maligned Luoyang Palace.

No one reacted negatively to the erection of the Daming Palace, because it was in accord with the Confucian principle of filial piety. But the new Luoyang project was a different story. It elicited several criticisms. The most severe one came from Huangfu Decan, a County official the Emperor had never heard of. In his memorial, he listed three malaises of society: the first was the renovation of the Luoyang Palace, which was too costly; the second was land taxes, which were excessively burdensome to farmers; and the third was the fashion of wearing high buns (first started by palace ladies in Chang'an), which was bad for morality.

The Emperor was so incensed that He condemned the letter at a Chief Ministers' Council meeting.

"Have you ever heard of Mr. Huangfu Decan?" asked the Emperor.

"No, Your Majesty," answered Fang Xuanling.

"Vice Magistrate of Shǎn County."

"In that case, he is rank 8, lower class, upper grade, almost at the bottom rung of the officialdom."

"How dare he attack Me like that? He won't be happy until the state levies no corvée duties and collects no land taxes, and until the palace ladies stop wearing buns on their heads!"

"Don't be angry, Your Majesty," said Fang Xuanling.

"How can I not be angry? If he had his way, neither the state nor the court would be able to exist for a single day."

"But he has committed no crime, Your Majesty," said Wei Zheng.

"I disagree," said the Emperor emphatically. Turning to Fang Xuanling, He continued, "I can have him prosecuted for libel, can't I?"

"Yes, Your Majesty," answered Fang.

Addressing an attendant, the Emperor said, "You are going to see to it."

Before the attendant started drafting His rescript, a husky voice interjected, "Could I say something, Your Majesty?"

"Yes?" answered the Emperor as He turned to Wei Zheng.

"I remember in his memorial to Emperor Wen of the Han dynasty, Jia Yi said, 'Concerning today's situation, one of the points I will make will cause one to break out crying; and two of the points will drive one to tears.' Since antiquity, no memorial has touched the heart of a sovereign without using radical language."

Emperor Wen of Han was the paragon of good government, someone the Emperor constantly looked up to. Jia Yi, although a tragic figure, was universally regarded as a loyal adviser. This opinion of Wei Zheng's could not be ignored.

Still, He said, "Just look at the language. If it is not vicious, I don't know what is."

"It is lèse majesté, to say the least," added Fang Xuanling.

"Well," Wei Zheng continued, "although the words maybe those of a madman, the intention is not necessarily malicious. Furthermore, does Your Majesty really want to criminalize someone just for writing a memorial?"

The Emperor reread the memorial, paused for a while, and said hesitantly, "If I send him to jail, I wonder what will happen to those would-be remonstrators."

"Your Majesty, am I still going to initiate the prosecution procedure?" asked the attendant who had drafted the rescript.

"I have to say 'no' at this moment," the Emperor said.

"I thank Your Majesty for His sagacious decision," said Wei Zheng. "In my opinion, instead of a punishment, Huangfu should receive a reward and be recruited by the court. We need fearless critics like him."

"I'll think about that," the Emperor said.

In fact, the Emperor felt very conflicted. While He was aware of the need to assert Imperial authority, He was also attracted to the idea of encouraging criticisms at court, a *sine qua non* for good government.

At night, when He was back in the residential basilica, His oddly distrait looks did not escape Empress Zhangsun, who asked, "What is bothering Your Majesty?"

When He told her of His concern, she said, "As usual, I should not meddle in state business. But my instinct tells me Wei Zheng is right. I suspect hiring this intrepid man will not diminish Imperial authority, but will enhance it instead."

On the next morning, the Emperor issued a reward of 24 bolts of silk to Huangfu Decan and an edict to transfer him to the court to work as Investigating Censor (*jiancha yushi*), with the duties of making sure that court officials behaved and of impeaching them if they did not.

49. The Christian Mission

THE CHINESE HAD BEGUN to have a detailed knowledge of foreign lands in the Western Regions (Central Asia, Western Asia, and beyond) after the Han emissary Zhang Qian's return from his mission in the late 2nd century BCE. Commercial and cultural contact had been maintained with the "West" ever since. Under the Tang, especially during the second reign, it had become much more extensive than previous centuries, with Central and West Asian traders (specially the Sogdians) and Indian Buddhist missionaries coming to China, and Chinese Buddhist pilgrims going to Central Asia and India. The Western Asian religions of Zoroastrianism and Manichaeism, brought by merchants and others to China, had taken root. Christianity, however, had to wait until Zhenguan 9 (635).

At the start of that year, a group of Christians from Sassanian Persia arrived in the western suburb of Chang'an. The Emperor Li Shimin sent Vice Premier Fang Xuanling to welcome them. A few days later, they were granted an audience in the Ganlu Basilica.

"I, Archdeacon Abraham (Aluoben), would like to thank Your Majesty for granting us an audience so soon after our arrival," said a man in his 30s through an interpreter. Obviously, this tall Indo-European man with brown eyes was the leader.

The Emperor extended His warmest welcome to Abraham and his party, and then said, "I heard that your country lies further to the west of Kangju. Could you tell me more about it?"

"Certainly, Your Majesty. We are from the land of Sasan, or the Sassanid Kingdom. The area was anciently known as the Arsacid Kingdom."

"Of course, the Han were already in contact with the Arsacids of Parthia. But we have not received a tributary mission from the Sassanids. Yours is the first."

"But ours is not a tributary mission, Your Majesty."

"Oh? What is it then?"

"It is a religious mission, Your Majesty. We are all believers in Christianity."

"Is that the state religion of your country?"

"No, most people there practice the religion of Zoroastrianism. Ours is a minority religion. It is practiced mainly by people in Francia, Italia, and the [Eastern] Roman Empire."

"Where did it come from?"

"Well, the branch of Christianity we belong to was started by Archbishop Nestorius in Constantinople, the capital of the Roman Empire. It believes in dyophysitism, and was quite popular until it was judged heterodox at the Ecumenical Council of Ephesus (431). After that his followers began to move east. Many ended up in the Sassanid Kingdom."

"I am flummoxed," said the Emperor with a puzzled look. "What's the doctrine they believe in?"

"They believe in the dual nature of the Messiah: one divine and one human."

"Who is the Messiah?"

"The Messiah is the prophesied savior. He is identified as Jesus Christ, the son of God. He gave his life on the cross for mankind."

"And the Council of…"

"Ephesus, Your Majesty, on the east coast of the Mediterranean," continued Abraham.

"What did the Council do to that priest by the name of Nei…?"

"Nestorius. Actually, it condemned him."

"Why?"

"It disagreed with his dyophysite doctrine."

"Your people then fled east to the Sassanids?"

"Yes, Your Majesty."

"Were you welcomed by them?"

"Oh, the Sassanids have treated us well."

"And the purpose of your journey here?"

"To spread the teaching of God, Your Majesty."

"Is this God of yours the supreme deity?"

"Yes and no, Your Majesty. Yes, He is all-good and all-powerful, and is the creator of the world. No, He is the only God, thus the term 'supreme' is unnecessary."

"Fascinating! I do want to know more about it. Have you brought with you your scriptures?"

"Yes, Your Majesty. In addition to the scriptures, we have also brought some scholarly treatises and holy portraits."

As the conversation continued, the Emperor became increasingly curious about the exotic religion and its Nestorian branch, and asked a host of questions. Abraham did his best to answer them.

After Abraham and his party left, the Emperor said to Fang Xuanling, "Can the Palace Library provide a space for these foreign people to translate the writings they brought with them?"

"There shouldn't be any problems," replied Fang. "I will check with Wei Zheng immediately."

50. The Da'an Palace

HAVING DECLINED TO MOVE to the Jiucheng Palace, Li Yuan continued to live in the Hongyi Palace, now renamed Da'an, near Chang'an. Ever since he had been forced off the throne in 626, he had often been in a mood of gloom, in spite of efforts by the Emperor to patch things up with him. After his stroke, he became hemiplegic. In spring 635, his condition showed some signs of improvement, only to decline precipitously when summer came and a vicious heat wave hit the capital. Before the more comfortable Daming Palace was made ready, Li Yuan succumbed in the Chuigong Basilica of the Da'an to the suffocating weather, poor health, and depression. On the day of his passing, June 25, Zhenguan 9 (635), his Testamentary Edict was released. It said, among other things,

For a period of three days, officials and commoners shall come to pay homage. Thereafter, they shall doff their mourning vestments. There shall be no banning of marriages, wine-drinking, and meat-eating. Three days after I breathe my last, my remains should be placed in the coffin...and my heir should attend to military and state affairs of major significance without interruption... The setup of my tomb park should be as frugal and simple as possible...

On December 12, 635, Li Yuan was laid to rest in a tomb park west of Chang'an, known as "Xianling." It was about that time that he was given the temple name "Gaozu" (Exalted Ancestor). Meanwhile, the remains of his wife, Ms. Dou, were transferred to the same tomb for reburial.

The moment a sovereign ascended the throne, He started reigning as the Son of Heaven. When He died, He would not be deified. Instead, His spirit tablet would be set up and His spirit worshipped in the Ancestral Temple. In Chang'an, the Temple was in the southeast corner of the Imperial City. Li Yuan's tablet was placed in the central chamber of its main hall. Because he was the founding Emperor of the Tang, his tablet would receive offerings as long as the dynasty lasted.

THE DEATH OF LI Yuan in June cast a dark shadow over his son the Emperor. According to tradition, upon the death of a parent, a filial son should suspend his official work while observing a lengthy mourning period, which could last up to three years.

Although as Emperor Li Shimin was exempted from this practice, He gave up His job anyway while Crown Prince Li Chengqian ruled on His behalf. He began to step back into power only after more than a month had passed and did not assume full control until the beginning of the next year (636).

It was about this time that the Emperor was apprised of the successful completion of the Histories of the Five Dynasties, those of the Liang, Chen, Northern Qi, Northern Zhou, and Sui—all predecessors to the Tang dynasty. No doubt, the good news lifted His spirits. On March 3, Zhenguan 10 (636), a solemn ceremony was held in which the Emperor received the Five Histories from Vice Premier Fang Xuanling and President of the Chancellery Wei Zheng, and gave generous rewards to all the participants of the project, from the Editor-in-chief down to Editorial Assistants. By an Imperial edict, the Histories were deposited in the Palace Library.

As Editor-in-chief, Wei Zheng had done a superb job guiding the historians responsible for different volumes through various stages of the project, and inserted his insightful comments in many chapters. Each of these Five Histories is comprised of two components, one of Basic Annals and one of Biographies. A Basic Annals chapter is constructed around important events that took place during a given reign and serves as its chronological framework. The Biographies are accounts of key figures and non-Han ethnic groups. Traditionally, there should be other components as well, particularly that of Treatises. The Treatises were chapters dealing with various institutions and specialized topics such ritual, law, officialdom, and astrology. But compilation of the Treatises for the Five Histories had hardly begun. Still, what the historians had completed was something to celebrate. In spite of its imperfections, this was the largest officially sponsored history-writing project up to that time, and a highly successful one at that.

51. Empress Zhangsun

THE EMPEROR'S REJOICING OVER the Histories, however, was overshadowed by His own on-going health problem—an enteric disease that had started ailing Him when He was in His late 30s. From time to time, He suffered from loose bowels accompanied by acute pain in the lower abdomen. When the palace physician treated it with the pueraria-coptis decoction, the symptoms disappeared. But in early Zhenguan 10 (636), He had a relapse that was resistant to the old formula. The physician switched to the herbaceous peony decoction and other formulas. They initially alleviated the symptoms. With the passage of time, however, the efficacy wore off.

Throughout His sickness, the Empress stayed by His side during the day and often late into the night. She did all she could to help, boiling the herbs and spoon-feeding the patient. One night, the Emperor slipped into a coma for the first time. The palace physician came rushing to the rescue, administering acupuncture needles to bring Him back to consciousness. Empress Zhangsun watched on in complete despair. She could not help thinking the unthinkable: surviving her husband. *It should not be allowed to happen. After Liu Bang of the Han died, His widow Empress Lü and her Lü clan dominated the court. But as soon as Empress Lü died, the Lü clan was exterminated.* By the time her husband came to, she had made up her mind: she would not outlive the Emperor. Secretly she had some highly poisonous gelsemium boluses prepared, which she would take as soon as the Emperor breathed His last.

In desperation, Wei Zheng turned to Chang'an residents for help. With the Emperor's permission, he put up public notices in the marketplaces imploring them to donate secret nostrums for the Emperor's disease. Wei was deeply moved by the overwhelming response, but, to his dismay, none of the many formulas offered worked. Then a certain Zhang Baozang presented one that was deceptively simple. It involved decocting a small amount of dried long pepper (*biba*) in a pot of milk on a slow simmer. All one needed was take the freshly made decoction twice a day. Since the long pepper was a tropical plant, it was grown neither in the North or the South. Fortunately, the eunuch officers were able to obtain a fair amount of it in the Western Market where it was sold by some foreign spice merchants.

After the Emperor was put on the long pepper formula for about a week, miraculously the diarrhea stopped. The Emperor was so pleased that He appointed Mr. Zhang to a rank-5 position.

As the Emperor's health was well on its way to recovery, Empress Zhangsun's own health, worn out by prolonged patient care, went into decline. Her trouble had started two years before when she accompanied her husband on a trip to the Jiucheng Palace west of the capital. One midnight in late spring, General Chai Shao, the Emperor's brother-in-law then in charge of Palace security, woke up the Emperor to report a mutiny. When the Emperor clad in armor was about to leave with the general, the Empress, then still suffering from a bad cold, asked to join Him. A lady attendant had advised against it for fear she might catch another cold. But the advice had gone unheeded, and off she went.

During the next two hours she spent with her husband outdoors she was assaulted by the chilly night air of the Tiantai Mountains (not to be confused with its southern namesake). On the following day she woke up with a high fever and severe cough. About a week later, the fever came down but the cough lingered.

After she returned to Chang'an with the Emperor in early autumn, she often ran a low fever. The palace physician diagnosed her as having a "pneuma disease," a kind of chronic bronchopulmonary condition. And on the physician's advice, she took the ephedra decoction daily to ease the suffering.

In the summer of Zhenguan 10 (636), her condition suddenly deteriorated as she began to cough up blood clots.

The Emperor visited the Empress daily, sometimes in the company of His close advisers, and always with the Crown Prince Li Chengqian in tow. On one such visit, the Emperor stayed for about half an hour and left. The Prince stayed on to attend on his mother.

"I feel miserable when I see you suffer like this, Mother," said the Prince.

"Don't feel bad, Chengqian. It's all in the destiny. And there is nothing you can do about it."

"Could I suggest something that might help?"

"Of course, what is it?" asked Empress Zhangsun, sounding interested.

"I heard that granting an amnesty to criminals and sponsoring Daoist ordinations by the court may bring blessing from the Beyond."

"Well, my son," replied the Empress, disappointed, "if doing good can bring blessing, I sure can benefit from it without causing harm. However, granting amnesty is an important state affair, and it can't be done for my benefit! And it shouldn't! As for ordaining people as Daoist adepts, I don't believe in Daoism or Buddhism. Neither does your father. How can I, a woman, force the Emperor to do something He would never do otherwise?"

Eventually, the Emperor learned of the Crown Prince's proposal, and wanted to grant an amnesty on her behalf Himself. But He had to give it up because of the strong opposition by the intended beneficiary.

Towards the end of the month, she began to have spells of unconsciousness. One night, the Emperor came on a routine visit and found her conscious and alert. A eunuch officer was present to carry out his scribal duties.

"Your Majesty, where is Fang Xuanling?" asked Empress Zhangsun. "I haven't seen him lately."

"I suspended him from office."

"Why?"

"He committed an offense."

"Well, as your wife, I have no business to meddle in court politics. But ever since Du Ruhui's death (in 630), Fang Xuanling has been the only truly great administrator left. He is loyal, extremely careful, and very resourceful. He has never revealed a secret entrusted to him. Unless there is a major problem, please call him back, and soon."

"I will," said the Emperor. In fact, Fang Xuanling was out of favor for a minor transgression. The Emperor was actually more annoyed by his wife, who had forced the uxorious Fang to give up two young ladies the Emperor had given him.

"Are there any other issues you want to talk about?" He continued.

"Yes, our sons. Crown Prince Chengqian is now 18. He has shown himself to be a dutiful son. Our second son Li Tai is just one year younger. He is doing well too. But everyday

I am worried sick about sibling rivalry between them. Showering favors upon Li Tai does not help."

"Chengqian, Tai, and their little brother Zhi—they are all our sons," said the Emperor. "I don't favor any one over the others. But I have to admit, Tai is the most learned."

"How about the Institute for Literature (Wenxue *guan*)?" Zhangsun asked inquiringly.

"Oh, that one. I set it up for Tai because of his love of literature. I wanted him to fully develop his literary talent."

"There is nothing wrong with that. But the last thing one wants is to see it evolve into an anti-Eastern Palace stronghold."

"I don't think it will ever happen," replied the Emperor, surprised. "But I will watch it carefully."

"Since you have chosen Chengqian as heir, you have to support him all the way," said Zhangsun emphatically. "Otherwise, you must depose him. The earlier the better."

"Don't worry. I support him."

Nodding her approval, Empress Zhangsun remained quiet for a long while as the Emperor waited patiently. Then she said, in a raised tone, "Now, Your Majesty, my biggest worry is about my relatives: how to prevent them from self-destruction. As consort relatives, they are already privileged and powerful. If you appoint them to key posts, they will amass too much power, something none of them can handle. Please, I beseech Your Majesty, don't appoint them to chief ministerial positions. They should feel grateful if they could serve as 'Audience Attendants.' "

"That is a prestige title, with no substantive power," said the Emperor smilingly.

"That is my point…" said she, interrupted by a convulsive cough.

A few moments later, she continued, "As your servant, I have not done anything to benefit the people in my entire life, and I deeply regret that. I hope my dying will not cause any harm to them. After I die, please don't create a large tumulus for my tomb; it will be such a waste of labor. Bury me inside a hill instead. Don't fill my tomb with gold and silver and other types of treasure. Instead, use furnishings made of pottery and wood…"

There was a long pause as she gasped for air. Then she resumed, "Now it is the time for my last advice. It may be hard to follow, but I want Your Majesty to listen."

"Yes, I am listening," said the Emperor, holding her hand.

"First, be close to gentlemen and stay away from caitiffs; second, always accept the remonstrances of loyal subjects and reject the praises of sycophants; third, reduce public works projects and stop making hunting trips."

"I will do My best," said the Emperor, with tears in His eyes.

"Now I am about to say good-bye, and I will go content, since I have no lingering regrets."

The Emperor was weeping in silence.

That night, Empress Zhangsun slipped into unconsciousness, from which she never recovered until her death in the early hours of July 28, 636. She was 35 years old.

At the Emperor's request, the eunuch officer created a scroll that preserved the "Testamentary Instructions" of the Empress before submitting the original record of her last conversation with the Emperor to the Institute of Historiography.

52. A Trip to Luoyang

AS THE EMPEROR WAS looking nostalgically through the belongings of His late wife, He came across a book in 30 scrolls entitled *Precepts for Women* (*Nüze*) compiled and meticulously copied by her. It was a collection of historical narratives on the exemplary and unworthy behavior of women. As He read through the scrolls, tears flew down His cheeks. He had the book taken to His study, where He saw the "Testamentary Instructions" lying on the desk. It reminded Him of her request to recall Fang Xuanling. He immediately issued a summons to Fang and his wife Ms. Lu. Early the next morning, the couple were brought into His presence.

"Ms. Lu, what happened to the two ladies I gave Xuanling?" asked the Emperor.
"Your Majesty, I turned them out," answered Ms. Lu.
"What? How did you do that?"
"I used a feather duster," answered Ms. Lu.

The Emperor's face crinkled into a light smile before He asked in a serious tone, "Don't you know what you have done? Defying an Imperial edict."

"I am awfully sorry, Your Majesty. But I cannot help it."
"Now you have two choices: either you allow Xuanling to take back the two ladies, or you drink this wine." As the Emperor said these words, He held up a small goblet.
Eyeing the goblet for a few moments, Ms. Lu said gravely, "I will drink the wine." Then she took the goblet from the Emperor, and gulped down its content.

It had happened so fast that Fang had not had time to stop her.

The Emperor, taken by surprise, sighed and said, "I am amazed by the bravery of women. They are even willing to die for jealousy. All right, I will take back My order."

"Your Majesty, should I go and find an antidote?" asked Fang Xuanling.
"That won't be necessary. Did I say the wine was poisoned?"
"No, Your Majesty."
"Exactly! What she drank was just rice wine."
Turning to Ms. Lu, the Emperor said, "You can leave now. Don't forget to take good care of Xuanling."

"Yes, I will, Your Majesty," said Ms. Lu as she stood up and left.

"Do you know who wanted to recall you?"

"I don't, Your Majesty."

"The late Empress. She made the request on her deathbed."

"May she rest in peace," said Fang.

There was silence for a few moments before the Emperor said, "Listen, Xuanling, can you report for work tomorrow?"

"Yes, Your Majesty," said Fang, full of gratitude.

ON DECEMBER 6, THE remains of Empress Zhangsun were buried in the Zhaoling Tomb Park on Mount Jiuzong, about 140 *li* west of Chang'an. Out of respect for her wishes, the tomb was built on a modest scale. It was completed after more than 100 laborers working at the site for about two months. The tomb did not contain gold, silver or jade objects. The tomb furnishings were either made of wood or pottery. The Emperor hoped that this frugal burial practice would set an example for future generations and that the dearth of valuables would deter tomb robbers.

By burying His wife in a naturally formed hill in place of a tumulus the Emperor created a burial convention for Tang sovereigns to follow.

SEVERAL MONTHS WENT BY and the Emperor still could not get over His grief. He had a watchtower erected in the Forbidden Park. Whenever He had time, He would climb to the top level to gaze ruefully at the Zhaoling Tomb Park in the distance. Once, after He ascended the tower with Wei Zheng, He asked, looking west, "Can you see the Tomb Park?"

"I am sorry, Your Majesty," answered Wei Zheng. "I have got poor eyesight. I can't see it at all."

"Look," said the Emperor, pointing a finger to the west, "the Zhaoling Tomb Park is just over there, on Mount Jiuzong."

"Oh, that one. Yes, I can see it. But I thought Your Majesty meant the Xianling Tomb Park."

"Where My father is buried?"

"Yes. I cannot see that one."

"Me either."

Upon return to the Palace, the Emperor felt uneasy about the subtle dig—clearly, Wei Zheng considered inappropriate His obsession with the loss of the late Empress. With great reluctance, He issued an order to destroy the watchtower in the Forbidden Park. But the Emperor continued to miss her. The basilicas, the corridors, and the Palace courtyards recalled her image and voice, which filled Him with a sense of regret. How He wished that He had spent more time with her as a loving husband!

While Wei Zheng appreciated the Emperor's decision to tear down the watchtower, he was still worried about His condition. At court, He was no longer His usual self, witty, self-confident, and authoritative. Instead He had become tired, withdrawn, maudlin, and sometimes absent-minded. *His Majesty needs a distraction, perhaps a long sojourn away from Chang'an. How about Luoyang? The Luoyang Palace has been sufficiently renovated. A new suburban palace, called "Feishan" (Flying Across the Hill), has been added. True, the expansive Sui Western Park is reduced by one third, and some of the Sui palaces inside the Park have disappeared. But those that remain have been lavishly restored, over my vehement opposition, of course. In fact, I have been the only reason that prevents the Emperor from making the trip.*

The next day, Wei Zheng submitted a memorial relenting on his opposition to the Imperial trip to Luoyang. The Emperor jumped at the chance.

ON MARCH 10, ZHENGUAN 11 (637), the Emperor and His entourage departed from Chang'an for Luoyang. Before reaching His destination, He spent a night in the Xianren, one of the many suburban palaces Emperor Yang had built in the Western Park near the city. Because of the short notice they received, the Palace personnel served food and drink that were not quite up to the Emperor's standards. It was unfortunate that after two bereavements in a span of two years, the Emperor became peculiarly fastidious. The Palace Director was made to stand in front of His Majesty, trembling with fear, as the Emperor upbraided him before meting out his punishment: suspension of salary for a year.

"The poor fellow certainly deserves his punishment, Your Majesty," said Wei Zheng. "But what I am concerned about is the wrong message it sends."

"What do you mean?" the Emperor said, His face turning glum.

"From here on, I am afraid," Wei Zheng continued, "all local officials along Your Majesty's travel route would vie against one another to squeeze the masses for the purpose of serving delicacies. This runs counter to the very purpose of Your Majesty's tour. Emperor Yang rewarded and punished His underlings in the Commanderies and Counties according to the quality of the food they provided. Your Majesty knows what happened. The entire world rose against Him. I am sure Your Majesty doesn't intend to follow His example?"

"Well, what can I say?" responded the Emperor.

Turning to Zhangsun Wuji, the Emperor asked, "What do you think?"

"Your Majesty went through much harder times before, did He not?"

"Yes, indeed. I used to eat tasteless tack and take shelter in ramshackle huts and campaign tents. How could I feel dissatisfied with the service?"

The Emperor thereupon withdrew the order to punish the Palace Director.

NOT LONG AFTER THE Emperor and His suite settled in Luoyang, a controversy over Buddhism flared up, something the Emperor did not relish dealing with at all. Since He reversed His father's edict to rein in Buddhism and Daoism, the Emperor had been on friendly terms with the Buddhist and Daoist clergies. During His reign, both Buddhism and Daoism had gained much ground, sometimes with His explicit endorsement. But the parallel growth of the two religions also triggered clashes between them. In Luoyang, the center of Buddhism in the Central Plain, the Buddhist monks and Daoist adepts constantly jostled for influence. The Emperor then issued an edict aimed at putting the rivalry to rest. It read,

The rise of the Great Dao, whose origin derived from the Nameless in the very beginning, can be traced to far antiquity. It is thus superior to and lies outside the form. Moreover, its veneration is part of the ancestral worship of the state. So it should be placed ahead of Buddhism. From this day forward, on occasions when offerings are made and titles are ranked, Daoist adepts and nuns should precede Buddhist monks and nuns.

To the Emperor's unpleasant surprise, His well-meaning edict provoked a firestorm of controversy. In Chang'an the Buddhist clergy started a petition movement to have the edict revoked. In Luoyang Monk Zhishi and others intercepted the Imperial procession to submit a memorial, which, while acknowledging the greatness of Lord Lao, lashed out at the Daoist adepts for practicing a demonic art.

Impressed with their courage, the Emperor issued a new edict in a conciliatory tone, but it fell short of revoking the earlier edict. On behalf of the Emperor, Vice President of the Secretariat Cen Wenben visited Monk Zhishi and announced the new edict to him.

But the monk refused to acknowledge receipt of the edict, as was required by ritual and law. Infuriated by the defiance, the Emperor had him flogged and banished to the far south. With its leader thus removed, the movement died down.

As for Zhishi himself, feeling bitter and abandoned, he succumbed soon afterwards at 37.

53. The Western Park

IN THE WESTERN PARK near Luoyang, spring was in full swing. While ubiquitous plum flowers with yellow and pink stamens and white pedals were blooming, peach flowers were making a display of their showy pink color. Bamboos, ever-verdant, had turned luscious green. Spring breeze scattered willow catkins around as weeping willow trees on the lake shores hung their heads so low that they dipped into the water. At break of day, the woods came alive with the chatter of birds—orioles, sparrows, swallows, pheasants, and others—punctuated with the hammering sounds of woodpeckers. On the surface of the Jadeite Pond, the main body of water inside the Park, flocks of ducks swam about as they quacked. In the sky, from time to time a school of wild geese flew by as they honked raucously.

Enticed by the sight and sound of nature the Emperor went on an excursion in the Park on April 15, His first since arrival in the city about a month before.

On board the *Dragon*, a large three-story pavilion-ship, the Emperor held a lavish banquet to entertain His close advisers and attending officials. It was accompanied by dancing and music, pleasant conversation, and wine drinking. As host the Emperor was especially convivial. After several rounds of wine, everybody loosened up somewhat. The Emperor good-naturedly asked the officials to compose poems on the spot.

Inspired by nature, Yu Shinan wrote one on "Spring Night," which read,
As the Moon lingered in the Park of Spring,
The doors opened at night in the Bamboo Hall.
Startled birds flew past rows of trees,
Flowers in the wind spread across the water.

"Wonderful!" the Emperor exclaimed. "No doubt, Mr. Yu lives up to his reputation as the first poet of the country."

After a few court advisers responded with their own improvised compositions, all focusing on the scenic beauty of the Park in spring, Wei Zheng's turn came.

"Well, I am no good at writing nature poems," said Wei. "I will compose one on history instead."

"I'd love to hear it, Wei Zheng," said the Emperor.

"It is called the 'Western Han,' " said Wei Zheng, who went on to recite the poem. It ended with,
Only thanks to the ritual of Shusun Tong
Did one know the dignity of the Emperor.

Shusun Tong, of course, was the famous scholar who advised the peasant-turned-sovereign Liu Bang on ritual.

"Even in poetry, Zheng tries to restrain Me with ritual," responded the Emperor half-jokingly.

"Don't be such a spoilsport, Wei Zheng," said Zhangsun Wuji. "Every time the Emperor throws a party you have to say something unpleasant."

"Don't stop him, Wuji," said the Emperor magnanimously. "Wei Zheng always reminds Me of the saying, 'Good medicine is bitter to the taste and loyal advice is unpleasant to the ear.' "

Turning to Wei Zheng, the Emperor continued, "I suppose ritual is not the only thing on your mind."

"Your Majesty is right," said Wei Zheng. "But today is probably not the right occasion. I do not want to spoil the fun when everybody is in such a good mood."

"Not at all, not at all," said the Emperor firmly. "Say it, please. I insist."

"All right, Your Majesty," said Wei Zheng as he took a sip of wine. "I have been thinking about this for a long time. That is, how Your Majesty's style of rulership has evolved over time. At the beginning of the Zhenguan reign, Your Majesty really encouraged people to remonstrate. Three years later, Your Majesty still gladly followed the advice of remonstrators. In the last few years, however, Your Majesty listened to remonstrations only reluctantly."

"Give Me an example."

"When Huangfu Decan memorialized against the restoration of the Luoyang Palace, Your Majesty followed my advice and rewarded him, but never acted upon his suggestions."

"You are right, I never did," the Emperor said, His face flushed with embarrassment. "But didn't you approve of the Luoyang trip as well?"

"Yes, I did, Your Majesty. But I did not expect this level of extravagance."

"Wei Zheng, you have gone too far!" snarled Zhangsun Wuji. "The Emperor owns all under Heaven. Why can't He have a good time in His own Eastern Capital?"

"But it is only one step away from falling into the trap of decadence. Just look at the Western Park with all its palace complexes! Look at the Palace City, and especially the Qianyuan Basilica! They have certainly outdone their Sui predecessors in extravagance."

"You have blown it way out of proportion," asserted Zhangsun Wuji. "Besides, these structures are already there. Would you rather see them fall into disrepair and disuse?"

"No, Wuji," said Wei Zheng. "I have no intention of stopping His Majesty from visiting the Luoyang Palace. But I want to remind Him of the danger Zhang Xuansu talked about before."

Looking sullen, the Emperor raised His hand and said, "All right, Wei Zheng, I've got your point." Addressing His attendants, He ordered, "Turn the Dragon Ship around. We are going back."

Everyone was quiet on the way back as the Emperor's first spring excursion on the Jadeite Pond came to an end.

THAT EVENING THE EMPEROR summoned Zhangsun Wuji and Hou Junji to His basilica to discuss what had happened during the day.

"What exactly did Zhang Xuansu talk about, Your Majesty?" asked Zhangsun Wuji.

"A few years back," answered the Emperor, "when he was remonstrating against the renovation of Luoyang, he compared Me with Emperor Yang of the Sui dynasty."

Zhangsun was stunned. *Emperor Yang? One of the worst despots in history?*

After composing himself, Zhangsun Wuji said, "In my opinion, Wei Zheng has become too much of a trouble-maker for the good of Luoyang. I would like to suggest sending him back to Chang'an."

The Emperor was inclined to side with him.

To that Hou Junji responded, "Wei's criticisms are sometimes overly harsh, but he has played an absolutely irreplaceable role in catching small errors before they became disasters. That's why the late Empress—may she rest in peace in Heaven—respected him tremendously."

Both the Emperor and Zhangsun Wuji fell silent for a while. Then the Emperor said, "You've got a point, Junji."

On the next morning, the Emperor issued a rescript to Wei Zheng, which read,

Wei Zheng, thank you for pointing out My errors yesterday. I would be really worried if people like you stop calling attention to them!

APART FROM THE MONK Zhishi episode and occasional gripes by Wei Zheng, life in Luoyang was pleasant and essentially uneventful for the Emperor. By far the most enjoyable activity was hunting.

In the winter of late Zhenguan 11 (637), the Emperor went on His sixth hunting trip with an old comrade-in-arms, President of the Board of Revenue Tang Jian. Tang had been His Chief Administrator in the old days when the Emperor was the "Superior General of Celestial Strategy." Accompanied by a small escort of attendants, they went to the Western Park, a favorite hunting spot thanks to its undulating hills and scenic lakes and rivers.

Howling and barking, about a dozen hounds dashed excitedly into the woods, flushing out a pack of boars. Galloping on horseback, the Emperor drew his bow, and shot at them, felling four in succession. Before He had time to savor the joy of triumph, He was suddenly set upon by a boar that emerged from nowhere. As it smashed its way towards Him, its tusks came dangerously close to His booted foot in stirrup. Tang Jian hurriedly jumped off his horse to distract the wild animal as the Emperor frenziedly slashed and hacked it with a sword to death.

"As Chief Administrator of Celestial Strategy," the Emperor said good-humoredly, "you must have seen how the Superior General killed the enemy!"

Tang Jian, who had considered the Emperor's hunting excessive but had been hesitant to voice his view, suddenly threw himself on his knees and said remonstratively, "Gaozu of the Han (Liu Bang) conquered the world on horseback, but did not govern it on horseback. Your Majesty, divine and martial, has subdued the Four Quarters. Does He still need to prove His greatness by killing animals on horseback?"

In a fit of annoyance, the Emperor retorted, "Hey, who are you to lecture Me like that?"

Tang Jian bowed his head to brace himself for an Imperial outburst.

But, to his surprise, the Emperor did not say a word more, and went on to call off the hunting trip, returning with His party to Luoyang way ahead of schedule.

That night, after dinner, the Emperor sat at His desk, upon which lay a pile of paper scrolls. One of them, the "Testamentary Instructions," caught His eyes, and it reminded Him of the Empress's plea, "Stop making hunting trips!" He murmured to Himself, with a sigh, "I don't need to kill animals to prove My greatness, do I?"

On the next morning, He granted Tang Jian a prestige title, which he accepted with a profusion of thanks.

TAKING TANG JIAN'S ADVICE to heart, the Emperor suspended all His planned hunting trips around Luoyang for the rest of the winter. When spring came in early Zhenguan 12 (638), He ended His long sojourn and departed for Chang'an.

When He and His retinue of eunuch officers, palace ladies, and court attendants, and the top leaders of the central bureaucracy arrived in Pu Prefecture (seat: southwest of Yongji, Shanxi) on March 31, thousands of local residents, led by Prefect Zhao Yuankai, thronged the main streets to give them a warm welcome. Dressed in yellow, the royal color, they chanted well-rehearsed slogans, and danced energetically to the rhythmic beating of drums. Veranda bungalows, loft-buildings, and pavilions in the Governor's Office compound were all lavishly decorated with yellow silk draperies.

At night, Prefect Zhao Yuankai hosted a banquet in honor of the Emperor, where a nice array of delicacies and vintage wines were served. For the occasion, more than 100 sheep were slaughtered and hundreds of fish were caught.

"Everything is delicious," observed one adviser.

"I have never tasted such fabulous wine before," opined another.

"Zhao Yuankai deserves an accolade," suggested the third, and everybody present assented.

The Emperor, however, was not pleased. Wei Zheng's remonstration against Him punishing the Director of the Xianren Palace was still fresh on His mind. So instead of commending the Prefect, the Emperor called him to account.

"All the expenses for My trip should come directly from the government storehouses," the Emperor said sternly. "But, can they cover this much extravagance? No! You must have spent a fortune at the expense of the masses. This is clearly the way of the degenerate Sui Dynasty. Not something we want to follow."

"Yes, Your Majesty..." said Prefect Zhao, too scared to finish.

After the Emperor sent him away, He asked His advisers,

"You don't think I should reward Zhao Yuankai for his wasteful behavior, do you?"

They all fell silent.

54. The Edict on Christianity

DURING THE EMPEROR'S ABSENCE from Chang'an, about 200 memorials had piled up in His study. Within days of His return, He began to read them. These were not of military and state importance. If they were, they would have been delivered posthaste to Luoyang for His immediate consideration. For one reason or another, neither could they be dealt with by Vicegerent Li Chengqian. In most cases, the Emperor just passed them on to the Secretariat. Only a few of them required His personal attention.

One was submitted by Assistant Editorial Director Deng Shilong. It was a proposal for compiling an anthology of the Emperor's writings. It set Him thinking.

Apart from several hundred poems and dozens of prose pieces, the bulk of My writing consists of edicts. If they are good and beneficial to My people, they will be included in the histories anyway. If they are no good, what is the point in collecting them? Emperor Wu of Liang, His son Emperor Yuan, the Last Sovereign of Chen, and Emperor Yang of Sui—all have their anthologies, and all of them are still in circulation. But these anthologies could not save their regimes from collapse. A sovereign's job, above all, is to prevent the loss of virtue. How can an anthology of writings be of any help? I just don't get it.

He rejected the proposal and the anthology was not compiled.

Another memorial was submitted by Archdeacon Abraham, asking for permission to proselyte in the Tang Empire. Ever since their arrival in Chang'an in Zhenguan 9 (635), Abraham and his associates had worked hard to translate their holy scriptures and related treatises. The translated works were then deposited in the Palace Library. Through reading some of them, the Emperor gained a firmer understanding of the fundamental concepts of Christianity, which He found enlightening and in no way contradictory to the "Three Teachings," that is, Confucianism, Daoism, and Buddhism. In response, He penned an edict in verse form:

The dao does not have a constant name,
Nor does the sage take a constant form.
The religion spreads wherever it goes,
The multitude of creatures reap the benefit.
From the state of the Roman Orient,
Came Archdeacon Abraham.
He traveled from afar with scriptures and portraits,
And presented them to the capital.

Examine its religious doctrine:
Mysterious, marvelous, and committed to non-action.
Behold its original purpose:
Nurturing life and promoting the essential.
Though its language is devoid of complex discourse,
Its reasoning has its share of trivialities.
But it benefits things and humans alike,
And should be allowed to spread among all under Heaven.

Thus for the first time in history, a group of Christian missionaries (albeit of the banned Nestorian sect) were given permission by the Chinese Emperor to freely practice their religion in the Central Kingdom. Not long afterwards, with the Emperor's blessing, a Nestorian monastery went up in Chang'an's Yining Ward northwest of the Western Market.

55. Yuchi Jingde

BECAUSE OF HIS HEAVY workload, the Emperor cancelled His planned trip to the Jiucheng Palace and stayed on in Chang'an well into the middle of the summer. It was on a torrid mid-summer day that He learned of the death of Yu Shinan. The Emperor was grief-stricken. Yu was the first close associate to die since the passing of Du Ruhui in 630. Although never included in the Emperor's inner circle, Yu was His only intimate "cultural friend."

"Now Yu is gone, with whom else can I discuss calligraphy and poetry?" the Emperor said with a sigh to Wei Zheng.

"Yu Shinan is indeed unsurpassable as a calligrapher and poet, Your Majesty," answered Wei. "But I know someone who is Yu's pupil and whose calligraphy can hold its own against that of his mentor."

"Who is that?"

"Court Diarist Chu Suiliang."

"I didn't know he is a calligrapher. Get him to see Me, will you?"

"Yes, Your Majesty."

In less than a week, the Emperor received Chu Suiliang in the Palace, who brought with him samples of his calligraphy. The Emperor was impressed and instantly appointed him "Court Calligrapher" (*shishu*). Like Yu Shinan, Chu Suiliang was given easy access to the Emperor. But unlike Yu, who held no important post, Chu was to become one of the most powerful advisers at court.

ALTHOUGH THE EMPEROR WAS pleased with the "discovery" of Chu Suiliang, the death of Yu Shinan left a permanent void and made Him painfully aware of the impermanence of life. He became more contemplative, and was often nostalgic for the past when He campaigned on horseback with His close associates. He wanted to see His old comrades-in-arms often. People like Zhangsun Wuji, Gao Shilian, and Fang Xuanling were senior civil officials at court, whom the Emperor met frequently. But others like Li Shiji and Li Jing were commanding officers often posted in the frontier provinces far away from the capital. So, whenever they were in town, the Emperor would make a point of inviting them to the Palace. In the early spring of Zhenguan 13 (639), Yuchi Jingde, another old comrade-in-arms, arrived in Chang'an. As expected, he was asked to pay a visit to the Emperor.

While the Emperor was anxious to see His old friend, He also had something else in mind: Yuchi Jingde had been implicated in a plot against the throne! *Jingde? That daredevil of a man who had risked his life multiple times to save mine?* The Emperor could not believe His eyes when He read the scandalous report. But the charge was too serious to be dismissed. The Emperor did not want to have him haled in for interrogation. That would be too humiliating. So He found a perfectly innocuous excuse to summon him to the capital: appointment to a new post.

"Somebody charges that you are plotting a rebellion—is that true?" the Emperor asked on seeing Yuchi.

"Of course, it is," said Yuchi angrily, his craggy face darkening. "I followed Your Majesty on expeditions all over China, took part in hundreds of battles, and helped Your Majesty pacify the world. Now they charge me with rebellion?"

The Emperor was silent.

"In fact, I am lucky to have survived these arrow and spear wounds," said Yuchi as he dropped his garments onto the floor to reveal the scars of battle wounds that covered his chest, arms, and back.

Struggling to hold back His tears, the Emperor said, "Put on your clothes, Jingde. I don't doubt you. That's why I want to talk with you. Don't be angry."

"No, I am not angry with Your Majesty. I am actually grateful that Your Majesty told me the charge."

"Don't worry about the charge. I know it is unfounded. Now, about your new appointment, can you take up position as Fuzhou Area Commander (in north Shaanxi)?"

"No problem, Your Majesty."

"Great," said the Emperor.

After Yuchi left, the Emperor felt somehow that the informal interrogation had hurt Yuchi's feelings, and decided to make it up to him by letting him marry one of His daughters.

When the Emperor made the marriage proposal to Yuchi a few days later, His old comrade-in-arms dropped down on his knees, kowtowed once, and said, "I want to sincerely thank Your Majesty. The trouble is, I am still married. My wife is lowly and ugly all right, but we have gone through thick and thin together. Even though I, your servant, do not have much book learning at all, I have heard that, in ancient times, people did not abandon their wives when they became rich. So I have to turn down Your Majesty's offer."

The Emperor did not press the issue. It was fine with Him so long as Yuchi understood His intention.

56. Master Falin

JUST AS YUCHI JINGDE was on his way to his new appointment, another religious scandal broke out. The Emperor felt obligated to intervene, because it involved a serious crime allegedly committed by Master Falin, a prominent member of the Buddhist community.

Falin had been a major figure in the Zhenguan-11 movement against ranking Daoism above Buddhism. Unlike the defiant Monk Zhishi, he was not obsessed with martyrdom, and advised his followers to back down from confrontation. He continued to live a peaceful monastic life in the scenic South Mountains south of Chang'an until his Daoist rival Qin Shiying filed a memorial against him. Qin claimed to have detected in the *Essays in Defense of the Correct* (*Bianzheng lun*), a collection of Falin's writings on Buddhism, irrefutable evidence of vilification against Daoism, a crime that might rise to the level of treason.

After Falin was taken into custody on November 27, 639, a tribunal was formed by Imperial edict under the headship of President of the Board of Justice Liu Dewei. In subsequent trials, the Master refused to admit his crime while stubbornly adhering to his extreme anti-Daoist views.

He was brought into the Palace for an Imperial interrogation. The Emperor was a bit taken aback when He saw the Master: a pale and frail-looking old man of small stature in his late 60s, with drooping shoulders.

"I am a descendant of Lord Lao, a virtuous recluse in the Eastern Zhou," said the Emperor. "Our more recent roots are traced to Longxi. Because Daoism is our ancestral tradition, we revere it above Buddhism. Who are you to gibe at our ancestors and speak irresponsibly of re-ranking the religions?"

Falin was silent, collecting his thoughts.

"You have to speak," said the Emperor impatiently.

"I heard," Falin finally responded, "wise sovereigns like Yao and Shun were afraid that people would not speak; despots like Jie and Zhòu were afraid that people would. Today I am living under the reign of a Yao or a Shun, how can I fail to speak!"

"You do have a smooth tongue. Go on."

"Let me start with Lord Lao. He was surnamed Li, and is known as Lao Dan or Li Dan. He was the natural son of a lonely beggar called Han Qian. His mother was a lowly maid. As for the Lis of Longxi, the alleged ancestors of Your Majesty, they had first settled there during the reign of Emperor Cheng in the Western Han. But Li was not the original surname of the Lis of Longxi. What really happened was this:

After an official called Li Yin was executed for libel against the throne, his family members were banished to Zhangye in Longxi. All of them perished along the way. Only the family slaves reached the final destination. It was they, the slaves, who assumed the Li surname."

"Are you intimating that My family descended from those slaves?" the Emperor asked, quite incensed.

"Of course not."

"From whom, then, did My family descend?" the Emperor asked sharply.

"The Dadus of Tuoba. Who were the Dadus? In my opinion, the Dadus were the nobles of the Tuoba Wei (Northern Wei) from the Yin Mountains (in central Inner Mongolia). The whole debate reminds me of a classical saying, *There is someone who trades gold for copper ore, and silk for flax; and gives up a treasured maiden for a slave girl.* Does it not apply to Your Majesty? I think, it does, because abandoning the Northern Wei in favor of Longxi is what Your Majesty has done."

Falin went on to cite passages from the Buddhist and Confucian sources to support his points. Only at the end of his long discourse did he hint at a desire for mercy.

Falin is a lost cause, thought the Emperor. *Of course I am familiar with the Tuoba, the most distinguished branch of the Xianbei from whom both My mother and wife descended. But I don't accept Falin's outlandish claim about My ancestors at all. Nor do I believe for a minute his stories about Lord Lao and the Li clan in Longxi. But I don't want to be held responsible for the death of a monk either, even an importunate one like Falin. In fact, I am not sure what to do. I need time.* He then said, "In your *Essays*, you say that those who recite the name of Bodhisattva Avalokiteśvara multiple times will be invulnerable to swords. I am now granting you seven days to recite his name while you wait for the verdict of the Board of Justice."

After seven days had passed, Liu Dewei went to see Falin in his prison cell.

"Now your time is up," said Liu. "Have you received divine protection from Avalokiteśvara yet?"

Falin answered calmly, "His Majesty brought an end to a chaotic age by campaigning against the guilty, by pacifying the multitude, and by ending the humiliating way of execution in the marketplaces. His Majesty *is* Avalokiteśvara. So in the past seven days, I have only recited 'His Majesty.' " Falin then cited a long list of reasons why the Emperor should be equated with Avalokiteśvara, the most worshipped Bodhisattva in China, who had delayed entering into nirvana in order to help creatures on earth to attain enlightenment.

"If His Majesty is in support of the loyal and righteous," continued Falin, "I will not lose even a single hair. If His Majesty is abusive and bent on imposing undeserved punitive sentences, I will end up dead soon. But the people will mourn for my death and cry over my corpse."

Liu Dewei had already made up his mind. As soon as he returned to his office, he prepared another report and sent it to the throne. It recommended in unambiguous language execution. The report, however, excited the Emperor's curiosity. So Falin was called into the Palace for another talk. But, in spite of the Emperor's effort, the Master refused to change his views.

Eventually, in the eleventh hour, the Emperor relented, sparing his life after all. It elicited a strong response from a law enforcement officer, who argued that anyone who disparaged the Imperial ancestors should be executed.

The Emperor answered, "Falin indeed denigrated My ancestors. However, he has not failed to cite evidence from the classics. That is why I spare his life. But he will be banished to a remote area, Yi Prefecture (in Sichuan)."

Falin was then sent directly from prison to his place of banishment, where he sank into a serious depression and died not long afterwards at the age of 68 in 640.

57. Gaochang

WHEN ADJUDICATING HIGH-PROFILE CASES involving Buddhist or Daoist clerics, the Emperor might not always hand down the most favorable judgment. But He consistently showed a high regard for Buddhism, and held in higher esteem its Daoist rival. His highest reverence, however, was reserved for Confucianism, not only as a religion, but as a set of moral principles to guide the day-to-day affairs of the state and human relations in general. So He followed closely academic trends in Confucianism and state-sponsored Confucian-style education.

Since antiquity, various schools had evolved around the Five Classics of Confucianism—the *Songs, Venerated Documents, Rites, Changes* (*Yijing* or *I-ching*), and

Spring and Autumn Annals. Followers of these schools were divided along academic as well as doctrinal lines. The Emperor did not like the chaotic situation, so He instructed Kong Yingda, Libationer (chief) of the Directorate of Education, to head a group of Confucians to compile a series of authoritative studies. The result was a set of subcommentaries on the Five Classics and their classical commentaries, collectively known as the *Rectification of Meanings* (*Zhengyi*). After their completion, they became the official interpretative works of the Five Classics that all scholars and students must read.

To help promote Confucian learning, the Emperor paid a visit to the office compound of the Directorate of Education (*guozi jian*) itself on March 7, Zhenguan 14 (640). There He watched with great interest the performance of the *shidian* (sacrificial offering) ritual in honor of Confucius and attended a showcase lecture by Kong Yingda, who spoke on the *Classic of Filial Piety* (*Xiaojing*). At the end of the lecture, a delighted Emperor gave out silk cloth to reward all the personnel of the Directorate from the Libationer down to lowly students.

The Directorate had on its teaching staff 26 professors (known as erudites) and lecturers. There were 2,260 students housed in dorms taking up 120 bays of floor space. In those days, it was not uncommon for the Emperor to drop in on student presentations. Those who had proven their mastery of one of the two major classics, the *Record of Rites* (*Liji*) and *Mr. Zuo's Commentary to the Spring and Autumn Annals* (*Chunqiu Zuozhuan*), were all offered official positions at court.

The Directorate supervised a number of learned institutions, notably, the National University (*guoxue*), with a predominantly Confucian curriculum and a student body of 8,000. On one of His visits, the Emperor had a casual chat with some of the students. He was pleasantly surprised to find a large number of them were foreigners, mostly sons of royals, nobles, and tribal chiefs from neighboring states such as Koguryŏ, Paekche, Silla, Gaochang, and Tubo. The Emperor showed a special interest in Gaochang students, not only because of their fluent Chinese, but also because of the strategic importance of their home country in Central Asia.

IN THE WAKE OF Xieli Khan's fall in Zhenguan 4 (630), a number of nomadic powers came to the fore on the vast steppes beyond the northern border. The most prominent one, Xueyantuo, took over much of the territory that had been controlled by Xieli, mostly in Mongolia.

In the northwest, there were the Tuyuhun, who had originally been a branch of the Xianbei in south Manchuria. In the late 3rd century, they migrated west to the Yin Mountains in central Inner Mongolia, and in the early fourth century moved south to east Gansu and Qinghai. In the early days of the Tang, they threatened the farming communities in Gansu and Sichuan for years until they were vanquished by Generals Li Jing, Hou Junji, Li Daozong, and Xue Wanjun. Thereafter, however, the Tuyuhun had stayed in the good graces of the Tang.

A late-comer was Tubo (ancient Tibet). In recent years, it had projected its power from time to time into the Gansu Corridor.

Further to the west, in Xinjiang and beyond, was Western Tujue, which had been at loggerheads with Xieli's Eastern/Northern Tujue.

Sandwiched between Tang China and Western Tujue were the oasis states, the largest of which was Gaochang. Its sovereign Qu Wentai had established close ties with the Tang, renewed each year by a tributary mission to Chang'an. But recently, the Gaochang missions had stopped coming after Qu Wentai had come under the wing of Western Tujue.

Following the collapse of Xieli's empire, many Han Chinese working for the Tujue had ended up in Gaochang. The Emperor considered these expatriates Tang subjects, and requested that they be returned, which Qu Wentai refused. What was worse, with the support of the Western Tujue, Gaochang encroached upon the oasis states of Yanqi to its west and Yiwu to its east. The Tang court was especially alarmed by the case of Yiwu, since it had already submitted to the Tang. So a consensus view began to take shape at court that Gaochang must be punished.

On January 2, Zhenguan 14 (640), the Emperor sent Qu Wentai a letter, requesting his presence at court. But Qu declined the request on account of an illness without sending a deputy. The Emperor lost patience and launched the Gaochang War with an expeditionary force headed by General Hou Junji and General Xue Wanjun, both heroes in the Tuyuhun War. Whereas Qu Wentai was supported by Western Tujue, the Tang allied themselves with Xueyantuo and Yanqi.

ALTHOUGH IN HIS 60s, Qu Wentai, the King of Gaochang, was in relative good health, mentally and physically. While he still looked forward to the day when he could host Master Xuanzang again after his long journey to India, he had severed his ties with Chang'an, largely to please Western Tujue. When warned of the Tang expedition, he was defiant:

The Tang capital and Gaochang are separated by a distance of 7,000 li, of which 2,000 li cuts through a desert. The barren land has neither water nor grass. And the wind is either piercingly cold or scorchingly hot. The Tang cannot possibly send a large army. If they try, they will have serious logistical problems. If the army they send is less than 30,000, we can deal with it. If they try to lay siege to Gaochang City, the siege won't last more than 20 days. So there is no reason to worry.

Thus essentially no important measures were taken to strengthen the defenses of Gaochang City, nor did the King make a request to his Tujue ally for immediate assistance.

By August, against all odds, the massive Tang expeditionary army had crossed the desert. On hearing of the news, Qu Wentai was struck with a debilitating disease and died a few days later. His son Qu Zhisheng succeeded to the throne in front of his father's coffin.

AS THE TANG TROOPS were passing through the Liu Vale in the east of Gaochang, Hou Junji received intelligence from his scouts that Qu Wentai's funeral would take place on the following day. That would be the ideal moment to strike—the entire country would be at its most vulnerable. But General Hou refused to give orders.

"The Son of Heaven has launched this campaign," argued Hou, "because Gaochang defies ritual. If we attack their funeral procession, we will lose our moral authority."

Thus the Tang army marched on at normal pace with drums beating and flags flying. Soon it reached the outpost city of Tiancheng. After his request for surrender was rejected, Hou launched an attack early in the morning, and stormed the city by noon.

Before long, the Tang army was at the walls of Gaochang City. Qu Zhisheng sent a conciliatory letter,

The person who offended the Son of Heaven was the previous King. Penalized by Heaven, he passed away. I, Qu Zhisheng, just succeeded to the throne, and am quite innocent of the offense. Hopefully, General Hou would have compassion for me and spare the city from the carnage of war.

Hou's reply was curt, "If you are really remorseful, you should be delivered with your hands tied behind your back to my headquarters."

Having received no further response, Hou ordered a massive attack. The city was surrounded by a moat, which contained little water. After the Tang soldiers filled up sections of it with soil, the commandos began to storm the wall using bamboo vaulting poles and scaling ladders. Meanwhile a kind of siege devices called "Nest Carts" were deployed. About 100 feet tall, these "carts" were mobile towers that allowed the Tang archers to provide cover for the attackers, and to target the wall guards and people inside the city.

The only possible threat to the Tang army had been Buddha City to the north (north of Jimsar, Xinjiang), where a Tujue garrison had been posted. But on hearing the arrival of the Tang army, the Tujue commander had fled, and Buddha City had fallen into Tang hands.

On August 13, all hope was lost for Gaochang. Qu Zhisheng, dressed in white, led his senior officials and generals in walking slowly out of the main gate to surrender. Thereafter, the Tang army went on to occupy the rest of the kingdom. All told, there were 22 cities. Gaochang, an independent state under the Qus for more than 140 years, finally ceased to exist.

KING LONG TUQIZHI OF Yanqi (Qarasahr) had been an ally of the Tang throughout the Gaochang War. Now that the War was over, he became increasingly disquieted by the rise of the Tang as the dominant power in the region. The only way to prevent the Tang from advancing further west, it would seem, was to ally himself with the Western Tujue. But he wanted to give diplomacy a chance first. So he sent a delegation to General Hou Junji's headquarters in Gaochang City.

After an exchange of compliments with his host, the Yanqi emissary said, "General, there are three Yanqi cities seized by Gaochang before the war."

"Oh?"

"We would greatly appreciate it if you could return them."

"The Great Tang launched the war to enforce justice. So we are morally bound to return to you what is rightfully yours."

"Thank you so much, General. In addition, there are 1,500 Yanqi subjects abducted by Gaochang. Could you have them repatriated?"

"That we can do as well."

Pleased with General Hou's promises, the Yanqi King decided to remain in the Tang camp.

58. Hou Junji

WHILE GENERALS HOU JUNJI and Xue Wanjun were still on their way back to the capital, a thorny issue cropped up at court regarding the status of Gaochang.

"What are we going to do with it, now that we are victorious?" the Emperor asked sharply.

"Your Majesty," answered Zhangsun Wuji, "I am in favor of inclusion."

"Elaborate, Wuji," said the Emperor.

"If we make Gaochang part of the Tang, we can use it as a forward base in the Western Regions."

"I disagree," interposed Wei Zheng. "In my opinion, Gaochang should be treated as a 'wild domain'. Its statehood should be revived, its King reinstated, and its people pacified. If we do that, we will convince more barbarian states to submit to our authority."

"The Gaochang people are predominantly Han Chinese, and would welcome Tang rule," said Zhangsun Wuji.

"That is not the issue," rejoined Wei Zheng. "If we convert the area into Prefectures and Counties, we need at a minimum a garrison force of 1,000, which will have to be rotated every several years. Up to 30 to 40 percent of them will perish in the process. In ten years' time, the financial resources of Longyou (Gansu) will be exhausted."

"You are exaggerating," said Zhangsun Wuji. "The area was already under the control of the Central Kingdom as early as the Western Han. By Emperor Xuan's time, a Commandant was posted there. If the Han could do it, why not the Tang?"

"The cost," said Wei Zheng, "will far exceed the pitiful amount of tax receipts in the form of wheat and silk Your Majesty can hope to derive from it."

The debate went on for hours until the pro-inclusion camp won the day.

Anxi Protectorate was set up as the overarching civil-military administration in the area west of Longyou with its seat located west of Gaochang City. The Kingdom of Gaochang itself was converted to Xi Prefecture (Western Prefecture), with Gaochang City as its seat, and the area to its north, to Ting Prefecture, with Buddha City as its seat. Both Prefectures were under the jurisdiction of the Protectorate.

BY EARLY ZHENGUAN 15 (641), the ex-king Qu Zhisheng and the royals, nobles, and high-ranking officials of Gaochang were settled in Chang'an. Qu Zhisheng himself was made General-in-chief of the Militant Guard Command of the Left and Prefectural Duke of Jincheng. Generous official appointments were granted to Gaochang royals and nobles. Gaochang's court entertainers were transferred to the Court of State Sacrifices. With their arrival, a new category of music, that of Gaochang, was added to the existing Nine Categories.

The heroes of the war, Hou Junji and Xue Wanjun, on arrival in Chang'an, were showered with rewards and accolades. However, before the joy of victory died down, both were thrown into prison. It turned out that in spite of his talk of moral authority, Hou Junji had a soft spot for gemstones and jewelry. It was an open secret that he helped himself to some of the royal treasures of Gaochang, including gold necklaces, bracelets, and rings, and other jewelry pieces adorned with precious stones, such as diamonds from India, carnelians from the Mediterranean, lapis lazulis from Afghanistan, and jadeites from Hotan (Hetian). His subaltern officers, taking their cue from their boss, openly pocketed war spoils. Discipline broke down in the days immediately following the conquest.

Xue Wanjun, on the other hand, had allegedly fallen for Gaochang women. At least one of them had come forward with the claim that she had had sex with the general. Under the Tang laws (just like under the Sui laws), fornication was a crime.

"It is a pity," said the Emperor, "that Hou Junji and Xue Wanjun are now in jail. They are such great generals! But I cannot ignore their crimes on account of their past merit."

However, for weeks, the Court of Judicial Review (*dali si*), which was charged with trying both cases, had not been able to make a decision. In the case of Hou Junji, the evidence seemed conflicting. Meanwhile the streets of Chang'an were abuzz with rumors about how the loyal general was dumped after he had won the war for the court. That made Vice President of the Secretariat Cen Wenben concerned enough to file a memorial,

…Because of the vacuity of the Gaochang King, Your Majesty ordered Hou Junji and Xue Wanjun to launch a campaign against him, which they carried out successfully. But within ten days of their arrival in Chang'an, both were imprisoned in the Court of Judicial Review. Although Hou and Xue deserve to be punished for their crimes, I am still concerned that people within the Four Seas will suspect that Your Majesty focuses too much on their transgressions, while ignoring their merit.

I heard that the main responsibility of a commanding officer is to conquer the enemies. If he defeats the enemies, he deserves his reward even though he may be avaricious. If he is worsted by the enemies, he deserves to be executed regardless how incorruptible he is.

That is why the Art of War *of Grand Duke Jiang handed down from the Lord of Huangshi says, "Use a general for his wisdom, his bravery, his avarice, or his folly. A wise one is fond of achieving merit; a brave one loves to carry out his wishes; an avaricious one is driven by profit; and a foolish one is not afraid of death."*

Therefore, I sincerely hope that Your Majesty would recognize their merit, no matter how insignificant, and look beyond their towering crimes so that both Hou Junji and Xue Wanjun would be able to once again serve the court and ride their horses into battle. Although these are avaricious and foolish generals, they are Your Majesty's avaricious and foolish generals.

Although Your Majesty may have to bend the law to follow my advice, the virtue of the court will spread farther for it. Even if Hou Junji and Xue Wanjun eventually receive a pardon, the exposure of their misdeeds will be even greater for it.

Neither was it any easier to deal with the case of Xue Wanjun. At several trial sessions where he was brought face-to-face with his Gaochang accuser, Xue strenuously denied every charge brought against him. The stalemate prompted Wei Zheng to submit a memorial, which said,

I heard that "A sovereign should employ the services of his subjects in accord with rites, and a subject should serve his sovereign with loyalty." Recently, General-in-chief Xue was ordered to confront a woman of the fallen country concerning their bedchamber affair. If the charge is true, there is little to gain. If the charge is untrue, there is much to lose.

Both Duke Mu of Qin (7th c. BCE) and King Zhuang of Chu (7th–6th c. BCE) pardoned minor crimes against them. Does Your Majesty, who looks up to such model sovereigns as Yao and Shun, want to do worse than local rulers such as Mu and Zhuang?

These two eloquent memorials left the Emperor in a conundrum. To maintain strict army discipline, it was necessary to punish generals and soldiers alike when they ran afoul of the law. But the negative publicity surrounding the trials of Hou and Xue was damaging to army morale and loyalty to the throne. Furthermore, He realized that by throwing them into prison and interrogating them in humiliating ways, the court had already punished them.

That night when the Emperor was reading the *Book of the Song* by the Liang historian Shen Yue, He was moved by the story of General-in-chief Tan Daoji, then the best commanding officer of the Song, executed on trumped-up charges. When the Emperor came to Tan's last words—"You are destroying your own Great Wall!"—His face flushed crimson as if Tan were addressing Him. On the next morning, He issued an edict to set free and reinstate both Hou and Xue.

59. Princess Wencheng

BEFORE THE CASES OF Hou and Wan were closed, the southwestern power of Tubo was forced upon the Emperor's attention.

At a meeting of the Chief Ministers' Council in the Liangyi Basilica, the Emperor said, "As early as Zhenguan 8 (634), King Songzanganbu sent an emissary to the court, requesting a marriage alliance after he had heard that the Tang had given Princesses in marriage to the Tujue and Tuyuhun Khans. I did not grant his request. At that time I did not know much about Tubo. Furthermore, we can not just marry off a Tang Princess to every local chieftain who wants one, can we?"

"Of course not, Your Majesty," said Fang Xuanling. "But the Tubo King did not take the rejection very well. He mounted a massive campaign against the Tuyuhun, because, for some reason, he was convinced that they had prevented him from getting his Tang bride. The Tuyuhun were their traditional rivals, and still are. To us, King Songzanganbu issued a threat. He said, 'So long as the Tang refuse to marry off a Princess to me, I will raid their lands.' He then mounted a massive invasion with an army of 200,000 deep into Song Prefecture."

"I had to order Generals Hou Junji, Zhishi Sili, and others to mount a counteroffensive," said the Emperor. "Eventually, he retreated because of our victories and because of the advice of his senior advisers. Recently, Tang-Tubo relations have seen much improvement. Late last year, they sent a tributary delegation, bearing as gifts a large number of gold vessels weighing about 1,000 catties. The King again asked for the hand of a Tang Princess. This time I saw no reason not to grant his wish. I have already requested the Board of Rites to start looking for a bride. As you all know, any female member of the Li royal house can be a Princess. If she does not have a Princess' title, it can be granted with special approval. In this particular case, I want someone who is highly cultured, and physically attractive."

Pausing briefly, the Emperor turned to Li Daozong and said, "The President of the Board of Rites, have you found someone suitable yet?"

"As a matter of fact, yes, Your Majesty," Li Daozong answered with confidence. "She is Princess Wencheng, a beauty of 16 with many cultural attainments."

"Is she willing to go?" asked the Emperor.

"Yes. In fact, she volunteered to be the Queen of Tubo."

"Wonderful," said the Emperor.

ON FEBRUARY 20, ZHENGUAN 15 (641), the Tubo delegation headed by Chancellor Mgar Stong-btsan arrived in Chang'an. Ten days later, a long cavalcade of horses and carriages departed from the Jinguang Gate of the Tang capital and proceeded west. In one of the carriages sat Princess Wencheng herself. She was accompanied by Tubo Chancellor Mgar Stong-btsan and Tang President of the Board of Rites Li Daozong, each in his own vehicle.

Almost the entire procession consisted of Wencheng's trousseau: bronze statues of Śakyamuni, precious stones, gold and jade objects, silk and cotton cloth, grain and turnip seeds, and boxes and boxes of books: the Confucian classics, histories, and those on divination, craftsmanship, architecture, and medicine. There were also attendants who constituted what may be called a "human dowry," including scholars, craftsmen, wet nurses, palace ladies, and court musicians.

About a month later, the procession arrived in Heyuan (northeast of Qumarlêb, Qinghai). King Songzanganbu under the escort of tens of thousands of troops had been waiting. In the marriage ceremony that followed, Li Daozong representing the Li royal house and the Tang played the role of the father, giving away Princess Wencheng, whereas Songzanganbu for his part piously performed the rite of becoming a son-in-law. Once the ceremony was over, a marriage alliance of Tang and Tubo came into existence, which would guarantee long-lasting peace between them.

60. The Crown Prince and Li Tai

IN EARLY ZHENGUAN 15 (641), the Emperor departed for Luoyang, leaving Chang'an in the charge of His eldest son, Crown Prince Li Chengqian, now serving as Vicegerent. For an extended period, he would be free from the watchful eye of his father. Within weeks of his father's departure, the Crown Prince threw his first party, an extravagant soirée, in the Eastern Palace. Among his invited guests were Du He (Du Ruhui's son, known for his occult knowledge) and Prince Li Yuanchang (Li Yuan's seventh son). There were his Tujue friends as well, including Dageyou, who had earned himself the reputation as a savage brawler in the marketplaces. Professional entertainers—singers, dancers, magicians, jugglers, and tumblers—from the Court of State Sacrifices (*taichang*) were the main performers, many of whom were from Gaochang. The Crown Prince particularly enjoyed their exotic dances and their colorful Western Regions music based on the diatonic scale—having grown tired of the Central Plain music of the pentatonic variety.

The party started in earnest after dark with the professional entertainers staging musical performances and acrobatic shows. After several rounds of drinking, host and guests joined the entertainers, dancing, singing, and carousing with abandon.

Chengqian was thrilled. In fact, he had never had so much fun in his short life of 23 years. For the first time he was able to enjoy life in his own way. To be sure, there were high-ranking court officials, such as Supervisors of the Households (*zhanshi*) and Mentors (*shuzi*), around him. Their sole task it was to make sure that he as Crown Prince acquitted himself in accord with ritual. Furthermore, Chief Minister Gao Shilian served as his adviser in dealing with government affairs. But at night the Crown Prince himself was the boss.

When the merrymaking ended in the wee hours of the morning, Chengqian graciously provided lodging for the invited guests and entertainers in the Eastern Palace.

The success of the soirée inspired Chengqian to hold night parties frequently, on average, about three to five times a month.

During the day, apart from discharging his responsibility as Vicegerent, he channeled his abundant energy into his own public building projects. One of them was the lavish renovation of the basilicas and auxiliary structures in the Eastern Palace (he had never found their architectural style and functionality appealing), using conscripted farm labor even during the busy farming season.

Supervisor of the Household Yu Zhining, the highest-ranking mentor of the Crown Prince, was alarmed by the night parties, by the presence of the Tujue in the Eastern Palace, and by the abusive use of farm labor. All this, he was convinced, had led the Crown Prince astray from the proper path for an emperor-in-waiting. In an effort to correct the Prince's misbehavior, Yu submitted a candid memorial that excoriated him and demanded, among other things, that he sever ties with Dageyou, "a beast in man's clothing." The hope was that by shocking the Crown Prince out of his comfort zone it would bring him back from the brink of a perilous abyss.

TWO DAYS LATER, ZHANG Sizheng and Hegan Chengji, two of the Crown Prince's myrmidons, both in their 20s, arrived at the north gate of Qinren Ward. It was well after dark and a city-wide curfew was in force. They entered the Ward after showing a special pass and proceeded to a corner residence. Scaling the six-foot wall, they landed inside the courtyard with hardly a sound.

"His bedroom should be in the eastern part," whispered Zhang Sizheng, as they moved quietly towards the main house.

"Look!" said Hegan Chengji in a muted voice, pointing to a nondescript mud brick structure in the middle of the courtyard. "What is that?"

"A hut," answered Zhang Sizheng.

"I know. But what's it for?"

Before Zhang said another word, Hegan drew closer to have a better look. Suddenly, he turned his head and whispered, "Our quarry is there!"

Without a word, Zhang Sizheng moved to the left of his partner, his hand firmly grasping the hilt of a poniard tucked inside his garment. They looked inside through the window lattice. Yu Zhining, a top-ranking member of the central bureaucracy, was lying on a rush mattress with his head rested on a pottery pillow, reading a scroll by an oil lamp on a side table. They were stunned by the complete lack of material comfort and stepped aside.

"What's going on?" asked Hegan.

"Now I remember. His mother died about two months ago."

"He has been living in this makeshift hut since then?"

"Some filial sons live in huts while in mourning for a parent up to three years."

"Amazing!" said Hegan.

After both fell quiet for a while, Zhang said abruptly, "You know what? I don't feel like doing it right now."

"Me either," said Hegan. "But the Crown Prince is going to be mad at us."

"Don't worry," Zhang said reassuringly. "I'll find a way to deal with him."

"You have to tell me why you blew it," the Crown Prince growled at Zhang Sizheng and Hegan Chengji on the following morning. "Didn't I tell you that I wanted that son of bitch dead no matter what?"

"Your Highness, the Yu residence is well guarded day and night," answered Zhang Sizheng. "We could not enter the courtyard unnoticed."

"But Yu has to go. His fucking memorial insulted me and called Dageyou 'a beast in man's clothing.'"

"Of course, he has to be bumped off, Your Highness. We'll do it next time."

"You'd better hurry. If you don't, there won't be a next time."

"Absolutely, Your Highness. We promise to do it soon."

UPON HIS RETURN TO Chang'an, the Emperor was briefed on the freakish behavior of Crown Prince Li Chengqian by his mentors. The Emperor called him in and gave him a serious warning, "If you don't want to be Crown Prince any more, you'd better say so." The Prince had no choice but to toe the line set by his father, and stop throwing wild parties. Naturally, his plan to take Yu Zhining's life was put on hold indefinitely.

His younger brother Prince Li Tai, meanwhile, was having the time of his life. On February 13, Zhenguan 16 (642), he officially presented a voluminous encyclopedic work, known as the *Comprehensive Gazetteer* (*Kuodi zhi*), to the throne. Comprised of 550 scrolls (including the table of content and abstracts in 5 scrolls), this thoroughgoing book on the Empire's administrative geography was the first of its kind, with elaborate information on the historical evolution and current status of the capital, and the three levels of regional administration—ten Circles, 358 Prefectures, and 1,551 Counties. The project had been launched five years before under Li Tai's general editorship with the Emperor's approval. Of course, much of the hard work was done by scholars at the Institute for Literature. But Li Tai was credited with bringing the whole project to completion. The Emperor was so delighted that He gave Li Tai in reward 10,000 bolts of silk, and significantly increased his stipend. It now topped that of the Crown Prince.

Of shorter than average height, Li Tai had an average-looking face and a corpulent body. Because of his gentle manners, kindly disposition, and impressive erudition, to most Li Tai was more like a pedantic scholar than an overbearing Prince. Not surprisingly, he was the most popular Prince with the high-ranking officials at court. The favors he received from his father only added to his popularity.

However, for Counselor of Remonstration (*jianyi dafu*) Chu Suiliang, Tai's growing popularity was a source of worry. In his memorial to the Emperor, he warned of the danger of showing too much favor to His second son. Impressed with his candid and well-reasoned argument, the Emperor paid an unannounced visit to Chu at the Institute of Historiography. Chu was now no longer a Court Diarist, but the senior court official in charge of the Court Diary.

At the Emperor's request, Chu Suiliang enlarged on his view of the Prince, citing past examples of favored princes coming to a bad end. Prince Li Tai, he argued, should be inculcated with such good values as compliance with ritual, modesty, and frugality. In a word, Chu was strenuously opposed to giving him preferential treatment.

After lavishing praises on Chu for his critical remarks, the Emperor asked casually, "Just out of curiosity, can I read the Court Diary?"

"Well," answered Chu, "the Court Diarists keep a thorough record of the words and activities of the sovereign, whether good or evil. The hope is that it will prevent him from doing harm. But I have never heard that one can read it before it is edited."

"If I have done something wrong, you will also record it?" asked the Emperor.

"As long as I hold the post of court historian," Chu Suiliang replied in all seriousness, "I don't dare not to record it."

"If Suiliang does not record it," echoed one of his colleagues, "it will be recorded by all under Heaven."

"Of course, of course," the Emperor assented.

AFTER THE EMPEROR HAD browsed through the *Gazetteer*, and liked what He had seen, He granted Prince Li Tai the rare honor of living in the Wude Basilica, the palatial structure east of the Liangyi Basilica, thereby reviving the practice of housing Princes inside the Taiji Palace, which had been abandoned after the Xuanwu Gate Incident.

For his part, Li Tai accepted the offer with alacrity and moved into the Wude. Less than two weeks later, Wei Zheng submitted a memorial to the throne. It read:

Your Majesty loves the Prince of Wei and wants to do everything possible to keep him from harm. To that end, one should abate his pride and extravagance, and make sure that he will not end up in a place subject to suspicion. The Wude Basilica, located west of the Eastern Palace, is where Prince Li Yuanji used to live. Yuanji perished in the Xuanwu Gate Incident. Thus Prince of Wei Li Tai's residence in the Basilica is now widely considered unacceptable. Although time has changed, I am afraid that, so long as he lives there, the Prince of Wei cannot find peace of mind.

Feeling irritated, the Emperor asked Himself, *Don't I have a right to house My son anywhere I want?* Before He was about to call Wei Zheng to account, He picked up Chu Suiliang's memorial and reread it. *Heaping favors and honors upon Tai*, He thought, *will probably do him no good after all.* He then issued an edict—not to summon Wei Zheng, but to order Li Tai to move back into his princely residence in Yankang Ward.

61. The Mirror of Man

PRINCE LI TAI WAS mortified by the Emperor's change of mind. For His part, the Emperor felt guilty and promised to make it up to His favorite son in some other way. Still, He was grateful that Chu Suiliang and Wei Zheng had cautioned against lavishing too much favor on Li Tai, and summoned the two remonstrators to thank them in person. Chu arrived on time but Wei was nowhere to be found. The absence was due to a chronic eye disease, which had gotten worse recently. The Emperor sent him a rescript, which, after asking after his health, said, "I haven't seen you only for a few days, and I have already made quite a few mistakes. I do want to pay you a visit. But I am afraid that it will cause too much trouble. In the meantime, whatever advice you care to give, please communicate it to Me directly in writing. I cannot wait to read it."

Wei Zheng sent a candid reply, which read, "Your Majesty likes to speak of the public at court. But Your Majesty's action seems to pay greater attention to private interest. When others find out about it, which Your Majesty clearly abhors, Your Majesty often flies into a terrifying rage. But the more one wants to cover up something, the more it gets out of control. It does not help things at all, does it?"

The Emperor was struck not so much by the sharpness of the criticism as by the calligraphy. The wavering strokes and uneven spacing of the characters revealed the extremely unsteady hands and poor eyesight of the calligrapher.

Thereupon, the Emperor sent a few eunuch officers to administer to his needs. When they reported that Wei Zheng's home did not have a main hall, the Emperor was surprised, because it was standard even in an average Chang'an home. He forthwith ordered to have one built for Wei, using materials originally intended for a small basilica in the Palace. On the occasion of its completion, the Emperor bestowed a number of gifts upon him, including a screen, a mattress, a comforter, a small table, and a cane—all practical items intended to make his life more comfortable.

Later in the year, Wei Zheng's health took a turn for the worse. On the Emperor's orders, several Commandants (*zhonglang jiang*) were billeted in Wei Zheng's home to monitor his health. On countless occasions, the Emperor dispatched eunuch officers to bring herbal medicines to the patient. Every now and then, the Emperor would visit his home in person. On one visit, He spent an entire day with him behind closed doors, discussing important government affairs and policy.

Not long thereafter, He came again, bringing with Him Crown Prince Li Chengqian and His daughter, the Princess of Hengshan. At the sight of Wei Zheng lying in bed and nearly blind but still wearing his official attire for court attendance, complete with a sash tied at the waist and a hat to match, the Emperor was moved to tears. Wiping off tears, He announced His decision to give His daughter in marriage to Wei Zheng's son, Shuyu.

"Sir, can't you see?" the Emperor asked anxiously. "This is the Princess of Hengshan, your new daughter-in-law!"

Wei Zheng scrunched his eyes to have a better look, but could hardly make out her face.

That night the Emperor had a dream of Wei Zheng. Like in previous dreams, His favorite adviser looked his usual self, dignified, acerbic, and intensely loyal. When the Emperor woke up the next morning He felt slightly relieved. By noon, He received the news of Wei's passing. It was February 11, Zhenguan 17 (643).

At Wei's funeral, the Emperor broke down into violent sobs. On His orders, a five-day suspension of court business went into effect, which was the longest ever for the passing of an official. Wei Zheng's remains were buried in the Zhaoling Tomb Park, the burial ground for Empress Zhangsun and eventually for the Emperor Himself. His epitaph was personally composed and brushed by the Emperor.

Several months later, the Emperor's longing for Wei Zheng had only grown stronger. Commenting on his death, He said, "I have only three mirrors: a mirror of bronze, a mirror of the past, and a mirror of man. By using the mirror of bronze, I could make sure I was properly attired; by using the mirror of the past, I could know the rise and fall of dynasties; and by using the mirror of man, I could understand the success and failure of things. These were the three mirrors I used to guard against My own errors. Alas! With the passing of Wei Zheng, I have lost My mirror of man!"

HOU JUNJI WAS GRIEF-STRICKEN over the death of Wei Zheng, who had recommended him for Chief Minister several times. Although Hou's pardon could be attributed to the memorial by Cen Wenben, it was Wei Zheng's remonstration against the continued incarceration of General Xue Wanjun that had caused the Emperor to change His mind about both of them.

Ever since his release from prison, Hou had been very unhappy. He knew that had it not been Cen's and Wei's petitions, he would probably have been sentenced by the Court of Judicial Review to flogging and banishment. His stint in prison was humiliating. For weeks he had to put up with the stench and bone-chilling cold of the cell, wearing fetters even in sleep. Now, in spite of his reinstatement, his career advancement had virtually come to an end.

One day when he was roaming about in the Eastern Market, he entered a tavern for a drink, where he met his old friend Zhang Liang. They started a casual conversation. Zhang told him that he was moving soon, having been transferred from the post of Supervisor of the Household in the Administration of Crown Prince Affairs to a provincial one, that of Commander of Luozhou Area Command. Hou was stunned. Gulping down the rest of his cup, he snarled, "It is unfair! You have been serving the Emperor since the days when He was the Prince of Qin."

"I am not too happy about it either," said Zhang. "But, to tell you the truth, the job of Supervisor of the Household was extremely challenging. One had to deal with Chengqian everyday."

"I know. That moron of a Prince is a pain in the neck. Still, it is a demotion to go from a key post at the center to a provincial one. I wonder who has pushed you out."

"Nobody but you," Zhang said somewhat facetiously.

"Me? No," Hou Junji said defensively. "Since my return from Gaochang, the Son of Heaven no longer trusts me. How can I push out anybody?"

After pausing for a few moments, Hou continued, "In fact, once I was so depressed that I thought of taking my own life."

"It was a shame you had to go through all that," Zhang Liang said with sympathy.

"As the saying goes, 'When all the hares are hunted down and killed, the hounds are cooked.' Sometimes, when I think of it, I am overwhelmed by a sense of total disillusionment, and that almost makes me want to quit."

"And do what?" Zhang Liang asked, startled at the tone of negativity.

"You know what I mean."

"Are you out of your mind?" Zhang asked severely, rising to leave.

Later Zhang Liang felt so disturbed that he reported his encounter with Hou to the Emperor, suggesting that Hou Junji might harbor sinister intentions.

62. The Lingyan Pavilion

THE EMPEROR FOUND ZHANG Liang's report hard to believe, but He launched a secret investigation anyway, which ended in two months after failing to uncover incriminating evidence. By then the Emperor was thoroughly absorbed in the renovation of an imposing structure, the Mist-transcending Pavilion (Lingyan *ge*), located north of the Wude Basilica, in Chang'an's Palace City.

On March 27, Zhenguan 17 (643), with much fanfare, the Emperor officially re-inaugurated the newly renovated Pavilion as the Tang "hall of fame." It featured prominently the portraits of 24 Tang heroes, such as Zhangsun Wuji, Fang Xuanling, Du Ruhui, Wei Zheng, Yuchi Jingde, Xiao Yu, Gao Shilian, Li Jing, Hou Junji, Zhang Liang, Li Shiji, and others—those who had played a pivotal role in consolidating the Tang Empire while serving under Li Shimin.

The idea of creating the hall of fame had emanated from the Emperor Himself, who wanted to permanently preserve the memory of His comrades-in-arms, half of whom had already departed from this world (including Qutu Tong, Du Ruhui, Li Xiaogong, Chai Shao, Yin Kaishan, Zhang Gongjin, Yu Shinan, and Wei Zheng). The artist who executed the paintings was Yan Liben, the greatest painter of the age, renowned especially for his figure painting. The renovated Pavilion provided a venue where the Emperor and His associates would be able to view the portraits of the heroes together or individually while reminiscing about their exploits and deeds.

A Tang scholar gave a poetic description of the building:

The Pavilion of paintings rises up in the void,
Seen from afar it sits amidst the nine heavens.
Its red pillars stand tall in splendor,
Its plain walls are painted with heroes.
Misty and obscure the primordial pneuma floats,
Skyward the auspicious smoke issues forth.
Up close one perceives the hundred officials attending court,

Bowing from a distance, one beholds a vision of many immortals.
The paintings are suspended on blue clouds,
The rituals there depicted unfold before the Forbidden Palace.
Staring into the rain-washed sky,
I lift my gaze to it again and again.

The number 24 symbolized the 24 divisions of the year, but it did not necessarily remain fixed. With the passage of time, it would increase to allow the addition of new hall-of-famers, and ascension to the Lingyan Pavilion, like the Roman Triumph, would become the greatest honor a Tang official could aspire to in his lifetime. When a hall-of-famer fell out of grace, however, his name and portrait were subject to removal.

63. The Pathic

AFTER THE EMPEROR'S CENSURE, Crown Prince Li Chengqian stopped throwing large-scale soirées in the Eastern Palace. His behavior showed marked improvement for a while. Then it took a turn for the worse and became outright bizarre as the Emperor turned His attention away from the Eastern Palace.

Apparently under the influence of his young Tujue friends, the Prince took a fancy to their way of life. He loved to speak the Turkic language and to dress up like a Tujue Khan. He picked out Tujue-looking slaves and organized them into five-man groups (called tribes). On his orders, they, wearing braided hair and sheepskin, herded and grazed sheep in the grounds of the Eastern Palace, all in supposedly Tujue style. A Khan's banner broidered with a five-wolf-head pattern was created as his flag, and a yurt was set up as his campaign tent. Oftentimes, in the company of his friends, the Prince would sit cross-legged on the grass, eating roast lamb with a dagger, in imitation of the Tujue way. Once he even staged a mock Tujue-style funeral for himself. As he was lying on the ground playing dead, his underlings went around him on horseback multiple times, wailing, cutting their ears and faces and cutting off their hair.

But most worrisome was Chengqian's obsession with a pathic, who was a great singer and dancer. His original name does not survive. We only know him by his pet name, "Chenxin" or "Heart Pleaser," given by the Prince himself. He and the Prince spent much time together during the day and shared the same bed at night. Frequently, Chenxin brought his entertainer friends, who would, with the Prince's permission, sleep over in the Eastern Palace.

The Prince also befriended two Daoists of dubious repute: Qin Shiying (who had brought charges against the Buddhist monk Falin) and Wei Lingfu, both of whom were allowed to join his entourage, practicing occult arts on demand.

Yu Zhining and Kong Yingda had remonstrated on numerous occasions. But all to no avail. Then, at the end of a night party, the fearless Zhang Xuansu confronted the Prince and told him bluntly, "Your Highness, I am worried about your personal safety. You should not allow the entertainers to spend the night in the Eastern Palace."

"Don't worry about them," said Chengqian dismissively. "They are my buddies."

"But it is inappropriate for Your Highness to rub shoulders with lowly entertainers."

"Why?"

"Because entertainers have been regarded as moral degenerates and caitiffs since antiquity. The music they play in the Eastern Palace is like the sound of Zheng and Wey. It is decadent." Zheng and Wey were two Central Plain states in the Spring and Autumn era. Their music had been considered "dissolute" since the times of Confucius.

"It is not decadent!" protested Chengqian. "It is exotic Western Regions music."

"Don't' argue with me. The Emperor will never approve of your listening to it."

Chengqian fell silent, looking very disappointed.

"Your Highness," Zhang Xuansu continued, "should stay away from Chenxin. He is dangerous."

"Why?" Chengqian asked incredulously.

"Don't you understand? The presence of Chenxin and his friends inside the Eastern Palace shows you are in undesirable company. What is even more troubling are the activities of those two Daoist adepts."

"What have they done?"

"Incantation, astrological divination, soul-calling, and internal and external alchemy. All this can have an evil influence on you. Most seriously, keeping such bad company can cast you in an unfavorable light in contrast with your brother Li Tai."

"Is that so?"

"Yes, Your Highness. Prince of Wei Li Tai has surrounded him with scholars and learned officials. After he presented the *Comprehensive Gazetteer* to the throne, the Emperor has often spoken highly of him."

"So?"

"Your Highness, haven't you noticed that when the Emperor goes hunting, He always brings Tai with Him, but never you?"

"Yes, I have noticed that. Maybe because I can't walk fast enough."

"You love hunting too, don't you? And the Emperor knows that."

"What are you driving at? Are you suggesting the Emperor will eventually replace me with Tai as heir?" Chengqian asked, without much conviction.

"I didn't say that. But one thing leads to another. Before long, you will find your position as heir in jeopardy."

"Are you sure?"

"Believe me, Your Highness. The danger is much greater than you think."

"All right, all right. I'll be careful in the future," said Chengqian as he walked away with a limp.

NOT LONG AFTER THE colloquy with Zhang, Crown Prince Chengqian resumed his old ways—keeping company with his entertainer friends and allowing them to spend the night in the Eastern Palace. His frustrated mentors had no choice but to send unflattering reports to the throne. When the Emperor read them, He was scandalized. *Not long ago*, He thought, *Chengqian clearly showed the filial side of his character during his mother illness and dealt with government affairs competently at the time of My father's passing. Today, he is hardly recognizable. What has happened? Has he become incorrigible?*

When Chengqian was brought into His presence, the Emperor asked casually, "I heard you made a new friend called Chenxin. What kind of person is he?"

"He is a smart young man from the Court of State Sacrifices (*taichang*)," answered the Prince.

"What do you do when you are together?"

"He teaches me how to sing and dance and play the flute."

"Did you allow him to stay in the Eastern Palace for the night?"

"Yes, Your Majesty. Sometimes I asked him to stay when it was too late."

"Where did he sleep?"

"It depends. Usually in one of the spare rooms in the Cheng'en Basilica."

"Really?"

"Yes, Your Majesty."

"Look at this," the Emperor said, handing a sheet of paper to him. It was a detailed account of his recent behavior submitted by one of the mentors.

When the Prince came to "shared the same bed and engaged in indecent acts with Chenxin," he dropped down on his knees, and said beseechingly, "Your Majesty, please give me a chance to correct my mistake."

"It is a disgrace!" the Emperor shouted, flying into a rage. "How can I entrust the fate of the country to a wastrel like you? Can't you be a little more like your brother Tai?"

With tears rolling down his cheeks, Chengqian said, "I entreat Your Majesty, spare me this time. I promise I will change in the future."

Still furious, the Emperor waved a hand to dismiss him.

SEVERAL DAYS LATER, THE Prince received an official notice that four of his friends, including Chenxin and the two Daoists, had been arrested on charges of endangering the safety of the Eastern Palace and of exerting an evil influence on the Crown Prince. Subsequently, all of them were found guilty, and executed by decapitation.

To the Emperor this was the only way to eliminate the source of evil in the Eastern Palace. To be sure, it would be a terrible blow to the Prince. But, in the long run, it would save him from disaster.

However, the Prince's reaction to the news was beyond description. His world simply collapsed. He was so grief-stricken that for days he could not think of anything but the tragic death of Chenxin. Over the strong protest of his mentors, he had a temple reared devoted to him. Hanging on its north wall was a portrait of his fallen friend; in the foreground were placed pottery human and animal figures and cart models, as one would find in a tomb. At the Prince's request, his maidservants visited the temple twice a day at dawn and dusk to pay homage to the portrait. Whenever the Prince showed up in person, he would be so overcome by sorrow that he would have a hard time tearing himself away. Inside the Eastern Palace, he had Chenxin's cenotaph created, marked by a tumulus with a stone tablet bearing an epitaph penned by the Prince himself and inscribed in his hand. At the obsequies held at the tomb, the Prince granted his deceased friend posthumous titles.

Meanwhile the Prince began to stay away from court sessions on pretext of illness. Inside the Eastern Palace, he would order 100 or so of his bondservants, clad in barbarian costumes, to perform barbarian songs and dances, and acrobatics such as bamboo-pole jumping, pole-climbing, and pole-balancing. The sound of drumming, horn-blowing, and shouting throughout the night often reached far beyond the walls of the Eastern Palace.

Eventually, he grew tired of singing and dancing, and began to contemplate his next move. He still blamed his austere father for the trouble he found himself in, but there was practically nothing he could do about it. Besides, the main source of his trouble was not Father, but Prince of Wei Li Tai. *That slicker,* he thought, *has done everything possible to make me look bad by comparison and to please Father. And Father has fallen for it. If I get rid of Tai, no one will be able to challenge me any more. Of course, there is my little brother Li Zhi. But at 15, he is way too young to amount to anything.*

The Crown Prince summoned Zhang Sizheng and Hegan Chengji, his bodyguards-cum-confidants, and told them to bump off the smart-ass. But it had to be done in such a way that it could not be traced to them. For their reward, each would receive 200 ounces of gold, plus promotion to at least General-in-chief when he himself eventually ascended the throne. Seeing that neither Zhang or Hegan was eager to take the offer, he warned them sternly, "We are all in on this together. If Li Tai is allowed to live, my chances of becoming Emperor will be ruined! If Li Tai seizes the throne, it is all over."

In the end, Zhang and Hegan verbally accepted this most challenging task, and at the urging of their master, started looking for ways to carry it out.

64. The Prince of Qi

WHEN CROWN PRINCE LI Chengqian counted his rivals, he only included Li Tai and Li Zhi, both born to his own mother, the late Empress Zhangsun. Non-heir sons born to other Imperial consorts were not eligible for succession (at least in theory), thus posed no direct threat to him. One of them was Prince of Qi Li You, who was only slightly younger than Li Tai. Like other Princes, he grew up in Chang'an in a privileged and secluded environment, where he learned archery and equestrian skills and fell in love with hunting.

When he came of age, he took up residence in Licheng (Jinan) in Shandong, where his hunting hobby matured into an obsession. "I can't live for a single day without hunting," he once confessed.

Although Li You was the lord of his domain, the Princedom of Qi, he was constantly subject to the tutelage of his Chief Administrator (*zhangshi*), the court-appointed official charged with his edification and the de facto general manager of the day-to-day affairs of the fiefdom. When the Administrator failed to cure the Prince of his obsession, the Emperor replaced him with Vice Censor-in-chief Quan Wanji, known for his Cato-like incorruptibility. As a leading official of the much-feared Censorate, the central government agency in charge of the moral oversight of officialdom, Quan had impeached many a high-ranking official with frightening zeal.

Upon arrival in Licheng, Quan Wanji resorted to draconian measures to correct the Prince's behavior, forbidding him to travel beyond the city walls, releasing all his hunting hawks and hounds, and barring his two favorite archery companions from entry into the Prince's residence. When Quan later found out that the Prince had secretly called the companions back, he reported it to the Emperor. In response, the Emperor wrote several damning letters to the Prince, chastising him for his lack of remorse.

After much prodding and pleading by Quan, the Prince wrote a self-incriminating reply letter to assure his father of his repentance. Quan journeyed with celerity to Chang'an, carrying the letter with him. Upon reading the letter, the Emperor was delighted. Thankful that His prodigal son was having a change of heart under the guidance of an able mentor, He showered Quan with gifts and accolades. However, in His reply letter to His son, the Emperor continued to play the role of an austere father, giving him another stern warning of the dire consequences if he failed to mend his ways.

To the Prince, the contrasting ways in which the Emperor had treated Quan and himself were grossly unfair. Weeks went by, but he still could not get over the insults he had endured as a result of what he considered Quan's machinations. He began to clash with his mentor with increasing frequency. On several occasions, he even made verbal threats.

For his part, Quan, intrepid though he was, began to worry about his own safety, with good reason. One night a large clod of earth landed in his courtyard with a loud thud. Quan concluded that the two archery companions had made an attempt on his life, and ordered their arrest. He then sent a letter posthaste to Chang'an to report the arrest and impeach the Prince and several dozens of his followers.

Upon reading a report in support of Quan Wanji, submitted by President of the Board of Justice Liu Dewei, who had investigated Quan's claim, the Emperor issued an edict summoning both Quan Wanji and the Prince to Chang'an for questioning. By that time, the Prince was furious beyond control and had started planning for Quan's murder.

While Quan was on his way to the capital, riding in a horse-drawn carriage, the Prince's hatchet man Yan Hongliang and 20 other thugs caught up with him. They attacked him with a barrage of arrows until he resembled a hedgehog. The angry mob then dismembered his body and dumped the parts into a toilet. Thus started Prince Li You's open rebellion against his father.

Under an Imperial edict issued on March 31, 643, Li Shiji, now President of the Board of War, and others, began to mass troops from nine neighboring Prefectures to fight the rebels. The Prince, for his part, mobilized all young men above the age of 14 to join his forces, set up his own administration, and opened the state storehouse to reward his followers. He also ordered a massive forced resettlement of suburban residents into the city proper, in an attempt to get ready for the inevitable clash with the Imperial forces.

Having finally rid himself of his nemesis, the Prince suddenly felt overwhelmed with a sense of euphoria. In the company of his consort (Wei Ting's daughter), his bosom friend Yan Hongliang, and three close followers, he spent night after night in an orgy of eating and drinking to the accompaniment of music. But when his orders to transfer troops from the Princedom's Counties fell on deaf ears, he became antsy; he was even tempted by the thought of abandoning the city and going into the marshes to live like a real outlaw.

Unbeknownst to the Prince and his confederates, in the suburbs, a low-ranking officer called Du Xingmin had already raised a sizeable anti-Li You army. One morning before dawn, they forced their way into the city through a tunnel dug under the wall. Encountering little resistance in the city, they headed for the Prince's residence, where they surrounded the principal house. Trapped inside was the gang of five—Li You, Yan Hongliang, and three of Li's close followers. Having barricaded themselves, using furniture and wooden planks, the gang held out from morning to early afternoon. Then Du Xingmin lost patience.

"Li You, you are no longer an Imperial Prince," shouted Du. "You are nothing but a rebel. Now I am fighting you on behalf of the country, and I don't have any misgivings. If you don't surrender, I am going to burn the house down."

His men piled up dry tree twigs and branches under the windows and on the door, and Du was ready to set the house ablaze.

"Don't!" shouted Li You. "I'll open the door!"

"Do it! Now!"

"But am I going to be safe? How about Yan Hongliang?"

"You'll be safe," said Du Xingmin. "I guarantee you."

After a heated argument inside the house went on for about three minutes, Li You and his men set to work to remove the barricade. As soon as the door opened, a rabble of soldiers rushed in. Some of them seized hold of the Prince; others wrestled Yan Hongliang to the ground, put out his eyes, and left him to die in agonizing pain. Still others captured the three remaining followers, broke their limbs, and dispatched them on the spot.

Having been paraded in front of the main gate of the Princely Administration, Li You was transported to Chang'an in manacles and fetters. While in custody in the Palace Domestic Service (*neishi sheng*), he committed suicide by an Imperial edict. About 40 of his accomplices were caught and most of them were executed. All others involved were let go. The hero of the anti-rebel operation, Du Xingmin, was promoted to Prefect of Ba Prefecture in the southwest.

65. The Prince and the General

FROM HIS SOURCE AT court, Hou Junji heard that he had been the target of a secret investigation. He felt outraged by the Emperor's distrust. He had long held the view that he had paid off his debt of gratitude to Him with the conquest of Tuyuhun and Gaochang. In spite of his total rehabilitation and induction to the hall of fame, he had come to believe that the Emperor was the ultimate obstacle to his success.

Through his son-in-law Helan Chushi, who served in the Personal Guard of the Crown Prince, Hou heard many things about the Prince, whom he regarded as a pampered brat. But to advance his personal goal, Hou was willing to make common cause with him. When he received an invitation to visit the Prince in the Eastern Palace, he accepted it without hesitation.

"What is your biggest worry, Your Highness?" Hou Junji asked inquisitively at the meeting.

"Prince of Wei Li Tai."

"What are you going to do about him?"

"Find a way to outmaneuver him," the Prince answered perfunctorily.

"That may be too late. He has the Institute for Literature under his thumb, and the *Comprehensive Gazetteer* under his belt. What do you have?"

The Prince fell silent, unable to think of anything that might rival his brother's strengths.

"He is even in better physical shape," continued Hou.

"He is fat."

"True, but he doesn't walk with a limp."

"Am I doomed?" asked the Prince, looking disquieted.

"Not really, Your Highness," replied Hou. "But you have to act soon. His allies at court have already started working on your removal. To be sure, the Emperor recently stated He intended to keep you as Crown Prince. However, after Chenxin's death, He may have already changed His mind."

"Can't I ask my supporters at court to counter the influence of Tai's allies?"

"Yes, you can do that. But they are not going to be so effective."

"Why?"

"You don't really have important court advisers who would go out on a limb for you. And it took a long time for the Emperor to change His mind about the Crown Prince. Once it happened, it would be almost impossible for Him to change again."

"There is no way out unless…" the Prince said darkly.

"Unless what, Your Highness?"

"Unless Li Tai disappears."

"You mean removing him?" Hou asked, sounding incredulous.

"Yes."

"I wouldn't do that if I were you. Tai is a very calculating man. He has surrounded himself with guardsmen and attendants."

"What do you think I should do then?" the Prince asked anxiously.

"There is a way out, if you really want to save yourself."

"Yes, I do want to save myself. Please tell me what it is."

"Take the throne yourself!"

The Prince was stunned.

"Look at this," said Hou, as he raised his right hand. "This hand has killed hundreds of enemy soldiers and conquered two states. Now it is ready to serve Your Highness. If we join forces, with your legitimate status as heir and my military background, there is nothing we won't be able to accomplish." Looking the Prince firmly in the eye, Hou asked solemnly, "Are you on board, Your Highness?"

For a long moment, Crown Prince Chengqian gazed into the air without speaking, as he tried to sort out the consequences of an alliance with the general. Then, he answered determinedly, "Yes, I am on board. With your support, I can do it!"

At the end of the conversation, Hou bound himself with an oath to give loyal support to the Prince. The Prince in turn gave him 200 ounces of gold in reward, promising to give more in the future.

CROWN PRINCE LI CHENGQIAN immediately contacted two of his close friends known to have been disaffected with the authorities, Prince Li Yuanchang and Du

He. The Crown Prince and Yuanchang, nephew and uncle, were about the same age. Yuanchang held a grudge against the Emperor for assigning him to a post in the northwest. Du He, Du Ruhui's son, took the Emperor to task for failing to recognize his own talent. Although the Emperor had given him a daughter in marriage, He had never seriously considered appointing him to a decent post. To the pleasant surprise of the Crown Prince, both Li Yuanchang and Du He were enthused about his plan and were anxious to play a part in it. Du He even went out of his way to provide astrological evidence for immediate action.

Two weeks later, the Crown Prince held a secret meeting with a dozen or so supporters, including Li Yuanchang, Du He, Helan Chushi (Hou Junji's son-in-law), Hegan Chengji, and Zhang Sizheng. Before the meeting started, the Crown Prince led his followers in performing a ritual ceremony. First, each one of them bared his left arm and made a small incision in the inside of the forearm with a dagger. He then wiped off the wound with a piece of white silk cloth, burned the stained cloth into ashes, and cast the ashes into a goblet of wine. Raising their goblets high, the followers pledged an oath of allegiance to the Crown Prince, and together they took an oath of loyalty to one another and drank up the wine.

A serious discussion followed on the mission of the group and ways to accomplish it. After a heated debate on how to break the defenses of the Taiji Palace, they settled on an idea proposed by Du He:

First, send a notice in the name of the Eastern Palace to the Taiji Palace that the Crown Prince has come down with a serious disease.

Second, waylay and kill the Emperor when He is on His way to the Eastern Palace.

After the meeting, Li Yuanchang pulled the Crown Prince aside and asked: "The Emperor has a beauty playing the *pipa* for Him. When you ascend the throne, could you allow me to have her?"

"Of course," the Crown Prince answered magnanimously, much to the delight of his young uncle.

When the news of Li You's (Prince of Qi) rebellion reached the Eastern Palace, the Crown Prince became very excited and said to his minions, "My Palace is just 20 paces away from the Taiji Palace. When we take action, we are sure to outdo the Prince of Qi!"

BEFORE THE CROWN PRINCE and his supporters could put their plan into action, they suffered a setback. Hegan Chengji, one of the Crown Prince's right-hand men was implicated in the Li You Rebellion, and thrown into prison in the Court for Judicial Review. For weeks, the Eastern Palace had made no attempt to save him—or so it seemed. Nonetheless, Hegan refused to betray the Crown Prince and his confederates, even under torture. He was holding out the hope that so long as he managed to stay alive, sooner or later, the Prince would come to his rescue. But he was stunned when he was read his sentence—decapitation in the Eastern Market.

Still, he refused to give up hope until the last day. With a cangue on his neck, he was paraded in the Wards, and transported to the Solitary Willow of the Eastern Market to face execution. As the slaughterer's broadsword was about to fall on his neck, Hegan suddenly shrieked at the top of his lungs, "Injustice! Injustice!" Every prisoner knew that this was the last opportunity for appeal, and the supervising officer of the Court of Judicial Review immediately stopped the execution. In the interrogation that followed, Hegan broke his oath of secrecy and loyalty and exposed the sinister scheme of the Crown Prince.

THE EMPEROR LI SHIMIN was devastated. Having already been deeply hurt by the Li You Rebellion, He found Crown Prince Chengqian's secret plot almost unbearable. Over the years, the tremendous effort to educate him must have been totally wasted. To say nothing of the loving care He and the late Empress had lavished on him as parents. Instead of showing his gratitude with action, the Crown Prince wanted to eliminate everyone who he believed stood in his way: his mentor, his brother, and even his father!

Because of the extremely grave nature of the case, the Emperor appointed a special task force to handle it, involving not only the Court of Judicial Review but also the Secretariat and Chancellery. Zhangsun Wuji, Fang Xuanling, Xiao Yu, and Li Shiji all took part in the investigation.

They did not take long to reach a unanimous verdict, "guilty."

With a heavy heart, the Emperor gathered His senior court officials to discuss punishment for the Crown Prince and his co-conspirators.

"What am I going to do with Chengqian?" asked the Emperor.

There was a long silence among the officials until a middle-aged man suggested, "If the Crown Prince is allowed to live out the remainder of his life, Your Majesty will be regarded by the public as a loving parent."

"Any objections?" the Emperor asked as He looked around.

No one answered.

"All right, I will follow this advice, and spare his life. Now, how about Prince Li Yuanchang? Even though he is about Chengqian's age, he belongs to My generation, and I have to call him brother. Can I spare the life of this young brother of mine as well?" Surprisingly, that question elicited strong opposition. The officials were not in a forgiving mood towards Yuanchang and recommended death by suicide (a privilege for men of rank 5 and above and for royalty), which the Emperor approved with great reluctance.

The other close associates of the Crown Prince, including Du He and Zhang Sizheng, were all executed. One exception was Hegan Chengji, who was spared death because of his collaboration.

The mentors were obviously ignorant of the plot, but they failed to remonstrate effectively with the Crown Prince. All except Yu Zhining were disenrolled and reduced to commoner status. Because of his strongly worded memorial Yu had nearly lost his life and was thus considered to have made a sincere effort to change the Crown Prince's behavior.

TO THE EMPEROR'S GRIEF and dismay, a Lingyan Pavilion hall of famer, Hou Junji, was also named as the Crown Prince's confederate. Because of his past merit and close ties with the Emperor, Hou was called to account by the Emperor in the Wude Basilica.

"I want to spare you the humiliation of being tried by a bunch of bureaucrats," said the Emperor. "So I am going to interrogate you in person."

"I am eternally grateful, Your Majesty," said Hou.

"Were you or were you not privy to Li Chengqian's plot against the throne?"

"No, Your Majesty. I did not have close contact with the Crown Prince at all."

The Emperor waved His hand, and a witness was brought in. It was Helan Chushi, Hou's son-in-law. He gave credible testimony to Hou's secret visits to the Eastern Palace. Then, on the Emperor's orders, Hou's incriminating letters to the Crown Prince, in which he repeatedly pledged allegiance to the Eastern Palace, were presented.

Falling down on his knees, Hou confessed to his crime, and asked the Emperor for mercy.

At the end of the interrogation, Hou was marched out.

TWO DAYS LATER THE Emperor saw Hou again.

"I had a meeting with the key officials," said the Emperor. "I told them, 'Junji wants leniency on account of his past merit.' But none of them was willing to grant it. So today, I have come to bid you good-bye." As the Emperor uttered these words, tears streamed down His face.

Hou Junji prostrated himself and sobbed remorsefully. Not only would he lose his life for his crime, his entire family would be extirpated.

On the day of execution, Hou caught the eye of the Supervising General and said, "I started serving the Emperor when He was still a Prince, and conquered two states for Him (Tuyuhun and Gaochang). I want to ask a last favor of Him. Could you communicate my request?"

"Yes, General," answered the Supervising General.

"Please ask Him to spare one of my sons to carry on my surname."

The Supervising General nodded his head and went on to finish the execution.

AFTER HOU'S DEATH, THE Emperor granted his last wish and spared the lives of Hou's wife and one of his sons. Hou was one of His most brilliant generals after all. For obvious reason, the fall of Hou Junji left Him in a foul mood. He was not worried about His own personal safety, because it had never been seriously threatened. He was more concerned about Hou's allies at court and cringed at the thought that the late Wei Zheng, His most trusted adviser and confidant, could be one of them. It was Wei Zheng who had repeatedly recommended Hou for the key post of Vice Premier. Having failed to uncover more evidence in support of His suspicion, the Emperor put it in the back of His mind until He received a report that Wei Zheng had shown his remonstrations to Chu Suiliang, then a Court Diarist. The Emperor was infuriated. These remonstrations contained sensitive information and highly critical remarks, which He had no intention of revealing to the outside world. In a fit of anger, He canceled the marriage agreement between His daughter and Wei Zheng's son, and ordered the felling of Wei Zheng's tombstone. Wei Zheng was now a disgraced man in death.

66. Succession Controversy

WITH THE DOWNFALL OF Li Chengqian, Prince of Wei Li Tai emerged as the frontrunner for Crown Prince. However, despite the promises He had made, the Emperor had refrained from making the official appointment, because the court was divided on the issue.

"For the sake of the country, a new Crown Prince should be appointed immediately," urged Vice President of the Secretariat Cen Wenben.

"Who do you think is the best choice?" asked the Emperor.

"Prince of Wei Li Tai, Your Majesty. Of all the Princes, he is by far the most learned."

"That may be the case," interjected Zhangsun Wuji. "But Prince of Jin Li Zhi is loyal, dutiful, and virtuous. These are more important qualities for a sovereign."

"Excuse me, Wuji," Cen Wenben replied sharply, "but you can't say that Li Tai is devoid of these qualities. Besides, Li Zhi, at 15, obviously lacks experience."

"Experience can be acquired," countered Zhangsun Wuji. "I doubt loyalty, dutifulness, and virtue can be acquired at all once one has entered adulthood."

Thus the debate went on as more officials took sides. The Emperor remained uncommitted until about two weeks later when He summoned a meeting of his senior advisers.

"Yesterday," the Emperor began calmly, "I was with My son Tai, the 'Black Bird.' As I held him close to Me, he told Me affectionately, 'Only today did I really become the son of Your Majesty. This is the day of my rebirth.' He went on to say, 'I have a son and I love him dearly. But before I die I will have him killed so that Li Zhi, my little brother, can succeed to the throne.' Who does not love his son? But Tai is willing to sacrifice his own son for the larger good."

"That means Your Majesty will make Li Tai Crown Prince?" Cen Wenben asked tentatively.

"What if I say yes?" the Emperor asked back.

"With due respect, I may have to disagree with Your Majesty," said Counselor of Remonstration Chu Suiliang, who had been noncommittal so far. "Your Majesty is gravely wrong."

"Oh?" the Emperor asked, surprised.

"Does it make sense," continued Chu, "that, after Your Majesty's passing and Li Tai's ascension to power, he will kill his own son and pass on the throne to his younger brother Li Zhi? In the past, after Chengqian was set up as heir, Your Majesty showered favors on Tai, treating him even better than the Crown Prince himself. That eventually led to Chengqian's disastrous fall. Today, Your Majesty wants to set up Li Tai. However, considering what he is willing to say to get appointed heir, I am very concerned about what he will *really* do to Li Zhi once he is on the throne."

The whole room fell quiet until the Emperor began to weep. The meeting broke up without reaching a decision.

ON THE FOLLOWING DAY, the Emperor saw Prince Li Zhi looking gloomy.

"You look terrible," said the Emperor. "Are you sick?"

"No."

"Are you concerned about your brother Tai becoming Crown Prince?"

"No."

"But why do you look so worried?"

"I am afraid they will go after me because of my relations with Uncle Li Yuanchang."

"Who told you so?"

"My brother Li Tai."

"Don't be silly," said the Emperor reassuringly. "The case of Li Yuanchang was closed a while ago. Nobody will go after you because of him. Besides, knowing him is not a crime."

Prince Li Zhi sighed with relief and said, "Thanks, Your Majesty."

In the evening, the Emperor summoned Li Chengqian, the disgraced ex-Crown Prince, for a talk. The Emperor could not help upbraiding him for conspiring against the throne.

"Your Majesty," Chengqian responded humbly, "what I did was an unpardonable crime. I am truly grateful for Your Majesty's leniency. However, as Crown Prince, what more could I ask for? I became restless only because of Li Tai. Tai did everything possible to bring me into disfavor with Your Majesty so that he could replace me. Your Majesty will fall into his trap if he is allowed to become Crown Prince. I do not think he will ever tolerate me and Zhi when he ascends the throne."

ON THE NEXT MORNING, after a court session in the Liangyi Basilica, the Emperor dismissed all the attendees except His most powerful advisers—Zhangsun Wuji, Fang Xuanling, Li Shiji, and Chu Suiliang—and Prince Li Zhi.

"Look at what My three sons (Li You, Li Chengqian, and Li Tai) and one brother (Li Yuanchang) have done," the Emperor said agitatedly. "The very thought of it drives Me to despair. I don't want to live any more." Suddenly, He threw Himself onto a couch as Zhangsun Wuji and others rushed forward to hold Him down. Unsheathing a dagger, the Emperor made an attempt to stab Himself. Chu Suiliang hurriedly grabbed the hand holding the dagger, and, after a violent scuffle, wrested it from Him; he then handed it over to Li Zhi.

"What does Your Majesty want exactly?" asked Zhangsun Wuji.

"I want to make Li Zhi Crown Prince," answered the Emperor.

"I agree with the Emperor," said Zhangsun. "I would also like to ask permission to behead anybody who opposes it!"

Li Shiji pursed his lips as if he were about to say something, only to change his mind. There was a silence for a few moments. Then the Emperor stood up and said to Li Zhi, "Zhi, your uncle has just made you Crown Prince. You should thank him now."

Li Zhi did obeisance to Zhangsun reverently. And Zhangsun made a gesture to stop him.

"Now then," the Emperor said to all present, "we have chosen Li Zhi as heir. But what about the opinion of other court officials?"

"Your Majesty," answered Zhangsun Wuji, "everyone knows Li Zhi is benevolent and filial, and has been the favorite with virtually all under Heaven for quite a while. There won't be serious opposition to this appointment. I will see to that."

ON THE FOLLOWING MORNING, in the Taiji Basilica, the largest building in Chang'an, were gathered civil officials and military officers of rank 6 and above. In His address, the Emperor brought up the succession issue, saying, "Chengqian is rebellious, and Tai is devious. Neither can be made Crown Prince. Who do you think should be My heir?"

"Prince of Jin Li Zhi," the crowd shouted almost in unison.

Delighted, the Emperor thanked them for their support and commented, "Chengqian is immoral and has to be deposed. But if I set up Li Tai as heir, it would mean that the post of Crown Prince can be acquired through manipulation. Furthermore, if Tai were allowed to assume the throne, neither Chengqian nor Zhi would come to a good end. However, if I set up Li Zhi, both Chengqian and Tai will be safe."

Subsequently, on April 13, Zhenguan 17 (643), Li Zhi's appointment as Crown Prince was officially confirmed with an Imperial edict. To mark the joyous occasion, the Emperor, accompanied by the court officials, mounted the Gatetower of the Chengtian Gate to announce a general amnesty and kick off three days of feasting and festivities.

ANXIOUS THAT THE NEW Crown Prince should avoid his predecessor's fate, the Emperor assembled a powerful team of advisers, with Zhangsun Wuji as Grand Preceptor, Fang Xuanling as Grand Mentor, Xiao Yu as Grand Guardian, and Li Shiji as Supervisor of the Household. A new title was invented for Xiao Yu and Li Shiji, "Equal in Status to Rank Three Officials of the Secretariat and Chancellery," which gave its bearer chief ministerial status.

"These are the best mentors I can find for you, Zhi," the Emperor said to the Prince. "I hope you won't disappoint Me."

"No, I won't."

"After My passing, you will probably go through a difficult period and be challenged by some disgruntled Princes or ambitious senior officers. The support of these four mentors will be crucial for helping you tide over the initial difficulties."

"Yes, Your Majesty," the Prince said reverently. "But are these advisers equally important?"

"To be frank with you, no. The most important person is Li Shiji, the last of the group. He is the only professional soldier of the four and the greatest general on active duty alive. The other great general Li Jing is in retirement. Li Shiji was not a firm supporter of you in the beginning, unlike Uncle Zhangsun Wuji. But he never opposed you. By the way, have you seen him lately?"

"No," answered the Prince. "I heard he has been sick with a serious disease."

"Really? How come I didn't know about that?"

"In fact, he has been on sick leave for about a week."

The Emperor immediately sent for a palace physician, who arrived momentarily with a large medicine bag. Accompanied by the Prince, the physician, and a small entourage of attendants, the Emperor set off in His Imperial carriage for Li Shiji's home in Puning Ward in the northwest part of the city.

The Emperor and His suite first traveled north through the Xuanwu Gate into the Forbidden Park, then turned west and continued for about 10 *li* before turning south to reenter the city through the Guanghua Gate. Since most of the area the cavalcade traversed was inside the heavily guarded Forbidden Park in the northern suburb, there was not much of a need for cordoning off the streets except for the last leg of the journey inside the city.

Li Shiji was lying in his sickbed when the arrival of the Emperor was announced. With the help of two attendants, he slowly walked into the main hall of the principal house, and was overwhelmed by the sight of the Emperor and His Crown Prince, both of whom went up to greet him.

The physician went to work, feeling his pulse, examining his tongue, and prescribing a formula with six ingredients. All were medicinal herbs in his medicine bag except for one, "beard ash."

"That's easy," the Emperor said as He cut off a lock of His beard using a sword.

Li Shiji, moved and awed by this gesture of Imperial munificence, fell on his knees and started kowtowing repeatedly until his forehead was covered with blood.

The Emperor stooped over to help him to his chair and said, "I did this not only for you, but also for the country."

The physician exited the main hall to decoct the medicine in the kitchen, taking with him the Emperor's beard, which he would burn to ashes, while the Emperor continued to talk with Li Shiji. About three quarters of an hour later, the physician came back with a bowl of medical soup. The Emperor took the bowl from him and stirred the soup for several minutes with a wooden spoon to make it cool, before passing it to Li Shiji. As Li Shiji supped up the soup, tears rolled down his face.

"Shiji," the Emperor said affectionately. "At court, nobody is in a better position than you to support My heir after I am gone. Considering the way you treated Li Mi, you should be able to live up to My expectations?"

Li Shiji nodded his head forcefully several times.

IN SPITE OF THE extraordinary lengths to which He went to insure a smooth succession, the Emperor was still worried. Yes, Crown Prince Li Zhi was kind-hearted and benevolent, but he was also sentimental, and weak-minded. It was doubtful that he possessed enough martial spirit to keep the Empire together in times of crisis. Sometimes, the Emperor was tempted by a desire to replace him with a non-heir son, Li Ke, who was similar to Himself in temperament and character. Eventually, only the strenuous opposition of Zhangsun Wuji prevented it from happening.

67. Veritable Record

AS THE EMPEROR GOT older, He became increasingly concerned about His place in history. He was worried that the recent deposition of Li Chengqian would reflect negatively on His legacy.

After His request to read the Court Diary had been rejected, He set his eyes on a different kind of records, the National History (*guoshi*), which was the court-supported history of the current dynasty, based on primary sources including the Court Diaries.

"Why is it that official historians refuse to let their sovereigns see what they have written?" the Emperor asked Fang Xuanling, who was in charge of the National History.

"An official historian is expected to write in such a way that he does not exaggerate the merit of the sovereign, nor does he cover up his evil. So if a sovereign reads the unedited writing of the historian, he will likely be angry."

"But I am not just another sovereign, am I?" said the Emperor. "As Emperor, I would like to read the National History so as to learn the lessons of the past. Why don't you compile the manuscript into a book and present it to Me?"

"But that would be unprecedented under the Tang," said Fang.

"Precedents are set by man, Xuanling. I think I have made Myself clear enough," said the Emperor.

"Yes, Your Majesty, I will see to it," answered Fang resignedly.

THE EMPEROR'S REQUEST, HOWEVER, prompted a memorial from a Counselor of Remonstration. It expressed the concern that later rulers might end up executing historians for writing candid history. The Emperor saw his point. But so great was His curiosity that He chose to ignore it.

Finally, on September 4, 643, the *Veritable Record of the Current Emperor* was presented to the throne. This was a result of Fang Xuanling, Xu Jingzong (Supervising Secretary in the Chancellery), and others working together for months on the manuscript of the National History.

To His surprise, the Emperor found little that was offensive. On the contrary, there were a few cases where history seemed to have been "sanitized." For example, the account of the Xuanwu Gate Incident intentionally withheld vital information about the Emperor's involvement.

Unhappy with this attempt at subterfuge, the Emperor said to Fang Xuanling sternly, "The Duke of Zhou executed Guanshu and banished Caishu, both his brothers, to consolidate the Zhou. It was thoroughly recorded by the ancients. What I did in the

Xuanwu Gate Incident was similar. Why did you and your colleagues try to cover it up?"

Apologizing effusively, Fang took the *Record* back, promising to have it revised for honesty.

Part III

Last War
(643–650)

68. Koguryŏ

AFTER THE TWO DISASTROUS wars against Koguryŏ in 612 and 613, Emperor Yang of the Sui launched a third one in 614, which ended in a whimper. The Tang condemned Emperor Yang's military adventurism, and maintained peaceful relations with Koguryŏ, which in turn recognized the Tang's superior status and periodically sent tributary missions to Chang'an. However, several thorny issues between the two countries remained unresolved. The most controversial one concerned Sui expatriates residing in Koguryŏ.

In the autumn of Zhenguan 15 (641), the Emperor dispatched a fact-finding mission to Koguryŏ, headed by Chen Dade, a middle-ranking official. While there, he visited more than half a dozen cities, where he came across quite a few quondam subjects of the Sui, including both deserters and captives. Many of them had married Koguryŏ women and had children with them. But they still missed friends and relatives in their hometowns or home villages now under Tang rule. Chen estimated (with much exaggeration) that as many as one half of the inhabitants in those cities were from the Sui.

Upon return, Chen Dade gave a briefing at the Emperor's request on September 20, 641.

"Recently, Koguryŏ has increased contact with her neighboring states," said Chen. "This, in my view, is driven by a growing fear of the Tang following the fall of Gaochang."

"Judging by your report, Koguryŏ now seems to be an easy target," responded the Emperor.

"Yes, Your Majesty," Chen said approvingly.

"The land now known as Koguryŏ used to be part of the Four Commanderies of the Han. That at least gives us some justification for action. We could start with an attack on Liaodong (in Liaoning) with a force of several tens of thousand men. That would compel Pyongyang to come to its rescue with most of its troops. We would then launch from Donglai (in Shandong) another expedition to take Pyongyang itself from the sea. With this joint land-and-sea offensive, we could take the entire country without difficulty."

"That is a brilliant idea, Your Majesty," echoed Chen.

"But the Prefectures and Counties in Shandong are not yet fully recovered from the ravages of the past Wars. I don't want to burden the people with another one."

So the Koguryŏ issue was put on the backburner for more than a year. Then the Emperor received a report from Prefect of Ying Prefecture Zhang Jian on a palace revolution in Koguryŏ. The gist of it is as follows:

Recently, when King Wu and his supporters at court were planning to eliminate his most powerful minister, Quan Gaisuwen, the latter got wind of the plan. At a military parade in the south of Pyongyang, Quan attacked and killed the key ministers and their associates. He then rushed to the Palace, where he killed the King in person and dumped his body in a ditch after dismembering it. Placing the late King's nephew Zang on the throne, Quan himself served as Grand Chancellor with dictatorial power.

Almost at the same time the Emperor received a request filed by Prefect of Bo Prefecture Pei Xingzhuang for a punitive campaign.

The report and request from the frontier sparked a heated debate among the Emperor's pro-war and anti-war advisers. After a careful assessment of the situation, the Emperor sided with the latter, saying, "King Wu of Koguryŏ had paid tribute to us continuously before he was murdered. I was deeply saddened by his death. But to invade a country when she is in chaos is not the noble way even if one can succeed. Furthermore, Shandong still worries Me."

69. Prelude to Conflict

IN THE ENSUING TWO years, all was quiet on the Tang-Koguryŏ border. Then on October 21, 643, a Silla emissary arrived in Chang'an to report a disturbing new development. Paekche, supported by Koguryŏ, had launched a massive invasion of Silla and taken more than 40 of her cities.

The Emperor immediately dispatched an emissary to Koguryŏ with an Imperial edict that said, "Silla is a faithful tributary state with her hostages at the Tang court. Koguryŏ and Paekche must stop military action against her. Or else the Tang will launch an expedition against Koguryŏ in the following year."

By the time the Tang emissary arrived in Koguryŏ, she had already conquered two Silla cities. To the edict, the Grand Chancellor of Koguryŏ responded, "In the past, at the time when the Sui invaded our country, the Silla seized from us an area of 500 *li* across. They have not offered to return it. I am afraid I can't stop the military action."

The emissary replied, "How can you sort out things that happened such a long time ago? Take those cities in Liaodong for example. They were originally under the Commanderies and Counties of the Central Kingdom. We are not asking to have them back. How can Koguryŏ reclaim her lost land from Silla?"

But the Grand Chancellor refused to listen.

The unflattering report the emissary submitted to the throne in March 644 threw into doubt the Emperor's pacifist policy.

At a Chief Ministers' Council meeting, the Emperor said, "Quan Gaisuwen committed regicide against his sovereign, murdered his ministers, and abused his people. Recently, he defied My edict and invaded his neighboring state. We have no choice but to launch a punitive expedition against him. What do you think?"

Chu Suiliang was the first to speak, "Your Majesty has pacified the Central Plain, subdued the barbarians in the Four Quarters, and extended His authority to all under Heaven. If the goal of this expedition across the sea against these small-time barbarians can be accomplished within a short span of time, there is no reason against it. But if it drags on, Your Majesty's authority will be eroded. In anger Your Majesty will probably send more troops. By then, success or failure will be hard to predict."

"Suiliang, cut to the chase. You are against the expedition, aren't you?"
"Yes, Your Majesty. I am against it."
"I would like to say something, Your Majesty," Li Shiji interposed. "In the past, when the Xueyantuo invaded our lands, Your Majesty wanted to launch a punitive campaign but stopped short when opposed by Wei Zheng. Even today, the Xueyantuo are still caus-

ing trouble. If we followed Your Majesty's strategy then, the northern frontier would have been safe today."

"Wei Zheng misled Me on Xueyantuo as he did on Hou Junji," responded the Emperor. "Later I regretted I did not take on Xueyantuo. Still, I didn't want to talk about it for fear it might discourage people from giving good advice. Anyhow, Shiji, you are in favor of fighting the Koguryŏ?"

"Beyond a shadow of a doubt, Your Majesty."

"Great. We will then launch the expedition. And I will lead it in person."

"May I say something, Your Majesty?" requested Chu Suiliang.

"Yes?"

"The world can be likened to a human body with the Two Capitals as the heart and the Prefectures and Counties as the arms and legs. These barbarians, however, lie outside the realm, and are not an essential part of the body at all. Even though the Koguryŏ deserve to be punished for their crime, the expedition only needs two or three top generals with an army of 40 to 50 thousands. If Your Majesty gives up the protection of the walled and moated metropolis and braves the dangers of land and sea, and something happens, what, then, will become of the young Crown Prince?"

"Concerning My personal safety," answered the Emperor, "you don't have to worry. I will be safe so long as we can be sure of victory. In war, everything is about timing. Now is the perfect timing for the conquest of Koguryŏ. Quan Gaisuwen has abused his Kings and people, and the Koguryŏ are dying to be liberated."

Thus the Tang Empire was set on a course of war with Koguryŏ.

IN AUGUST, ZHENGUAN 18 (644), war preparations were underway. Chief of the Directorate for the Palace Buildings Yan Lide (brother of Liben, the famous painter) went to north Jiangxi, where he started building 400 transports for shipping grain and military stores. Tens of thousands of Tang troops from Ying and You Prefectures were deployed in Liaodong, where they were joined by the Qidan, Xi, and Mohe auxiliaries. Grain would be shipped from Hebei to the Liaodong front, and from Henan to the naval base in northeast Shandong.

On October 30, a Koguryŏ delegation arrived, sent by the Grand Chancellor himself, bringing with it a piece of "white gold" (platinum) as tribute to the Tang.

"The Koguryŏ have quailed," said the Emperor to Chu Suiliang. "What do you think?"

"Your Majesty, white gold is extremely rare among tributary goods from neighboring states. The fact that the Koguryŏ have brought such a large piece as tribute shows they want to avoid war. Personally, I am not very much in favor of this war, but I am suspicious of the Grand Chancellor's intentions. This reminds me of the Quadripod of Gao in Spring and Autumn times."

"The gift the state of Song used to bribe the state of Lu with."

"The state of Song had stolen it from the state of Gao in the first place. Similarly, the Koguryŏ want to use bribery to stop us from taking action."

"You think I should ignore it?"

"Yes, Your Majesty."

"I am with you on that one."

On the morrow, at the meeting with the Koguryŏ emissary and his associates, the Emperor said sternly, "You all served King Wu as his ranked officials. But after the King's murder, you all have failed to revenge it. Now you want to represent the Chancellor the regicide himself? No crime is greater than this!"

The Koguryŏ made an attempt to defend themselves. But the Emperor did not find it convincing. So instead of treating them as foreign visitors, He ordered their incarceration in the Court of Judicial Review.

ON DECEMBER 28, THE Emperor while still in Luoyang made two crucial appointments—President of the Board of Justice Zhang Liang as Commander-in-chief of Pyongyang Circle, and Li Shiji as Commander-in-chief of Liaodong Circle. The war would start in the third month (mostly April) of Zhenguan 19 (645) when winter was coming to an end. Zhang Liang was to lead a force of 40,000 in 500 transports to cross the sea from Lai Prefecture in Shandong to fall on Pyongyang. Li Shiji was to lead 60,000 infantry and cavalry to invade Liaodong.

Meanwhile a nationwide campaign was underway to recruit new soldiers; in Chang'an and Luoyang alone, 3,000 men were newly enlisted in the army. There was no lack of young men offering their services; and many subjects, official and nonofficial, voluntarily provided logistical support. But government resources had to be tapped into, and taxes and use of corvée labor increased. Concerned with the economic burden on the populace, the Emperor issued an edict that urged local officials not to waste money on Himself and His entourage when they were on their way to Liaodong. The local governments subsequently reduced their budgets for such expenses by half.

Chu Suiliang reminded the Emperor of another problem. "How do we," said he, "make it clear that this campaign is different from the Wars launched by Emperor Yang? They all ended in disaster and were in part responsible for the downfall of the Sui dynasty."

In response, the Emperor wrote a rescript, which read:

At the time of the Wars of Daye 8 and Daye 9, the Sui Emperor was despotic and His people were rebellious, whereas the Koguryŏ King was benevolent and his people united. To fight a united enemy with an army bent on rebellion was bound to fail. Today, we are bound to succeed for the following five reasons: first, we greatly outnumber them; second, we are just while they are not; third, our people are at peace whereas theirs are rebellious;

fourth, we are well rested while they are fatigued; and fifth, our subjects are joyous while theirs are discontented. With these five reasons, how can we not succeed?

Handing the document to Chu, the Emperor asked, "What do you think?"

Upon reading it, Chu Suiliang said, "Excellent, Your Majesty! It would go a long a way toward addressing the image problem." Thereupon he had it disseminated among the military and civilians.

LIKE MOST OFFICIALS, CHU Suiliang was genuinely pleased with the rescript. But he was soon alarmed by another not entirely unrelated problem. Tens of thousands of Tujue had recently been settled, with the court's approval, in the Ordos area south of the Yellow River in central Inner Mongolia. They had been under the command of the Caucasian-looking Silibi Khan (also known as Li Simo), a friendly Tujue leader. At the request of the Emperor, Silibi had led them north to contain the growing threat of the Xueyantuo. But the Tujue masses had subsequently abandoned their leader and gone south. Mortified by his failure, Silibi had returned to Chang'an, where he now served as General of the Right Martial Guard.

"When Your Majesty," said Chu, "is away in Liaodong, the presence of so many Tujue south of the Yellow River may pose a direct threat to Chang'an. It would be better if Your Majesty would stay in Luoyang and send a general to lead the expedition against Koguryŏ instead."

"You still want Me to stay, eh? But the barbarians are people too. They are no different from the people of the Central Kingdom. A sovereign should stop distrusting non-Han people and should instead worry about failure to extend his virtuous grace. If there is enough virtuous grace, the barbarians and the Han can become one family. If there is too much distrust, even blood relatives become sworn enemies. We all know that Emperor Yang was immoral and had long lost popular support. During His Liaodong campaigns, people cut off their hands and feet to avoid conscription, and Yang Xuangan rebelled in Liyang. These were not caused by the barbarians!

"In our expeditionary army today, all new recruits are volunteers. In fact, each time we want ten recruits 100 men will show up. It is those who have failed to enlist who are angry and depressed. What a contrast with the Wars of Emperor Yang! As for those Tujue, we went to their rescue at a time when they were weak and vulnerable. They will be deeply grateful; and I can assure you they will not make trouble."

70. Master Xuanzang

AFTER AN ABSENCE FROM China for more than 17 years, Master Xuanzang with his party crossed the border into the northwest in late Zhenguan 18 (644) and reached the western suburb of Chang'an on February 2, Zhenguan 19 (645). He was greeted by deputies of Vicegerent Fang Xuanling. By then the Emperor had already left for Luoyang.

As Xuanzang and his party were approaching the city proper, throngs of Chang'an residents streamed out to watch them. A large crowd followed the Master all the way to the Duting Post House in Tonghua Ward west of Zhuquemen Avenue, just one Ward away from the Imperial City.

On the following morning, in the spacious square south of the Zhuque Gate (the southern main entrance of the Imperial City), Master Xuanzang displayed the treasures—carried on the backs of 20 horses—he had brought back from the Subcontinent: 150 Buddhist relics (called *sarira*), several Buddhist statues, and 657 Buddhist works on palm leaf. After the display was over, the precious items were carefully packed and transported by a cavalcade of carriages fitted with silk baldachins to the Hongfu Monastery. Hundreds of Chang'an monks dressed in their best cassocks poured into the streets to escort the carriages, carrying canopies, flags, and jeweled tents with them. Some of them walked in a single file at the head of the procession while melodiously chanting sutras in Sanskrit. Others walked in the rear, swinging thuribles with burning incense that filled the air with a pungent, fragrant aroma.

From the Zhuque Gate, the procession turned west and traveled two Wards before turning north to reach Xiude Ward and the Hongfu Monastery therein. Along the way a multitude of Chang'an residents—court and capital officials, and ordinary subjects—lined the streets several rows deep to pay homage, and to bear witness to this historic moment.

AFTER A BRIEF STAY in Chang'an, Xuanzang journeyed further east to Luoyang, where he was granted an audience in the Yiluan Basilica of the Palace City on the afternoon of March 3.

As Xuanzang entered the audience hall, the Emperor, accompanied by His close advisers, went up to give him a warm welcome. After host and guest sat down, the Emperor asked somewhat reproachfully, "Why didn't you report to the authorities when you set off on your journey to the West?"

"Indeed, I am guilty of unauthorized travel," answered Xuanzang. "Before my departure, I made several requests for permission to travel. They were all rejected, probably because I was too insignificant. But my desire to learn about the Law (Dharma) was so strong that I set off on my own without official permission. Now I am fearful of the consequences."

"You don't have to worry about unauthorized travel," the Emperor said reassuringly. "In fact, I greatly appreciate the endeavor you undertook as an ordained cleric to follow your own destiny in quest of the Law with the noble aim of benefiting the people." Pausing briefly, He continued, "Out of curiosity, I would like to know how you survived the grueling journeys—across the desserts, over the mountains, and through the waterless valleys; and how you dealt with different local customs, mores, and beliefs."

"I heard," said Xuanzang, "that for those who travel on strong wind the Celestial Pond is not far; for those who ride on dragon ships sailing through the billows is not difficult. Your Majesty has dominated the universe and cleared the Four Seas with virtue that spreads to the Nine Provinces, with benevolence that extends to the Eight Regions, with a simple style that reaches the sun-scorched far south, and with an august authority that prevails over lands west of the Pamirs. Whenever those tribal chieftains saw a high-flying bird from the east, they suspected it was a creature from the superior state (China). So they treated the bird with great respect. Let alone yours truly, who was a proper human being with his round head and square feet, and who had been edified by Your Majesty. Thanks to the celestial authority, I had not encountered much hardship on my way thither and hither."

After thanking him for his complimentary remarks, the Emperor directed His attention to the foreign lands the Master had visited, especially those that lay to the west of the Pamirs and in India—their social customs, produce, and institutions, the monuments left by King Asoka, and the holy sites associated with the Buddha. Xuanzang answered each one of them with great erudition and lucidity.

"This is really exciting," said the Emperor to His advisers. "Master Xuanzang has far surpassed Zhang Qian in his knowledge of the Western Regions. Most of the information he has acquired can't be found either in the *Grand Scribe's Records* by Sima Qian or the *Book of the Han* by Ban Gu."

Sima and Ban were the leading historians of the Western and Eastern Han dynasties. They provided the earliest detailed accounts of the Western Regions based extensively on the reports of the Han emissary Zhang Qian.

"In the past," the Emperor resumed, "Former Qin Emperor Fu Jian spoke highly of Dao'an, and the entire court worshipped him. Today Master Xuanzang is far more knowledgeable than Dao'an."

"What Your Majesty has said is true indeed," chimed in Zhangsun Wuji. "I have read about Dao'an in the *Annals of the Thirty States*. No doubt, Dao'an was a monk of noble character and profound knowledge. But he lived in an age when Buddhism had not been in China for long and when there were not many sutras and treatises in circulation. Dao'an did some research, but it was quite limited. And he cannot be compared with Master Xuanzang when it comes to exhaustively studying the origins of various Buddhist doctrines and investigating Buddhist monuments."

"I completely agree," said the Emperor. Turning to Xuanzang, He continued, "You can write a book on those faraway kingdoms, and their Buddhist monuments."

"Yes, Your Majesty," Xuanzang said in agreement.

"Apparently, you are not only a first-rate Buddhist monk and a great scholar, but are possessed of the talent of an administrator. Why don't you quit the monastic way of life and join us? You can head a central government agency."

"Thanks, Your Majesty," said Xuanzang, tensing up. "Since I devoted myself to the Buddha as a young man, I have been immersed in the study of Buddhist doctrines, of which I am a firm believer. But I have no knowledge of the Confucian Teaching at all. If I were laicized to engage in secular work, I would feel like a boat out of water traveling on land. I would become useless, and my whole being would begin to fester. On the other hand, it will be my great fortune if I am allowed to dedicate my entire life to Buddhism so as to repay my debt to my country."

"I won't insist," the Emperor said, detecting a determination in the Master's voice, "if you are not so inclined."

Noticing the sun was already setting, Zhangsun Wuji said to the Emperor, "Master Xuanzang is staying in the Court for Tributaries. If he leaves late he probably won't be able to make it back before dark."

"I didn't realize it is getting late," said the Emperor. "Master Xuanzang, I find today's talk most fascinating. We must continue some other time. How about this: you come with Me on the expedition? You can observe the local customs and have a talk with Me every now and then."

"Well," replied Xuanzang, "during my journey to distant places, I caught a disease, and I am still troubled by it. I am afraid, I am not in a position to accompany Your Majesty."

"Since you have visited the remotest places, this trip to Liaodong should be like a picnic," said the Emperor.

"Well," said Xuanzang, knitting his brows, "when Your Majesty leads the Six Armies on the expedition to penalize the rebellious state and its renegade ministers, Your Majesty is bound to score a victory of Muye and achieve a triumph of Kunyang. However, I, as an ordained monk, will not be able to contribute anything to the combat-effectiveness of the army. On the contrary, I will only add to the expenses along the way. Moreover, the Buddhist discipline, the Vinaya, prevents us from watching a battle in action—this is something I dare not withhold from Your Majesty. May Heaven have compassion on me so that I will be fortunate enough not to go." Of the two historic battles he cited—Muye and Kunyang, the first one led to the fall of Shang and the rise of Zhou in antiquity, and the second one preceded the fall of the Xin and paved the way for the rise of the Eastern Han.

"If you can't join Me on the expedition, that is fine," the Emperor said, seeing no point in pressuring the Master on the issue. He then asked, "Do you have any requests?"

"As a matter of fact, yes, Your Majesty," answered Xuanzang, more calmly. "I have brought with me more than 600 works in Sanskrit. They have yet to be translated. In the

Song Mountains not far from here there is the Shaolin Monastery set up by Emperor Xiaowen of the Northern Wei."

"More than 100 years old," interjected the Emperor.

"Yes, Your Majesty. Far away from the hustle and bustle of city life, it offers an extremely quiet environment. Bodhiruci from North India did his translation work there under the Northern Wei. By Your Majesty's leave, I hope to be able to work there as well."

"Well," said the Emperor, "you don't have to live in the mountains. After you left for the Western Regions, I set up the Hongfu Monastery in Chang'an in memory of My mother Empress Dowager Dou. It has a meditation courtyard, which is extremely quiet. You can do your work there."

"Thanks, Your Majesty. Here is another: When I returned from the West, the multitude in Chang'an crowded around to watch. It was quite a circus. They did not break any laws, but they made it hard for me to do my work. I wonder if some gate-keepers can be posted in my monastery to prevent people from trespassing."

"Absolutely. This is a necessary protective measure," the Emperor said smilingly. "Once you are back in Chang'an, for whatever you need, just contact Fang Xuanling."

With a profusion of thanks, Xuanzang took leave of the Emperor.

71. Off to War

ON MARCH 14, THE Tang expeditionary armies moved out of Luoyang and went on the long trek north. Along the way, the Emperor made a point of visiting sick soldiers, making arrangements for them to stay behind for treatment when necessary. For fear of disturbing the local communities, He instructed His eunuch officers to stop serving fresh vegetables. And His meals now only consisted of preserved meat and rice.

The soldiers were in high morale, as were the "volunteers"—unenlisted men organized into "private" units that followed the regulars. Some of them said that they did this "not for money nor for official titles but for an opportunity to serve the Emperor in Liaodong."

ON APRIL 10, THE Emperor arrived in Dingzhou, the seat of Ding Prefecture. Prior to departure for the Liaodong front, He said to the Crown Prince, "During My absence, I want you to remember three points: first, try to promote the worthy and stay away from the unworthy; second, reward the good and penalize the evil; and third, do everything for the public good, but never for self-interest. So long as..."

By then Crown Prince was already in a flood of tears.

"What's matter with you, My son?" said the Emperor, greatly annoyed. "Don't be such a crybaby!"

"I am afraid," the Prince blubbered out, "I won't be able to see Your Majesty again."

"Don't be silly. My time has not come yet."

"I fear I will lose my way when Your Majesty is not by my side."

"Now you will have a perfect opportunity to prove your worth to all under Heaven. You should welcome it! Besides, you will not be alone. Fang Xuanling is now in Chang'an, and both Li Shiji and Chu Suiliang are coming with Me. But Grand Mentor Gao Shilian, Uncle Wuji's stepfather, is staying with you in Dingzhou. You can always consult him on important matters. Do you understand?"

The Prince nodded his head.

An attendant came rushing with a sealed envelope. The Emperor sent the Prince away. Upon opening the envelope, He found a letter from Fang Xuanling and a report by an unknown informant. In the letter, Fang requested His Majesty to assess the enclosed report that accused Fang of sedition. Infuriated by the letter and the report, the Emperor asked rhetorically, "Didn't I make Myself clear that Fang as Vicegerent in Chang'an doesn't have to refer these cases to Me?"

Handing the letter and report to Chu Suiliang, the Emperor said, "Now, write down the punishment for the informant: *execution by severing the torso.*"

"Your Majesty," said Chu Suiliang. "Severing the torso—is that not a cruel punishment?"

"Yes. But the informant has committed a heinous crime: reviling a honest court official."

"But the newly revised Tang Code does not contain that particular form of punishment."

"It does contain 'execution,' doesn't it? Severing the torso is a form of execution. Furthermore, as Emperor, I have some latitude in interpreting the law, don't I?"

Chu Suiliang did not know how to answer. The Emperor then had an edict created bearing the Imperial seal and sent to Fang Xuanling in Chang'an, in which He said, "You must have more self-confidence. From this day forward, you will have the exclusive power to deal with cases like this."

THE NEXT MORNING, THE Prince and his associates rode out to see Him off. The Emperor was riding a white horse, with a bow and a quiver full of arrows slung over His shoulder, and an oilcloth raincoat secured to His saddle. The rising sun accentuated the streaks of grey in His hair, which filled the Prince with gloom.

After father and son rode along silently for a while, the Emperor said, "Zhi, My son, it is not going to take very long." Pointing to the yellow silk robe He was wearing, He continued, "I won't change this robe until the campaign is over. That's a promise." The Emperor then bid good-bye to the Prince and rode away.

As the image of his father going to war receded into the distance, the Prince could no longer restrain his tears.

IN THE PREPARATORY STAGE of the Koguryŏ War, a civil official known as Wei Ting played a crucial role. It all started on August 30, Zhenguan 18 (644), when he was summoned to the Taiji Palace.

"I am appointing you as Grain Transportation Commissioner," said the Emperor to Wei. "The Liao River extends about 2,000 *li* beyond You Prefecture. In that area there are no Tang Prefectures and Counties, nor are there grain suppliers. Thus it is essential to store up enough grain locally."

"Yes, Your Majesty," said Wei Ting.

"You are temporarily relieved of your duties as Director of the Court of State Sacrifices. But your new assignment is far more important. You will assume administrative authority over all the Hebei Prefectures. I am also appointing a deputy commissioner to assist you. Moreover, you can select 10 rank-4 officers as branch commissioners. Two hundred warriors and 200 horses will be placed at your disposal immediately."

The Emperor then bestowed upon him His own sable coat, and two fast steeds from the Palace stable. Wei Ting had banked on Li Tai in the recent succession struggle. Instead of punishing him, the Emperor, after the struggle was over, decided to tap into his organizational skills. The Emperor's trust in Wei Ting was based on the latter's excellent track record. There were marriage ties between the Li and Wei families—His son Prince of Qi Li You was the husband of Wei's daughter. But after Li You's ignoble suicide, those ties were no longer meaningful.

ON ARRIVING IN YOU Prefecture in late Zhenguan 18 (644), Wei Ting spent a considerable amount of local government money to build a large number of transports, which he then used to ship grain northwards by water. Not long afterwards, a bone-chilling cold descended on the area. It was then that he was informed by one of his deputies that much of the route to the north beyond Lusitai—a place about 800 *li* north of Youzhou—was clogged and unnavigable.

"Obviously, it will be difficult to make any progress under these conditions," said Wei Ting to his deputy.

"If not impossible," echoed the deputy.

"Are there storage facilities near Lusitai?"

"Yes. There are some souterrains that can be used for storage."

"Good. Let's have future shipments of grain sent to Lusitai. Next spring, as soon as it gets warm, we will start working on the river route and ship the grain further north."

"Yes, Commissioner."

Wei Ting sent a report to Chang'an to explain the situation, and ordered all the transports—there would be more than 600 of them—to unload their shipments at the new destination. Eventually, there was not much left to do except to hold frequent drinking parties for his men, as they waited patiently for the long winter to pass.

Wei Ting's report—when it reached the Palace—sent the Emperor into a towering rage. In reply, He issued a scathing edict, which said, "In war, one would rather have speed and inferior quality than slowness and superior quality. I want to start a major operation in the 19th year (645), but you talk about completing the shipment of grain in Zhenguan 20 (646). It does not make sense at all!" When an investigation confirmed Wei's incompetence, the Emperor replaced him with Li Daoyu, Vice Chief of the Directorate for the Palace Buildings.

After his dismissal from office, Wei Ting was brought back to Luoyang in chains, where he was disenrolled. Later, he was set free and allowed to follow the Emperor on the expedition, but only as a commoner.

Because of the delay caused by Wei Ting, the Emperor had lost at least a month's valuable time. It was not until May 1, 645, that the Tang forces reached key outposts on the front.

72. Liaodong City

IN THE INITIAL PHASE, the Koguryŏ War went very well for the Tang. By early June, they had captured several Koguryŏ cities, including Gaimou City in the west, and Beisha City in the east. They then moved forward into the suburbs of Liaodong City. However, Tang Commander-in-chief Li Shiji did not launch an attack on the city proper. He knew very well that Liaodong City would not be an easy target, having withstood the ferocious attack by Emperor Yang's mighty army 32 years before. Instead he was waiting for the Emperor's reinforcements.

The sudden approach of a numerous Koguryŏ rescue force—40,000 infantry and cavalry—on June 7, complicated the situation. Unlike the defenders of the well-fortified city, who could easily hold a large enemy force at bay, the rescue force was outside the city's protective walls and was thus vulnerable to attack.

Li Shij isummoned a war council, at which his second-in-command General Li Daozong urged an immediate attack on the enemies before they got a foothold.

"But we have only 4,000 cavalry," cautioned a Commandant. "The enemies have a much larger army. We should wait for the Emperor's troops."

"Their numerical strength is also their weakness," said Li Daozong. "It causes them to underestimate us. After a long-distance march they must be exhausted and can be worsted with a surprise attack."

In the end, Li Shiji sided with Li Daozong.

A fierce assault on the Koguryŏ rescue force ensued, with Courageous Commandant Ma Wenju leading the charge, cutting a swath into their ranks outside the city. Taken aback, the Koguryŏ were soon on the verge of collapse. But the Tang detachment commanded by Area Commander Zhang Junyi failed to push through the enemy flank, and the Koguryŏ rallied for a counterattack and reversed the battle. General Li Daozong ordered a hasty retreat. Climbing onto a hilltop, he closely observed enemy troop movements for a while. It turned out that the Koguryŏ counterattack was poorly organized and soon lost momentum. The Tang army then mounted another assault, in which Li Daozong led the charge with a small troop of cavalry, and Li Shiji followed with the main force of horse and foot. Before long, the Koguryŏ were put to rout.

STARTING OFF FROM YOUZHOU on May 14, the Emperor and His troops crossed the Liao River Bridge into the war zone on June 9. He then issued an order, "Burn the Bridge."

"Do I understand that Your Majesty wants to destroy the Bridge?" asked Zhangsun Wuji, who could not believe his ears.

"Yes."

"Your Majesty, to fight with one's back to a bridgeless river is considered taboo in the *Art of War*," responded Zhangsun Wuji.

"I know. But what's more important here is another principle in the *Art of War*: he who is placed in a position of death shall live. You still remember the Battle of Jingxing fought by Han Xin more than 800 years ago? He used the same strategy and defeated a much larger army." Han Xin under Liu Bang was the greatest general in a civil war that gave rise to the Han dynasty. The Battle of Jingxing (204 BCE) was crucial in tipping the balance of power in favor of Liu Bang against his rival.

"All right," said Zhangsun, "I will make sure the order is carried out immediately."

Having arrived in Liaodong, the Emperor bivouacked His troops in Mount Mashou. At the first meeting He held with His commanding and middle-ranking officers the Emperor rewarded Li Daozong for bravery, promoted Ma Wenju, and ordered the decapitation of Area Commander Zhang Junyi for his failure on the battlefield.

The next morning, under the escort of several hundred cavalry, the Emperor rode to the Liaodong City front to survey its fortifications. When He saw Tang soldiers were busy at work filling sections of the moat outside the city, the Emperor, throwing off His robe, loaded two bags of soil on the back of His horse and led him to the bank of the moat. And His attendants rushed to join Him.

AS THE EMPEROR WAS still deploying troops under His direct command to environ Liaodong, a day-and-night general assault, amid shouting and howling, began.

For days, the Koguryŏ garrison soldiers held their own. Then came June 16 when there was a strong southerly gale early in the morning. The Emperor saw His chance, and ordered the elite commandos into action. With the aid of long bamboo vaulting poles, some of them sprang onto the city wall in the southwest corner to attack the defenders while others engaged in storming the gatetower. Soon a fire that started in the arch of the gatetower got out of control, spreading into the city proper. A massive number of Tang troops climbed over the wall or forced their way through the gate. Within hours, the Koguryŏ were thoroughly defeated with about 10,000 killed and another 10,000 captured. The 40,000 surviving residents suddenly found themselves at the mercy of the Emperor Li Shimin and His generals.

"WHAT IS GOING TO happen to Liaodong City, Your Majesty?" Chu Suiliang asked the next day.

"We will make it into the seat of a new administrative area, Liao Prefecture," the Emperor answered with decision.

"But the declared aim of this War was to penalize those rebellious ministers and revenge the death of the Koguryŏ King."

"You are absolutely right about that. But Liaodong City is strategically too important to be left in the hands of the Koguryŏ. Furthermore, the Koguryŏ are sedentary farmers and their officials and scholars read the Confucian classics. They are not like the true barbarians of the steppes, and can be easily governed."

"I see, Your Majesty," said Chu Suiliang, who saw no point in challenging Him.

Thus, the newly conquered Liaodong area was absorbed into the Tang administrative network. Similarly, the Gaimou area was converted to Gai Prefecture, with Gaimou City as its seat.

HAVING LEFT A TANG garrison to guard Liaodong, the Emperor and His troops moved northeast to lay siege to Baiyan City. A barrage of arrows kept the Tang troops from approaching the city walls. The defenders of Baiyan seemed to have learned the lesson of Liaodong.

The initial attack by the Tang army did not go as planned, and had to be called off when the commanding officer, General Silibi (Li Simo), was wounded in the leg. The Emperor, with a few attendants, rushed to his tent to see him. As Silibi struggled to raise his upper body on the pallet, the Emperor hastened to hold him by the arm, and gently guided him down. The Emperor then knelt down besides the patient, undid the dressing on his leg, and sucked on the wound, drawing out reddish pus into His mouth, before spitting it out onto the dirt floor. As He did so, tears rolled down Silibi's cheeks, and there was not a single dry eye in the tent.

Before the Tang army could rally for another attack, a Koguryŏ rescue force of more than 10,000 strong arrived from neighboring Wugu City. The Tang-Tiele general Qibiheli led 800 mostly Tujue cavalry to meet the enemies head-on. Cut off from his comrades, Qibiheli soon found himself surrounded. In spite of his repeated efforts, he failed to break through the enemy lines, and in the process had sustained several spear wounds in the back. On the Emperor's orders, a cavalry commando fought his way through and rescued him. Having stayed in his tent long enough to have his wounds dressed, Qibiheli returned to the battle to fight more vigorously until the Tang forces gained the upper hand.

BY JUNE 29, THE Koguryŏ Commander of the garrison, Sun Daiyin, had enough. He sent a secret emissary to negotiate the terms of surrender.

"The Commander wants to surrender, but there are those who won't follow his lead," said the emissary.

"First, take a few Tang banners with you," said the Emperor. "Set them up on the city walls if you really want to surrender. Others will lay down their arms."

As soon as the emissary left, Li Shiji said abruptly, "Your Majesty, now the city is just about to fall. Why accept the surrender? That will disappoint the troops. One of the reasons they braved the arrows and risked death to fight the enemies is their greed for booty."

"What you said is true," said the Emperor. "But I can't bear seeing innocent residents killed and their wives and daughters abducted. That's why I want you to spare this city."

But Li Shiji then raised a thorny issue: how to recompense his troops without war spoils. A heated discussion followed. Li Shiji finally dropped his opposition after the Emperor pledged to open the state storehouse to reward the meritorious officers and men.

ON THAT NIGHT, Sun Daiyin had the Tang banners unfurled on the walls, and the Koguryŏ defenders gave up fighting. On the next morning, in a huge tent set up near a river, the Emperor personally took surrender from Sun Daiyin and his officers. Meanwhile measures were taken to pacify the Koguryŏ. Grain was distributed to the more than 10,000 starving residents and the soldiers, and one bolt of silk was bestowed upon each elderly man of 79 or older. A new Prefecture, that of Yan, was created with Baiyan as its seat and the Koguryŏ general Sun Daiyin as its first Tang Prefect. Sun's troops were permitted to leave or stay as they pleased.

HAVING LEARNED THAT QIBIHELI had become bedridden, the Emperor went to see him in his tent. As He knelt down and removed the dressing on his back, the sight of the festering wounds brought Him to tears. In a fit of rage, the Emperor ordered His aides to find the perpetrator. A few moments later, a Koguryŏ officer called Gao Tubo, with his hands bound behind his back, was delivered to the tent.

"I want you to kill him in person," said the Emperor to Qibiheli.

"It is true that he stabbed me, Your Majesty, but he did it for his master. He is a brave, loyal warrior and I don't want to kill him."

"What do you want to do with him?" asked the Emperor.

"I want to release him, Your Majesty."

The Emperor nodded to his aides, who untied the Koguryŏ and set him free.

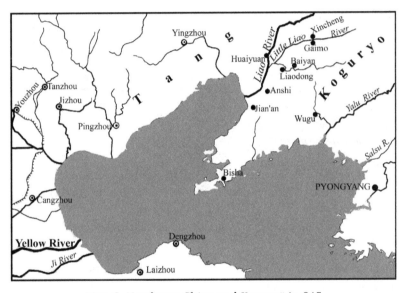

Map 6. Northeast China and Koguryŏ in 645

73. Anshi City

ON JULY 18, THE Tang troops set up camp in the suburbs of Anshi City. Located to the southwest of Baiyan, it was the next Koguryŏ stronghold to conquer. On the morrow, the Emperor received intelligence that a massive Koguryŏ-Mohe rescue force of 150,000 led by Generals Gao Yanshou and Gao Huizhen was approaching. The Emperor had no choice but to confront it before laying siege to the city itself. Although outnumbered five to one, the Emperor's army was of superior quality, with squadrons of the formidable Tujue cavalry and battle-hardened Tang officers and men. After an analysis of the situation, the Emperor put forward three choices the enemy rescue army was likely to make:

1) link up with the well-fortified and well-provisioned Anshi City;

2) flee together with the defenders of the city;

3) immediately engage the Tang army without properly assessing its strength.

The Emperor's generals made more suggestions, but none of them went far beyond the three choices. Because of the situation was still in flux, the Emperor decided to wait for more intelligence before making tactical dispositions.

AT A KOGURYŎ WAR council, an experienced general proposed something quite different, "We are not likely to win if we try to confront the enemies on the battlefield," said he. "Our best choice is to stay put and refuse battle while sending small attack forces to cut off their grain supply."

Commander-in-chief Gao Yanshou, young and self-confident, rejected it and instead ordered his troops to march at full speed towards Anshi until they were about 40 *li* from the city.

A small troop of Tang-Tujue cavalry sent to test the strength of the Koguryŏ army was soon scattered, or so it seemed. On General Gao Yanshou's orders, his vanguard forces gave chase until they were about 8 *li* southeast of the city and positioned themselves close to the mountains.

UNDER THE ESCORT OF several hundred cavalry, the Emperor and His generals rode to a hilltop overlooking the enemy lines. They were surprised to see that the Koguryŏ and Mohe forces spread out along the foot of the mountains for as far as the eye could see. However, the terrain of dells, hills, and mountains instead of open country seemed to favor the Tang attackers.

"Your Majesty," said Li Daozong, "apparently, the Koguryŏ have deployed the bulk of their forces to fight us. Their capital, Pyongyang, must be vulnerable at this time. Please allow me to lead 5,000 cavalry to sack it. I am sure that will force the Koguryŏ army to surrender."

"Good idea, Daozong," replied the Emperor. "But, at this moment, we cannot spare 5,000 cavalry." Pausing for a few moments, He continued, "We need time to position our attack forces. Let's try to throw the enemies off guard first."

Thereupon, a Tang emissary was sent to the Koguryŏ camp, bearing a letter from the Emperor addressed to the Koguryŏ Commander-in-chief. It said,

The purpose of our expedition is to penalize the regicide who murdered your King, not to fight the Koguryŏ army. Once we entered your country, our provisions were found in short supply, so we took several cities. We will return them to you once Koguryŏ becomes a tributary state again.

By then, the deployment of the Tang troops had begun: Li Shiji with 15,000 infantry and cavalry would be positioned in the west mountain; Zhangsun Wuji with 11,000 crack troops would move into a dingle in the north mountain, laying an ambush for the enemy's rear; and the Emperor Himself with a mobile force of 4,000 infantry and cavalry would quietly ascend the north mountain, whence they would launch an attack when the opportunity arose.

On the following day, it was overcast with dark clouds swirling in the sky. As Li Shiji was moving his troops into position, Gao Yanshou mounted an attack. A sudden burst of drumming and horn-blowing from elsewhere caught the Koguryŏ general by surprise. Amidst the fluttering of banners, the three Tang forces began to advance simultaneously, kicking up a tremendous dust storm. It happened so fast that Gao Yanshou and his generals did not have time to arrange their troops into effective formation. Under fierce attack by Tang archers and cavalry, the Koguryŏ officers and men began to rout. It was at that moment that lighting and thunder struck, followed by a downpour that drenched the battlefield. By then the Koguryŏ had lost more than 20,000 men. The survivors made an attempt at retreat, only to find themselves trapped in the valleys—the bridges leading to the escape routes had been destroyed by Zhangsun Wuji's men.

On July 22, Gao Yanshou and Gao Huizhen surrendered with 36,800 officers and men, 50,000 horses, 50,000 oxen, and 10,000 sets of iron armors. The Emperor treated most of the captives with clemency, appointing Gao Yanshou and Gao Huizhen as Director of the Court for Tributaries and Director of the Court of the National Granaries (*sinong qing*), respectively; and granting official ranks and titles to the 3,500 officers and local chieftains before sending them to the hinterland for resettlement. The rest of the Koguryŏ soldiers were given permission to return to Pyongyang if they so chose. The 3,300 Mohe cavalry mercenaries, however, were executed, probably in an attempt to deter Mohe from meddling in Tang-Koguryŏ relations. The north mountain where the Emperor and His 4,000 troops had lain in wait before the start of the battle was rechristened Zhubi Mountain (the Mountain of Imperial Presence) in honor of His Majesty.

THE EMPEROR NOW TURNED to Anshi City itself, a castle town that rested on a high mound dominating the surrounding landscape. Its vantage location and strong fortifications made it almost impregnable. Its defenders were known to have been fiercely independent. Previously, when Quan Gaisuwen usurped power in Pyongyang, Anshi had refused to recognize his authority. Subsequent efforts to bring it to heel had failed.

On August 2, the Emperor set up camp in the mountain east of Anshi City. From there, He attempted on numerous occasions to lure the defenders out of their fortress so that the superior Tang forces could engage them. But the enemies refused to take the bait.

One month had passed, and the Tang army had made no progress. On September 6, the Emperor moved His headquarters south to get closer to the city. On the morrow, under the escort of a cavalry squadron, He ventured out of camp to survey the front. As He and His escort rode to the bank of the moat, He heard a barrage of noise coming at Him. Raising His head, the Emperor saw in the distance some Koguryŏ soldiers atop the city wall shouting and gesticulating amidst a roll of drums.

Annoyed, the Emperor asked an interpreter, "What are they saying?"

"They are cursing."

"Your Majesty," Li Shiji interposed. "These bastards need to be taught a lesson. May I propose that we give no quarter to all the inhabitants—men and women, old and young— after we sack the city?"

"Well," answered the Emperor, "we should let it be known that My patience has its limits. If they continue to offer resistance for long, we will probably have to revoke our policy of leniency."

The Emperor's warning seemed to fall on deaf ears. The Koguryŏ defenders shut themselves up inside the fortress city and vigorously fought off any Tang attempts to storm its walls and gates.

ONE AFTERNOON, THE EMPEROR was out at the front again. He heard pig squeals and chicken squawks from inside the city.

"Did you hear that?" the Emperor asked Li Shiji.

"Yes, Your Majesty."

"We haven't heard that kind of noise for a long time. Does it mean anything to you?"

"Nothing out of the ordinary, Your Majesty. Just some poor pigs and chickens are getting slaughtered."

"It means the Koguryŏ will feast their warriors before sending them out to attack us."

On the Emperor's orders, the security of the Tang barracks was tightened and more guards were posted at the front to closely monitor enemy movements.

About midnight, hundreds of Koguryŏ commandos were quietly let down the wall by rope. No sooner did their feet touch the ground than they were set upon by the Tang troops lying in wait and were forced to retreat back onto the wall, leaving behind several dozens of their dead and seriously wounded.

ANSHI CITY HAD TURNED out to be a hard nut to crack. The city walls were too high and too well fortified for any siege techniques the Tang had at their disposal. Gao Yanshou, the erstwhile Koguryŏ general, proposed an alternative plan: to bypass Anshi altogether and fall on Wugu City to the east instead, which was now being defended by a dotard. Wugu could then serve as a springboard for a campaign to capture the capital Pyongyang.

"It sounds like a great idea," the Emperor said approvingly.

"However, Your Majesty," said Zhangsun Wuji, "this campaign is different from all others because it is led by the Emperor Himself. Pushing on to Wugu will expose the Emperor to an unacceptable degree of danger. Nor can we afford to leave so many enemy troops in our rear in places like Anshi. It is far better to take Anshi first."

Neither did His senior generals want to give up the city. The siege continued.

Li Daozong then resorted to a new tactic that promised to break the logjam. On his orders, his men started raising a mound next to the southeast corner of the city. The work pressed ahead in spite of repeated Koguryŏ attempts to disrupt it. Eventually, the mound was raised higher than the wall, which would give Tang archers a vantage point over the defenders of the city.

To counter this tactic, the Koguryŏ defenders increased the height of the city wall opposite the mound accordingly. When attacks by the Tang soldiers destroyed a section of the city wall in the southeast corner, the defenders hurriedly erected a tall fence made of wooden stakes to close the gap.

Li Daozong was at the site every day until he tripped and fell, and was carried back to camp. On that night, the Emperor paid him a visit. Lying on his pallet Li Daozong was moved to tears when the Emperor knelt by his side and administered acupuncture to his hands and legs.

Meanwhile, the mound continued to grow. Now Courageous Commandant Fu Fu'ai was in charge of the work with a platoon of soldiers. One day, when the Commandant was away on private business, the mound collapsed, destroying a section of the city wall nearby. Out from the gap came several hundred Koguryŏ warriors, who drove off the ill-prepared Tang soldiers. Hastily, the Koguryŏ dug a moat around what remained of the mound and left a small force to guard it.

The Emperor was furious.

Sitting in His tent, He asked Fu Fu'ai sharply. "Do you know what you have done?"

"Yes, Your Majesty," answered the tied-up Commandant. "Dereliction of duty."

"Because of your irresponsible action, hundreds of Tang soldiers have lost their lives, and the entire operation may fail. I have to make an example of you." Fu was then frog-marched out of the tent to execution.

Next, Li Daozong was brought in. Limping along for a few steps, he dropped on his knees, saying, "Your Majesty, I am awfully sorry."

"You deserve to die because of your crime," the Emperor said angrily.

"Yes, Your Majesty, I do," said Li Daozong, without attempting to defend himself.

After a pause, the Emperor said, "Considering your merit in the siege of Gaimou and Liaodong, I have decided to pardon you this time. But don't ever let it happen again!"

After a profusion of thanks, Li Daozong limped away.

The Emperor ordered a fierce attack on the mound. For three days, the Koguryŏ defenders stood their ground, and the attack was abandoned.

ONE MORNING IN EARLY October, the Emperor woke up to find the outside blanketed in white. He immediately summoned a meeting with His top generals in His campaign tent.

"The infamous winter of the northeast has arrived," said the Emperor.

"Pastures have gone yellow, and our provender is running low," added Zhangsun Wuji.

"We are also running out of grain," said the Emperor. "It is increasingly difficult to keep the troops fed."

"It can last another ten days," said Chu Suiliang.

"Now," the Emperor said with decision, "we are pulling out. Do you have anything to say?"

"Your Majesty, give me another three days," requested Li Daozong. "I can storm the southeast corner."

"What if you can't?" asked the Emperor.

Li Daozong fell silent.

"The best time for war in the northeast is the third to the eighth months (April through September). Because of Wei Ting's incompetence, the whole operation was delayed by at least a month. That has cost us dearly. If we stay, more and more of our soldiers will freeze to death. Should that happen, how can I face their parents and wives?"

On the morning of the next day, October 13, the Tang forces held a military parade outside Anshi City as the Koguryŏ defenders, seriously starved, watched quietly from atop the city walls and from embrasures in the gatetowers. No one bothered to hurl execrations at the Tang invaders. When the defenders realized the Tang forces were leaving, their Commander mounted the wall to bid farewell to their worthy adversaries. The Emperor, for His part, stopped on His white horse and started talking to him through an interpreter, "You have fought bravely in defending the city. To express My admiration, I have left a modest gift." He then turned around and rode off, followed by His escort.

After the Tang forces were out of sight, the Koguryŏ came down and collected the 100 bolts of silk lying on the ground left by the Emperor.

THE TANG KOGURYŎ WAR finally came to a close. On that occasion the Emperor issued an edict that took stock of the situation:

[In this campaign,] we have conquered ten cities—Xuantu, Hengshan, Gaimou, Momi, Liaodong, Baiyan, Beisha, Maigu, Yinshan, and Houhuang—and have acquired a population of 180,000 in 60,000 households... After a number of battles, including three major ones, we have cut off more than 40,000 enemy heads, captured two Generals-in-chief, 3,500 lesser officers and local chieftains, and 100,000 soldiers, who, having been issued with grain rations, were allowed to return to their hometowns or home villages...

But the Emperor did not mention the high cost, in terms of men and horses lost, maimed, or wounded, nor the failure to achieve the ultimate goal—the conquest of Koguryŏ. Neither did He say anything about the 14,000 Koguryŏ civilian captives, who would be awarded to officers and soldiers as slaves. The Emperor did not like the idea at all, but He was reluctant to disappoint His troops. After an intense debate with His advisers, He had the captives ransomed with money from the state treasury so that they could be reunited with their families.

THE TANG ARMY WAS marching deep into Tang territory. After crossing the Liao River, it was bogged down in muddy roads. Zhangsun Wuji led 10,000 troops to strew the roads with reeds to make them passable. The Emperor Himself did His bit by carrying reeds on the saddle of His white horse. Then, on October 26, a major snowstorm hit, exposing the ill-clothed soldiers to dangerously low temperatures. To boost morale, the Emperor stood by the roadside, firebrand in hand, cheering on His soldiers as they marched by. Still, many of them succumbed to the bitter cold.

On November 5, the Emperor and His troops crossed into Ying Prefecture. In the southeast of Liucheng, on the Emperor's orders, a pyramid was created out of the skulls and bones of Tang fallen soldiers. In front of this monument, solemn obsequies were held in which the Master of Rites made a sacrifice of oxen and lambs to the Lord on High. The Emperor read out a commemorative speech composed for the occasion, knelt down, and wailed sorrowfully for a long time.

The march continued.

"I wish Wei Zheng was still alive today," the Emperor said ruefully to Chu Suiliang. "He would have opposed this War and I probably would not have started it." After a contemplative pause, He continued, "Suiliang, write down My edict:

Wei Zheng shall be rehabilitated immediately; his tombstone shall be repaired and re-erected; a minor sacrifice in honor of him shall be conducted at his tomb at the earliest possible date."

TEN DAYS LATER, AS the Emperor was approaching the Linyu Pass (west of Qinhuangdao, Hebei), He was met by Crown Prince Li Zhi on the road. On hearing of his father's return, the Crown Prince, under an escort of 3,000 light cavalry, had rushed hundreds of *li* to greet Him.

"How have you been, My son?" asked the Emperor, who could hardly contain His joy.

"Very well, Your Majesty," the Crown Prince answered, as tears streamed down his cheeks. To him, Father looked haggard and weary with thinning white hair and bleary eyes. His yellow silk robe was so tattered that much of the undergarment could be seen.

"Stop crying. I am back!"

"Your Majesty does not feel cold?" the Crown Prince asked as he eyed His threadbare robe.

"I am fine. Oh, this is the same robe I wore when I embarked on the expedition. You see: I have kept My promise to you, wearing the same robe in the last five months. Actually, it was already worn out in early autumn; and My aides kept asking Me to change. But how could I wear new clothes when My soldiers were in rags? Besides, I had to keep My promise to you."

"Your Majesty can change now?"

"Of course, Zhi," the Emperor said merrily as He doffed what remained of the old robe and put on the new robe brought by Li Zhi.

WHEN THE EMPEROR ARRIVED in the eastern suburb of Youzhou, the seat of You Prefecture, on November 30, He was startled to see a large crowd—approximately 10,000 people—lining the road to welcome Him.

"How many times have I said," the Emperor shrieked, "that I don't like staged spectacles like this? It is a complete waste of time and money. We have to hold the Prefect responsible."

"Yes, Your Majesty," said Chu Suiliang, "but..."

"But what?"

"This is not staged. They are not You Prefecture residents."

Only then did the Emperor realize that these were the Koguryŏ civilian captives who had recently been freed. They screamed and shouted, cheered and danced in a whirl of dust. Moved by the outburst of enthusiasm, the Emperor got off His horse to mingle with them.

STARTING ON DECEMBER 30, the Emperor began to be carried in a palanquin— a large boil in His thigh had made it too painful to ride a horse or sit in a carriage. The Emperor's condition worried people around Him, most of all, the Crown Prince. When the Imperial procession was on the move, the Prince would often walk behind the palanquin, lending a hand to the bearers every now and then. When it stopped for a rest, he would go up to inquire after the Emperor's health and kneel down to examine His boil and sometimes suck the pus out of it.

74. Zhang Liang

BACK IN CHANG'AN, THE Emperor Li Shimin did not feel well enough to resume all of His Imperial duties, so He delegated much of His power to the Crown Prince. Everyday, the Prince, after his official work in the Eastern Palace was over, would come rushing to the neighboring Taiji Palace to attend on the Emperor.

With a reduced workload, the Emperor hoped to have more time to enjoy himself while recuperating. It was then that a serious scandal broke that demanded His full attention. It concerned Zhang Liang, one of His old comrades-in-arms.

In early Zhenguan 20 (646), Zhang Liang was taken into custody by officers of the Board of Justice from his Chang'an home. It was a rather awkward moment. Not only was Zhang not fully aware of the charges, he was also the President of the Board.

Recommended by Li Shiji and Fang Xuanling, Zhang Liang had been one of the Emperor's original sworn followers. As early as Wude 9 (626), still during Gaozu's (Li Yuan) reign, he was sent by then Prince Li Shimin to Luoyang to develop a regional power center to counter the influence of Crown Prince Li Jiancheng. Soon, he was accused of cliquishness and thrown into jail. But he survived the ordeal without betraying his master. Later he was rewarded with a series of key appointments by Li Shimin after He had come to power, and was eventually inducted into the hall of fame at the Lingyan Pavilion. Indeed, it was Zhang's report that first alerted the Emperor to Hou Junji's criminal intent. In the recent Koguryŏ War, Zhang was given a decisive role to play, as Commander-in-chief of the eastern column. Throughout his career, Zhang was known as a fair and incorruptible official who often stood up for the downtrodden against the rich and powerful.

Trouble started when he divorced his first wife and married a termagant, Ms. Li, 20 years his junior. She had led a promiscuous lifestyle, which she continued even after the marriage, with the tacit approval of her uxorious husband. At her urging, the couple adopted as their son one of her paramours, a young dancer named Shenji. Thereafter, they went on to adopt so many sons that Zhang lost count. Equally troublesome was his association with some theurgists, especially Cheng Gongying and Gongsun Chang, who would use a variety of magical methods to make politically sensitive predictions. It was this association that landed him in jail.

"ARE YOU AWARE OF the crime you have committed?" the judge asked Zhang Liang at his trial.

"I am not, Your Honor."

"Plotting rebellion!"

"Never! I was a close follower of the Emperor when He was still a hidden dragon. I have continued to serve Him in various capacities after He became Emperor. And never once have I betrayed His trust."

"Well, you can refuse to own up to your crime, but we have witnesses," said the judge menacingly. Addressing his attendants, he continued, "Bring Cheng Gongying and Gongsun Chang."

The two theurgists appeared, their hands tied behind their backs. The blood stains on their faces showed signs of torture.

"Mr. Cheng," said the judge, "tell us, how did you get to know Mr. Zhang?"

"Several years ago," said Cheng Gongying, "when Zhang Liang was posted to Xiang Prefecture (in south Hebei), he secretly summoned me to his home."

"Why?"

"Because of my reputation as the best-known theurgist in the area."

"What did Mr. Zhang say to you at that meeting?"

"I remember he asked me a peculiar question:

It is said that Xiang Prefecture has an extraordinary terrain and that a king will rise there in a matter of years. What do you think?"

"Your answer was?"

" 'The way you lie down is reminiscent of a dragon. Thus you will achieve great nobility.' "

"What did Mr. Zhang say to that?"

"He said, 'When the country sinks into chaos, it is my son Shenji who will rise to a position of great nobility.' "

"That's a lie," shouted Zhang Liang, "I never said 'the country sinks into chaos.' "

The judge signaled to have Cheng Gongying taken out of the room. Now it was Gongsun Chang's turn.

"I got to know Mr. Zhang through my brother Gongsun Jie, who is his adopted son."

"Did you notice anything suspicious about them?"

"Yes. My brother Gongsun Jie once discovered a *chen*-prognostication phrase. It goes like this, 'A Zhang with a long bow will dominate another capital.' Gongsun Jie identified this Zhang as Zhang Liang, because his last name *zhang* is comprised of two parts: *gong* (bow) and *chang* (long)."

"What was Zhang Liang's reaction?"

"He was beside himself with joy."

"Did he believe it?"

"Yes, absolutely."

"Did he say anything to you that you wish to report?"

"Yes. Zhang Liang once said to me, 'A physiognomist told him that his wife would become the consort of a Prince.' "

"Meaning his wife, Ms. Li, would marry a Prince?"

"No. It means 'her husband, Mr. Zhang, would become a Prince or sovereign.' "

"Liar! Liar!" shouted Zhang Liang, as the judge gestured to have Gongsun Chang marched out of the room.

"These two persons," continued Zhang Liang, "know they are in trouble. They want to defame me in order to avoid the death penalty. What they said is absolutely untrue."

"How about those adopted sons of yours?" the judge asked sharply.

Zhang Liang suddenly fell silent.

"How many do you have?"

"I don't know. I have lost count."

"How about 500?"

"I really don't know."

The judge nodded to his attendants to dismiss Zhang.

A COURT DISCUSSION FOLLOWED. Li Shiji and Fang Xuanling, who had vouched for Zhang Liang before, did not dare to do it again for fear of incriminating themselves. In fact, no officials stood up for him except for Li Daoyu, Deputy Chief of the Directorate for the Palace Buildings, who insisted, "There is not enough evidence for plotting rebellion. Although Zhang Liang is guilty, he does not deserve to die."

The Emperor responded, "He kept 500 adopted sons. What were they for if not rebellion?" And that question sealed Zhang's fate.

On the Emperor's orders, Fang Xuanling and Zhangsun Wuji visited Zhang Liang in prison to bid him farewell. After his request to see His Majesty was rejected, Zhang Liang, loudly protesting his innocence, was beheaded together with the theurgist Cheng Gongying (Gongsun Chang had committed suicide) in the Western Market. Thereupon, his image and name were removed from the hall of fame in the Lingyan Pavilion.

AFTER ZHANG LIANG'S DEATH, the post of President of the Board of Justice was left vacant. For Vice President Cui Renshi, the workload had become overwhelming. Since nobody was deemed qualified to serve as President, it was decided to appoint another Vice President. The court vetted a number of candidates, but none was satisfactory.

When the Emperor was briefed about the situation, He paused for a while and said, "I know who you should use: Li Daoyu. The one who said 'There is not enough evidence for plotting rebellion' about Zhang Liang."

"Yes, Your Majesty," said Chu Suiliang. "But Your Majesty did not follow his advice."

"No," said the Emperor with a sigh. "If Wei Zheng were there he would have stood behind him. Oh, how I miss him. I would probably not have allowed Zhang Liang's execution to take place."

75. Xiao Yu, Fang Xuanling, and Gao Shilian

ZHANG LIANG WAS NOT the only hall-of-famer who had bothered the Emperor lately. Xiao Yu had been acting weird. A quintessential political survivor, he was already a top-ranking official under Emperor Yang. But the latter's distrust drove him into the arms of Gaozu (Li Yuan).

At the time of the Xuanwu Gate Incident, Xiao, as one of Gaozu's top advisers, firmly supported Li Shimin and played a crucial role in helping him tide over the extremely challenging period of transition. As Emperor, Li Shimin respected him tremendously for a variety of reasons, not the least of which was his pedigree. In fact, few people alive were more blue-blooded. The Emperor once said jokingly to him, "You are the son of a Liang Emperor, the brother of a Sui Empress, a Tang Vice Premier, and the father-in-law of My daughter."

Understandably, Xiao Yu felt superior to upstarts like Fang Xuanling and Du Ruhui. But his power soon began to erode as Fang and Du took over the helm with the Emperor's encouragement. Bitter about his treatment, Xiao could not get along with other colleagues at court and complained to the Emperor about them, "Little does Your Majesty know, Fang Xuanling and his chief ministerial associates have formed a small clique to monopolize power."

"What have they done?"

"Cronyism, partisanship, and disloyalty."

"That is troubling. Doesn't Confucius say, 'Gentlemen gather but do not form their own parties'?"

"Yes, Your Majesty. But it has not yet risen to the level of treason," Xiao Yu added.

At the Emperor's insistence, Xiao offered a few pieces of evidence.

The Emperor, who found none of them convincing, responded, "You are going too far. The people I have appointed to the leading posts are not perfect. Actually, nobody is, including Myself. What is most important is how to manage them, maximizing their strengths while minimizing their weaknesses."

In the end, the Emperor not only rejected his charges, but also warned him against making them again. But Xiao Yu remained restless and offended the Emperor on several occasions. The Emperor would have dismissed him from office had it not been for his past merit.

After the Koguryǒ War, Xiao Yu showed a growing interest in Buddhism. When the Emperor learned about it, He gifted him with a large silk brocade painting that featured the Buddha at the center with Xiao by his side; a *Mahaprajna-paramita-sutra* in the hand of Wang Bao—a leading man of letters in the late sixth century whose calligraphy was highly sought after; and a cassock to be worn on the occasions of chanting religious hymns and lecturing on sutras.

Then Xiao Yu formally requested His Majesty's permission to join the Buddhist clergy.

The Emperor was taken by surprise, but nonetheless gave His approval.

A few days later, He received a report from Xiao, which said, "Upon careful consideration, I have decided not to join the clergy after all."

The Emperor was duly annoyed. When He noticed his frequent absence from court sessions on the pretext of a foot trouble, He lost his composure, and said, "He's not supposed to flip-flop like this in dealing with the Emperor."

All senior advisers shared this sentiment. In fact, not a single one was willing to put in a good word for him. That prompted the Emperor to issue a harsh edict,

I am not a believer in Buddhism. There is no evidence that it brings blessings to its faithful followers. In fact, the followers have suffered in spite of their belief. Take, for instance, Emperor Wu of the Liang and His son Emperor Jianwen. Both used the state treasury to support the clergy and exhausted the labor force to build pagodas and monasteries. Then turmoil broke out, spreading from the Huai to the far south. Both sovereigns died in custody, their descendants perished, the whole country collapsed into ruins. How absurd is the law of reward and retribution!

Xiao Yu has been going down the same disastrous road and has inherited the style of a fallen country. He has given up public service in favor of private interest, and failed to distinguish between reclusion and secular life. He has disobeyed the sovereign at court and contributed to the trend of ostentation in society. Recently, he requested permission to join the clergy, only to take it back after it had been granted. I have tolerated him for a long time, but he has shown no intention to mend his ways. I hereby demote him to Prefect of Shang Prefecture, and deprive him of his fief and ducal title.

Eventually, Xiao Yu, due to his advanced age and his past merit, was not requested to take up position in the prefectural seat after all. A few months later, his fief and title were restored.

IN THE WAKE OF the Koguryŏ War of 645, the Koguryŏ began to send their tributary missions to Chang'an, in acknowledgment of the Tang's dominance. But the Emperor felt vexed by their continued encroachment on Silla. By late Zhenguan 20 (646), the Tang court had stopped accepting Koguryŏ tributary goods, an act tantamount to the severing of diplomatic relations. Soon discussion was underway for a second Koguryŏ War.

Fang Xuanling, now old and sick, spoke strongly against it, much to the chagrin of the Emperor, who clearly preferred the obedient and meek Fang of the past. In a fit of anger He had Fang taken into custody after berating him and depriving him of all his powers.

Chu Suiliang was alarmed at what he considered the Emperor's overreaction and could not help but think of the fate of His close advisers in recently years: Hou Junji, Zhang Liang, Xiao Yu, and others. He shuddered at the thought that disgrace could befall Fang Xuanling as well, the Emperor longest-serving adviser. After much hesitation, he summoned enough courage to write and submit a memorial to address the issue. It read,

Fang Xuanling has fully supported the Imperial cause from the earliest days of the Righteous Uprising, and risked his life when he helped make the crucial decision at the time of the Xuanwu Gate Incident. He was instrumental in recruiting the worthy and formulating key policies in the early Zhenguan years. Of all the public servants at court, Xuanling is the most meritorious. If he has committed an unpardonable crime, the scholar-officials will all condemn him. But he should not be forsaken. If he has become senile, Your Majesty should ask him to retire in accord with ritual. But it will never do to cast him away—a worthy friend of old who has rendered decades of faithful service—for the slightest of errors.

The memorial did not enrage the Emperor as Chu had feared but set Him reminiscing about the darkest days of the Wude reign when His own life was in danger. Fang Xuanling was the first of His close followers to urge Him to confront Li Jiancheng and his gang. To this day, Fang remained loyal to the Emperor, in spite of the recent unpleasant episode.

On the next morning, the Emperor made a trip to Hibiscus Garden in Chang'an's southeast corner. On His way back, He paid a surprise visit to Fang Xuanling's home in Wuben Ward to pick him up. From there sovereign and subject rode in the same carriage to the Taiji Palace.

BECAUSE OF HIS RECENT bouts of sickness, the Emperor became acutely aware of His own deteriorating health. He took a great interest in various ways to preserve and prolong life, especially the Daoist technique of "external alchemy." The practice was well documented in the works of such famous masters as Ge Hong and Tao Hongjing of the previous age, and Sun Simiao of the Tang. It was grounded in the belief that a wonder drug called the "gold cinnabar"—alchemized from lead ore, sulfur, and mercury—could make the body resistant to decay and bring about longevity.

By early Zhenguan 21 (647), the Emperor had been taking the wonder drug for a while, and His constitution had been seriously weakened by its toxic side effects. He suffered from constant dizziness, nausea, and an overwhelming sense of malaise. But these were supposed to be signs of a genuine metamorphosis that would lead to longevity, so long as He avoided exposing Himself to the extremes of heat and cold, and to emotional ups and downs.

It was then that the Emperor received the news that Gao Shilian was dying. Gao was not just another Lingyan Pavilion "hall-of-famer," a living hero, who had been at His side at the time of the Xuanwu Gate Incident. Gao was also the maternal uncle and adoptive father of His wife Ms. Zhangsun and her brother Zhangsun Wuji. It was Gao who had married off his adopted daughter and niece to Him.

On February 21, the Emperor made an unannounced visit to Gao Shilian's home. He stayed with the unconscious Gao for about half an hour, and left the sickroom teary-eyed. On the following day, Gao passed away.

As the Emperor was getting ready to attend his funeral, Fang Xuanling made an urgent attempt to stop Him on account of His poor health.

"Mr. Gao," said the Emperor, "was not only a subject of mine. He was an old friend, a relative by marriage, and a dear uncle. What reason do I have *not* to attend his funeral and bewail his passing? Stop trying to persuade Me. I am going."

Fang Xuanling fell silent.

As the Emperor and His entourage arrived at the gate of Gao Shilian's home, where his coffin was placed in the center of the main hall, as was the custom, Zhangsun Wuji, the chief mourner, rushed out to greet Him.

"Your Majesty," said Zhangsun Wuji as he stood in front the Imperial carriage, "has been taking the gold cinnabar, and is not supposed to attend funerals. For the sake of the country, Your Majesty should take good care of His health. Moreover, before his death, Uncle said that the last thing he wanted was to cause Your Majesty to pay a visit because of his death and funeral service."

"For Me, Uncle Gao was family," said the Emperor firmly. "I must attend his funeral."

The Emperor signaled His carriage driver to move forward. But Zhangsun Wuji was already on all fours in the middle of the road, wallowing in the dust and desperately imploring His Majesty not to proceed any further.

With great reluctance, the Emperor granted His brother-in-law's request and turned back north. He then entered the Forbidden Park, where He climbed to the top story of a tall pavilion. Looking towards the south, He stared at the vague contour of Gao Shilian's home in Chongren Ward, as tears poured down His face like rain.

On the day of Gao's burial in the Zhaoling Tomb Park, the Emperor went to Han Chang'an, the old city, and mounted a loft-building in its northwest corner. From there He fixed His gaze on the Horizontal Bridge below, and waited and waited... When Gao's hearse, followed by a long procession of horse-drawn carriages draped in white, passed through the Bridge, the Emperor broke down into uncontrollable wailing.

76. The Cuiwei Palace

AS WINTER TURNED TO spring, the Emperor Li Shimin had a stroke, and became hemiplegic. The disease seemed to run in the family. His father Gaozu (Li Yuan) had come down with hemiplegia before His death. Now the Emperor had all the more reason to take the gold cinnabar in order to improve His health. One noticeable effect of the drug was the accumulation of excessive internal heat. Unfortunately, the Emperor's permanent abode in the Taiji Palace was situated in a low area. In summer, it was humid and hot, extremely uncomfortable for someone taking the gold cinnabar.

As soon as summer arrived, on the Emperor's orders, the defunct Taihe Palace was revived as a summer resort with a new name, "Cuiwei" (Jadeite Tenuity). The Cuiwei was situated in a scenic area south of Chang'an in the South Mountains. In early June, it was ready, and on the 10th, the Emperor moved in, entrusting government affairs in Chang'an to Crown Prince Li Zhi.

During His sojourn in the Cuiwei, the Emperor never gave up control of the country. It was there that He was briefed about General Li Shiji's recent victory in Liaodong. Now by design, the Tang was in a constant state of hostility with Koguryŏ. There had been no large-scale campaigns with the purpose of conquering the country. But a significant number of Tang troops were inside Koguryŏ attacking and sacking cities on a year-round basis.

While the Emperor was encouraged by the news from the Koguryŏ front, He was frustrated by the slow recovery of His health. The stroke had left His left hand semi-paralyzed. He missed the days when He could draw a bow and shoot arrows. Now even getting up in the morning became a struggle, let alone riding a horse into battle.

UPON RETURNING TO CHANG'AN on August 31, the Emperor was very pleased with the way the Prince had handled government affairs during His absence. The Prince had now virtually taken over the day-to-day running of the country. This prompted a man of Qi Prefecture called Duan Zhichong to write a petition letter in which he suggested that the Emperor hand over the reins to the Prince. The Emperor did not think much of it, since He did not intend to abdicate. But when the Crown Prince read the letter he was so horrified that he broke into tears. Uncle Zhangsun Wuji came to his rescue by requesting the execution of the madman Duan Zhichong—there were a number of laws on the books that could be used to condemn him. However, the Emperor was not in a mood to forfeit the life of someone for writing a petition. So Duan got away with banishment to a remote place.

IN LATE ZHENGUAN 21 (647), the King of Qiuci died, and his younger brother succeeded to the throne. The oasis state had been a thorn in the flesh of the Tang Empire. For years, it had allied itself with the Western Tujue and refused to pay homage to the Tang court. The death of the old King brought a glimmer of hope that the new King would switch allegiance. But the hope vanished when he challenged the Tang's supremacy and impinged on neighboring states.

"It is intolerable," said the Emperor. "A punitive expedition must be launched."

"But the Koguryŏ War is still going on," said Fang Xuanling. "If we start another war, we will have two major international conflicts on our hands."

"Our war effort in Koguryŏ," said the Emperor, "is only a limited operation. The Qiuci expedition will be similar in nature. We can use troops in the Western Regions without having any impact on the hinterland."

Thus a sizeable military force comprised of troops from Tiele, Tujue, Tubo, Tuyuhun, and Western Regions Protectorate was dispatched against the small oasis state. Its Commander-in-chief was the Tang-Tujue general Ashina She'er, with General Guo Xiaoke as his lieutenant.

77. The Yuhua Palace

ON THE EVENING OF February 6, Zhenguan 22 (648), Crown Prince Li Zhi paid a routine visit to the Emperor in the Taiji Palace. The Emperor seemed to assume an unusually serious tone when He said, "Zhi, it is about time that we had a talk about My legacy. Since Wude 9 (626), I have been on the throne for more than 20 years. The rule of the Li house over the country is secure; and all under Heaven are at peace. I think this success has much to do with my style of rulership. Essentially, there are five characteristics:

First, in the past the Emperors and Kings were often jealous of those who surpassed them. I am not. On the contrary, I take pride in other people's abilities as I would My own.

Second, I know no one can excel in everything. So when using people, I try to bring out their strengths while avoiding their weaknesses.

Third, oftentimes when the sovereign sees a worthy, he wants to take him into confidence; when the sovereign sees an unworthy man, he wants to throw him into the ditch. I, on the other hand, respect the worthy, but commiserate with the unworthy. Thus both the worthy and unworthy are in their proper places.

Fourth, the sovereign often abhors the just and honest, killing them either secretly or in public. At My court, there are many just and honest officials. Since My enthronement I have never killed one of them. Not only do I tolerate their presence at court, I also act upon their suggestions.

Five, there has been a tendency since antiquity to prize the Han Chinese and despise the barbarians. But I love them all with equal measure. Thus the barbarians attach to Me as they would to their parents."

"Thank you, Your Majesty. These five points will be a tremendous help to me..."

"However, since My enthronement, many bad things have happened. There is a constant supply of silk brocade garments and precious jewels and jades at court; palace basilicas, terraces, and pavilions are frequently built; hounds, horses, hawks, and falcons accompany the Imperial procession no matter how far it goes; too many Imperial tours have been made in the Four Quarters at enormous cost to the local providers of service and goods. These are serious mistakes. You should never, never repeat them.

"Instead, you must model your behavior on the wise Kings of the past. Even though I may have achieved certain accomplishments that surpassed them, I am not nearly as virtuous as they were. To My subjects, during My reign of more than 20 years, gains outweigh losses. So they are not complaining, and the Great Cause is not in danger. My son, however, you don't have My merit, but still, you will inherit My vast riches. If you try your best to do good, the most you can achieve is peace in the country. If you become arrogant, indolent, extravagant, and wasteful, you won't be able to survive for long, nor will the dynasty! Do you understand?"

The Prince nodded his head.

"Now, let Me ask you this: what is your idea of a state?"
"A state is a territory ruled by a particular government."
"But viewed from a different angle, a state is something that takes a long time to found and a short time to destroy."
"I see."
"What is your idea of the throne?"
"The throne is the place from which the sovereign governs."
"To Me, the throne is something that is hard to acquire but easy to lose. When it comes to governing the country on the throne, you simply can't be too careful!"

The Prince listened submissively, dipping his head every now and then to show his appreciation.

As the Prince was about to take leave, the Emperor presented him with a rare gift, a short book entitled *Models for the Emperor (Difan)*. It was a collection of 12 essays—"the Essence of Being a Sovereign," "Enfeoffing Royal Relatives," "Searching for the Worthy," "Vetting Official Candidates," "Accepting Remonstrations," "Eliminating the Sycophant," "Guarding Against Extravagance," "Venerating Frugality," "Reward and Punishment," "Focusing on Farming," "Practicing Martial Skills," and "Venerating Civil Virtue."

Looking His son in the eye, the Emperor said, "I thought the book would take a long time, maybe two or three years. But recently I decided to finish it ahead of schedule. Do you know why?"

"No, Your Majesty."

"Because, I've got a feeling that I won't be in this world for long."

"Daddy," said the Prince, as his eyes became wet.

"Don't be sad, Zhi. You should be happy instead. See, even after I pass on, this little book will always be there to keep you company and to help you carry on the Great Cause."

WHILE ON HIS RECENT summer visit to the Cuiwei Palace south of Chang'an, the Emperor had authorized the expansion of the Renzhi Palace (north of Chang'an) into the nearby Phoenix Valley. The Cuiwei, as it turned out, was too narrow to accommodate all the court officials and attendants in His entourage. Furthermore, access to the Cuiwei was hindered by perilous road conditions.

After the rebuilding of the Renzhi was underway, it was renamed "Yuhua" (Jade Flower), and the Emperor gave instructions to its designers and builders to be frugal. Only residential basilicas were allowed to have tile roofs. All other types of structures must be topped with thatched roofs instead. However, because of the large scale of the Palace, complete with its own Eastern Palace and government office buildings, it was costing the court an enormous fortune.

In March of Zhenguan 22 (648), the Yuhua was completed, and the Emperor moved in on March 23. The Palace was set in a valley surrounded by tree-clad mountains and hills with countless springs and streams. The Emperor soon felt the salubrious effect of the new environment. The crisp air sharpened His mind and lifted His spirit. In fact, He felt recovered enough to try His hand at hunting.

But His mood turned sour when He read a report on Cui Renshi, a rising star at court, who was already a de facto Chief Minister. Recently, he was involved in a case in which a petitioner had gone as far as the entrance pavilion to the Inner Area of the Palace City to lodge a complaint. Cui failed to refer the case to the court, as he was expected to. Chu Suiliang, who was Cui's rival, reported this lapse. The infuriated Emperor disenrolled Cui for "deceiving the sovereign," before banishing him to the far south.

About the same time, He received an even more unpleasant report by Xu Hui, an Imperial concubine from the South in her early 20s, known for her literary accomplishment. In it, she chastised the Emperor for warring against the Koguryŏ in the east and Qiuci in the west; for constructing the Cuiwei and Yuhua Palaces; and for enjoying extravagant raiments and playthings. It even cautioned against following the example of the First Emperor, whose Empire collapsed after His death.

The Emperor was incensed by the scathing criticism. *What does she know about the complex relations between Tang and her neighboring states?* Of course, He would not call a stop to the military campaigns already underway, nor would He do much with the two

Palaces. When His rage cooled down, however, He realized that nobody had dared to criticize Him with such candor since the passing of Wei Zheng, and was inadvertently impressed with her brutal honesty. Instead of punishing her, He granted her a handsome reward.

WHILE WAITING EXPECTANTLY FOR news from the Western Regions as the Qiuci War was underway, the Emperor received an unusual report on the distant land of India that piqued His curiosity. The author of the report, Wang Xuance, was an officer of relatively low rank. But his exploits were nothing short of extraordinary. Previously, Wang had gone on a Zhenguan 17 (643) mission to India in response to a friendly mission sent by King Harsha Vardhana, who had learned much about Tang China through Master Xuanzang. This report, however, was about Wang's more recent, adventure-filled second mission.

After giving an account of how he and his party traveled from Central Asia to north India, Wang Xuance continued,

By the time we entered the kingdom of Magadha, King Harsha had already passed away. His successor Arunasva ambushed us, took us prisoner, and seized the tributary goods we had received from other states. I managed to escape east to Tubo. After listening to my appeal for assistance, the Tubo King lent me 1,200 crack troops. We further received 7,000 cavalry from the King of Nepal. With these expeditionary forces under the command of myself and my lieutenant Jiang Shiren, we returned and fell on the Central Indian City. After an attack lasting three days, we sacked the city on June 16, Zhenguan 22 (648). We beheaded more than 3,000 enemy soldiers, and drove another 10,000 into the Ganges River where they drowned. We captured 12,000 men and women and 30,000 oxen and horses. Although the usurper Arunasva escaped the sack of the city, he was later captured. We then returned to Chang'an through the Western Regions and the Hexi Corridor, bringing with us the spoils and important prisoners of war, including Arunasva himself and the theurgist Nārāyaṇasvāmin.

In response, the Emperor said in an edict,

It pleases Me to hear the great victory won by Wang Xuance. This is a cautionary tale for those avaricious sovereigns. Had it not been for his avarice, the Indian sovereign Arunasva, who abducted our men and goods, would never have been taken prisoner.

For his valor and distinguished service, Wang Xuance was awarded the title of "titular counselor." Although this was a rank-5 "prestige title" with no substantive power, it carried a sizeable stipend and greatly enhanced the recipient's social standing.

WHEN THE EMPEROR LEFT for the Yuhua Palace for the summer, He had deliberately included Xiao Yu in His entourage as a way to gradually bring the hall-of-famer back into favor. In spite of his capricious behavior, Xiao Yu was a loyal follower after all. Upon arrival in the Palace, sovereign and subject were settled in different quarters. The thought of Xiao never crossed the Emperor's mind until July 19, Zhenguan 22 (648), when a eunuch officer informed Him that Xiao had passed peacefully in his sleep and handed Him Xiao's Testamentary Will. It said,

It is only natural that death follows life. After I breathe my last, you can don me in a single garment. Only one mat should be placed inside my coffin. Not a single more item should be added. Hopefully, my body will decay soon. For the sake of expediency, you shall not necessarily choose an auspicious day for my burial. Among the sage and worthy since antiquity this practice is not without precedent.

His eyes wet with tears, the Emperor said, "Even in death, he set an example of simplicity." He ordered a day of fasting in mourning, and granted Xiao two posthumous posts—Commander of Jingzhou Area Command and Minister of Works—and the honor of burial in the Zhaoling Tomb Park.

THE LOSS OF XIAO Yu left the Emperor acutely aware of His own mortality. More than ever He yearned to discuss the meaning of life and death with learned scholars. The first one that came to mind was Master Xuanzang, who subsequently arrived in the Yuhua on an Imperial summons.

"Recently Xiao Yu passed away," said the Emperor upon meeting the Master. "I was impressed with the nonchalant way he dealt with death. I suppose it had something with Buddhism?"

"Yes, Your Majesty," replied Xuanzang. "From a Buddhist perspective, life is an illusion and death is an illusion."

"Does it mean life is without purpose?"

"No. Only that life is an illusion brought on by the effect of karma in an unending cycle of rebirth accompanied by tremendous suffering."

"Explain the Buddhist idea of suffering," requested the Emperor.

"Yes. Suffering or *duhkha* in Sanskrit is a fundamental concept of the Buddhist tradition. In ordinary lives, it is ever-present and inescapable. One suffers at birth; one suffers when getting old; one suffers when experiencing sorrow, lamentation, pain, grief, and despair; one suffers when failing to acquire what one desires; and one suffers when forced to separate from the loved ones. In short, all five forms of existence are suffering."

"Five forms of existence?"

"They refer to the five states of existence or the 'five aggregates' that define what we are: corporeality, feeling, perception, mental formation, and eventually, consciousness."

"Well, that is really profound. My question is, if what you just said is the truth, how can one get out of this predicament, this endless suffering?"

"In Buddhism, the ultimate goal is to break the cycle of rebirth to achieve the final deliverance: nirvana."

"Is that achievable for everyone?"

"Potentially, yes. Nirvana is achievable not only for all humans but for all creatures. But the path to nirvana is full of twists and turns. This is where Bodhisattvas can play a crucial role. As Your Majesty knows, a Bodhisattva is a being who has reached an advanced stage on the path to enlightenment. Instead of attaining the final stage, that is, nirvana itself, the Bodhisattva chooses to live among the humans. The purpose—to salvage as many humans as possible. The best example is Guanyin or Avalokiteśvara Bodhisattva."

"No wonder Avalokiteśvara is so popular among My subjects. By the way, what have you been working on recently?"

"I just completed the translation of the *Yogācārabhūmi-śāstra* in 100 scrolls," Xuanzang replied, not without a sense of achievement.

"This is a massive work. Which sage wrote it?"

"Maitreya Buddha."

"The Future Buddha."

"Yes, Your Majesty."

"What's it all about?"

"It elucidates the meaning of the seventeen stages."

"The seventeen stages?"

"These are the stages one goes through as one progresses towards enlightenment or nirvana. We just mentioned the stage of the Bodhisattva. That is one of the more advanced stages. At any rate, one starts with the stage of the five consciousnesses and the stage of mental intent. Eventually, one reaches the stage of the Bodhisattva, the stage of nirvana with residue, and the stage of nirvana without residue."

"Fascinating!" exclaimed the Emperor.

Xuanzang went on to give a discourse on the meaning of each of the stages with examples. The Emperor was so intrigued that, after the meeting, He sent an envoy to Chang'an to acquire a copy of the *Yogācārabhūmi-śāstra* itself.

Through reading on His own and through subsequent conversations with the Master, the Emperor gained a much deeper appreciation of Buddhism. He commented, "The Buddhist scriptures are so vast and profound, like the wide sky and blue sea, simply unfathomable. Previously, because I was busy with state and military affairs, I had no time to explore Buddhism. Today, I have spent much time studying it and come to appreciate its enormous depth and vast extent. What the Confucian and Daoist classics are to them is like what a pondlet is to the vast ocean. It is nonsense to speak of the equality of the Three Teachings."

On His orders, nine more copies were made of the newly translated *Yogācārabhūmi-śāstra*, which were then sent to the Nine Provinces.

78. Fang Xuanling

TWO MONTHS PRIOR TO His visit to the Yuhua, a secret dispatch from the Astrological Service under the Department of the Palace Library reached the Emperor. It registered several occurrences of Venus (Grand White) in broad daylight. One of the Five Planets, Venus was in charge of killing and war. It was also a *yin* planet that normally made its appearance at night. Its apparition during the day was an aberration with serious consequences. The phenomenon, in which a *yin* planet competed for brilliance with the sun, suggested the rise of a throne-challenger (as in the case of Wude 9 [626]) or a female sovereign! And the latter possibility was confirmed by a telling message in a widely circulated book called *Secret Records*. The message said, "After three reigns of the Tang, a female *wu* (martial) sovereign will take over all under Heaven for generations to come."

Usually, the Emperor did not put much stock in astrology. But when an astrological phenomenon and a prognosticatory message occurred simultaneously, He could ill afford to ignore the implications. So He instructed his aides to undertake a secret investigation to uncover this potential female martial sovereign. But the investigation yielded nothing conclusive.

One evening, at a banquet He held in honor of the Guard officers working for the Palace, the Emperor stood up and proposed to play a game of "Drinking by Command," in which everyone present was to play a word game under the supervision of a "wine officer." Losers would be required to drink a cup of wine. The Emperor good-naturedly offered to serve as the wine officer. To break the ice, He asked everyone to tell Him his pet name. When his turn came, Li Junxian, General of the Left Martial Guard (*zuo wuwei*), said, "My pet name is Wuniang (meaning 'fifth daughter')."

The Emperor could not help commenting, "You are not a woman, you are a man!"

After the banquet was over, He uncovered some disturbing facts about Li Junxian. His noble title was the County Duke of *Wu*lian; his place of origin or choronym was *Wu*'an; his military unit was the Martial Guard (*wuwei*); and his pet name was *Wu*niang! So many *wu* were associated with this man. Wasn't he the future *wu* (martial) sovereign? The connection was too obvious to ignore even though the sex was wrong. The Emperor thereupon transferred him to a provincial post as Prefect of Hua Prefecture. Once there, Li Junxian made friends with a theurgist who claimed to have lived for years without consuming grain and to know the law of the Buddha.

It was during the Emperor's sojourn in the Yuhua that Li Junxian and his theurgist friend were implicated in a rebellious plot and were subsequently executed. But the Emperor was not sure if Li Junxian was that "martial sovereign" predicted in the *Secret Records*. By then, Fu Yi had passed away. The Emperor secretly sent for Fu's successor

Grand Astrologer Li Chunfeng, the foremost authority on astrology in the nation, who wrote the definitive work on astrological fortune-telling called *Yisi Divination* and was charged with writing the "Treatise on Astrology" for the Histories of the Five Dynasties.

"Is the passage in the *Secret Records* on the throne-challenger believable?" the Emperor asked anxiously.

"Yes," answered Li Chunfeng, "it is believable, Your Majesty."

"Can you fill Me in with details?"

"Certainly. Based on my study of celestial phenomena and calendrics, I can assure Your Majesty that the person in question is already inside the Palace. She is a relative of sorts, who will reign over all under Heaven within 30 years, and will try to destroy the sons and grandsons of Your Majesty."

"Oh? The person is a woman?"

"Yes, she is a woman."

"Can we kill out all the suspects?" the Emperor asked, his face turning ashen.

"That will not do, Your Majesty. This is the will of Heaven, and cannot be defied by humans."

"Really?"

"If humans try, not only will many innocent people get killed, but the targeted person—that future sovereign—will survive. Thirty years later, she will be quite old. She will probably develop a conscience, and the harm she will cause will not be so severe."

"Are you sure about all this?"

"Yes. I swear by the honor of my ancestors. Even if by chance this future sovereign *were* killed, Heaven would probably produce another one who would be even stronger and much more vicious. Should that happen, I am afraid, the entire clan of Your Majesty would be extirpated."

The Emperor was left speechless. His instinct compelled Him to take action. But the Grand Astrologer's stark warning gave Him pause.

INITIALLY, ON THE EMPEROR'S orders, Fang, had been left in the capital as Vicegerent to help the Crown Prince deal with government affairs. The death of Xiao Yu, however, changed His mind. The Emperor was seized by a fear that He would not be able to see Fang again. He issued an urgent summons to request His longest-serving adviser's presence in the Yuhua Palace.

Fang Xuanling, in his late 60s, was in failing health. After arrival at the Palace gate, he was expected to go to the Emperor's residential basilica on foot. But he was too weak to walk, and had to be carried in a litter into the Emperor's presence. The Emperor was reduced to tears when He saw His favorite courtier dismount awkwardly with the help of attendants. The sight of the aging Emperor crying brought a flood of tears to Fang's eyes as well.

At the Emperor's request Fang was settled in a basilica close by. His condition was to be closely monitored by the eunuchs, who would periodically report directly to the Emperor.

Fang Xuanling was immeasurably grateful to the Imperial attention lavished on him. But he nonetheless felt obligated to submit one more memorial before he expired. It read,

...Lord Lao says, 'He who feels content will not be humiliated; he who knows where to stop will not fail.' Your Majesty has acquired sufficient merit and authority; and now is the time to stop territorial expansion. Before a death sentence is carried out, Your Majesty will have it checked three times and reported five times; on the day of the execution, Your Majesty will require that no meat and wine be served and that the playing of music be stopped. All this shows that Your Majesty values human life.

Today, however, innocent soldiers are put in harm's way, exposed to the danger of being wounded and maimed by spears and swords and of getting their brains dashed out. How come they alone do not deserve our compassion? In the past, when the Koguryŏ behaved immorally, it was justifiable to launch a campaign against them; when they harassed the masses, it was justifiable to destroy their state; if they posed a threat to the Central Kingdom, it was justifiable to eliminate them.

In today's world, however, none of these three points exists. And the current war purports to avenge the insult of the previous dynasty and to take revenge on behalf of Silla. Therefore, I beseech Your Majesty, instead of continuing the war effort, to give the Koguryŏ an opportunity to correct their past errors; and to burn the boats and dismiss the recruits. Then both China and foreign lands will be overjoyed, and people far and near will be pacified. I sincerely hope that Your Majesty would carefully consider this last appeal from me, your faithful subject, who already has one foot in the grave.

As He read the memorial, the Emperor burst into tears, saying, "Xuanling is lying on his deathbed, but he is still worried about the fate of the country." The Emperor went straight to see him. Soon afterwards, Fang Xuanling died on August 18, Zhenguan 22 (648) at age 69. Heart-broken, the Emperor ordered a suspension of court business for three days in mourning.

79. The Hanfeng Basilica

AFTER HE RETURNED TO Chang'an in late October, 648, the Emperor was confined to the Taiji Palace. Crown Prince Li Zhi came to see Him daily. On January 12th, Zhenguan 23 (649), the Prince came again on a routine visit.

"Finally, the Ci'en (Loving Grace) Monastery was inaugurated," the Prince said, hardly able to contain his excitement.

"Wonderful," the Emperor said, brimming with a smile.

"I want to thank Your Majesty for His patronage all these years."

"Well, initially, I was somewhat unsure about Buddhism and chary of its expensive building projects. But through close contact with Master Xuanzang, I acquired a much better understanding of the religion. The Ci'en Monastery in particular serves an important purpose: to seek posthumous blessing for your deceased mother. So I didn't hesitate to approve the project at all. Its location in Jinchang Ward is a bit off the beaten track though."

"Yes, Your Majesty. But it is beautiful and quiet, and is perfect for Xuanzang's translation project."

"Indeed. Has Master Xuanzang moved into the Monastery already?"

"Yes, Your Majesty. Master Xuanzang is the Abbot. In fact, he was involved in the building of the Monastery from the beginning. At present, there are 300 monks working for him; all of them were ordained at the time of the Monastery's inauguration."

"That's great. Xuanzang really needs a secluded place for his translation work." After a brief pause, the Emperor asked, "Can you tell Me more about the Monastery?"

"Certainly. It has almost 1,900 bays (1,897 bays to be precise) of floor space and a great variety of architectural forms, including loft-buildings, two-storied basilicas, tall pavilions, and cavernous houses. The premises are covered with trees and bamboos. In the central courtyard, there are a number of stone stelae. One of them is graced by Your Majesty's calligraphy."

"Oh? You mean the 'Preface to the Sacred Teachings of the Tripitaka Master?' "

"Yes, Your Majesty."

"That is a short piece of less than 800 characters. I wrote it at the request of the Master."

"The stele was installed in front of the entrance to the Ci'en Pagoda, and looks really nice."

"I must see it soon."

A FEW WEEKS LATER, good news arrived from the Western Regions. About one year after the start of the Qiuci War, the Tang forces under General Ashina She'er brought the kingdom into submission. The entire Western Regions was shaken. Khotan (Yutian), Western Tujue, and even Bokhara (the state of An) all tried to befriend the Tang. Not long afterwards, the Qiuci King was taken in chains to Chang'an and brought into the Emperor's presence. The Emperor went through the ceremonial process of scolding and releasing the ex-King, before appointing him Commandant in the Left Militant Guard. That night, a banquet was held in the name of the Emperor to honor the meritorious Tang generals. The Emperor, having been exhausted by His meeting with the ex-King, had to cancel His appearance, which was particularly alarming, given that He had been under treatment by the famous doctor Nārāyaṇasvāmin, whom Wang Xuance had brought back from India. Allegedly 200 years old, Nārāyaṇasvāmin was a Buddhist and occult practitioner probably of the Tantric tradition, which stressed the importance of ingesting purified mercury.

When the end of spring came, the Emperor headed for the Cuiwei Palace, the summer resort in the South Mountains, and arrived on May 17. He brought the Crown Prince and Master Xuanzang with Him.

The mountain air, the breath-taking scenery, and the cool temperatures delighted and invigorated the Emperor. And there were encouraging signs that His health was on the mend.

About a month later, when summer came into full swing, unexpectedly, the opposite happened. The long-term accumulation of toxins from the longevity drugs, both Daoist and Indian, began to have a devastating effect on His constitution. Suffering from a complexity of symptoms, the Emperor was most troubled by loose bowels. For more than 20 days, He was confined to bed. Crown Prince Li Zhi was almost always in His company except when he had to deal with government affairs or catch a few hours of sleep at night.

"You are so filial," the Emperor said gratefully one night. "That alone makes My life worthwhile. If I have to go today, I'll go without regret. The key advisers Zhangsun Wuji, Chu Suiliang, and others are loyal to Me. I have no doubt their loyalty will continue when you become Emperor. But Li Shiji keeps Me awake at night. He was a good friend of Shan Xiongxin and recommended Zhang Liang. Both I executed. Prior to the Xuanwu Gate Incident, I sought his help, and he refused to get involved. What is more important, he is the only one among the key advisers who does not owe anything to you. But he is extremely capable. So before My death, I am going to help you test him."

"How?"

"I will demote him to a provincial post. If he leaves immediately for the new post, call him back after My death and promote him to Vice Premier to ensure his personal loyalty. If he hesitates, kill him."

BY EARLY JULY, THE Emperor's condition worsened. Having being tormented by a splitting headache for a few days, he suddenly became aphasic. On the morning of July 10, He woke up to find His symptoms in remission, and urgently summoned Zhangsun Wuji and Chu Suiliang to his sickroom, where Crown Prince Li Zhi was sitting by His bedside.

"I heard Li Shiji moved to Dié Prefecture (in east Gansu) already," said the Emperor.

"As soon as he received the edict," said the Prince, "he left without so much as asking a question, Your Majesty."

The Emperor nodded with an almost imperceptible smile and said, "It is all up to you now, Crown Prince. You've got to do what you've got to do."

"Yes, Your Majesty."

"You see, life is just like a long boat ride. Sooner or later one has to get off the boat. I've got a feeling that My time will come soon."

"Daddy," murmured the Prince, as tears welled up in his eyes.

"Don't worry about Me, Zhi. I'll reach the other shore and be in safe hands."

Addressing the two advisers, He said beseechingly, "Wuji and Suiliang, now I have to leave everything in your care. The Crown Prince is humane and filial. Do take good care of him."

Both Zhangsun Wuji and Chu Suiliang broke into quiet sobs.

That night, the Emperor breathed His last in His sickroom in the Hanfeng Basilica (Basilica of Wind) of the Cuiwei Palace at age 50.

CROWN PRINCE LI ZHI was beside himself with grief. Clinging to his uncle Zhangsun Wuji, he wailed inconsolably. Shedding his own tears, Zhangsun managed to keep his presence of mind. In the wake of the Emperor's death, suddenly, the court was confronted with a host of issues. *How to secure the Palace City? How to prevent the rise of the "martial sovereign"? How to avert provincial rebellion? Or failing that, how to squash it? Above all, how to ensure a safe transfer of power?* He urgently needed to discuss them with the Crown Prince, the ruler-to-be. But, overcome with sorrow, the Crown Prince could not say a word.

"Stop it! Crown Prince," Zhangsun shouted in frustration. "The late Emperor has entrusted the fate of the country to Your Highness. How can you cry like a commoner?"

"What should I do, Uncle?" the Prince blubbered.

"Listen carefully. Go back to Chang'an immediately, bringing with you the Palace Guard units, and the trusted generals. Set off today, or tomorrow at the latest. Anything could happen if you procrastinate."

"Yes, Uncle," the Prince said, sobering up somewhat. "I will leave."

"As soon as you are in Chang'an, appoint your mentors to take charge of the Chancellery and the Secretariat. I will then follow with the Emperor's remains."

"Do we announce the Emperor's passing now?"

"Of course not. Keep it secret until I am back in Chang'an."

"Yes, I will, Uncle."

TWO DAYS LATER, CROWN Prince Li Zhi officially announced the Emperor's passing. He mounted the Taiji Basilica, where the coffin containing the Emperor's remains lay in state on a catafalque, and released the late Emperor's "Testamentary Edict." It demanded, among other things, that the Crown Prince ascend the throne in front of the coffin; that one not stop dealing with military and state affairs of great importance; that officials and officers of rank 3 and above take part in ceremonial wailing only twice a day (morning and afternoon) for a total of three days (on each occasion, one should cry only 15 times); that the military campaign in Liaodong be suspended; and that all palace construction projects be stopped.

Thereupon, the Crown Prince ascended the throne (posthumously known as Gaozong).

Tens of thousands of civil officials, military officers, and others filed into the Basilica to pay their last respects. All the Princes and Princesses residing in Chang'an were present. Conspicuously absent were Emperor Li Zhi's two brothers—ex-Crown Prince Li Chengqian, who had died of sorrow in 645, and ex-Prince of Wei Li Tai, who lived far away in his place of banishment. The Buddhist monks headed by Xuanzang were clearly visible with their yellow cassocks, in contrast with the Daoist adepts wearing white robes who merged imperceptibly into a sea of white. The presiders of the ritual ceremonies, however, were neither Buddhist nor Daoist, but "Confucian" ritualists from the Board of Rites.

Among the thousands of barbarian mourners were those visiting Chang'an on tributary missions and, more importantly, those serving the court as Tang officers. They not only wailed like the rest of the mourning crowd, but also expressed their grief by cutting their faces and ears, and by cutting off their hair.

On September 19, the deceased Emperor Li Shimin was laid to rest in the Zhaoling tomb where Ms. Zhangsun was buried. Several non-Han officers including Ashina She'er and Qibiheli made a request to kill themselves so as to accompany the Emperor to the Underworld. The request was rejected by the Emperor Li Zhi on grounds of the late Emperor's ban on human sacrifice.

80. Zhaoling

IN THE SUMMER OF 650, on the first anniversary of His father's death, the Emperor Li Zhi (Gaozong) paid a visit to the Zhaoling Tomb Park. He was accompanied by a small retinue of key officials, among whom was a distinguished-looking old man in his mid-60s, who walked with an upright, military bearing. It was Li Shiji, who had been serving as Vice Premier since last October.

Stopping at the central structure, a large stepped altar located in the north of the premises, the Emperor knelt down to perform the kowtow ritual. He then rose and stepped away for some distance, only to turn around to view the six tall steeds in marble bas-relief, three each on the east and west sides of the altar. These were the beloved warhorses the deceased Emperor had ridden in wars against Wang Shichong and Dou Jiande in Henan, Song Jingang in Shanxi, Liu Heita in Shandong, and Xue Rengao in west Shaanxi.

Along the central pathway, the Emperor took a walk to the north until He came to a stop in front of the northern gate (Beisima Gate) of the Park. He found himself flanked by 14 life-size statues, seven on each side, representing foreign leaders who had been subdued by His father in person or submitted to the Tang during His reign: four Tujue Khans, a Tubo King, a Khotan King, a Gaochang King, a Yanqi King, a Xueyantuo Khan, a Tuyuhun Khan, a Qiuci King, a Linyi King, a Silla Queen, and an Indian King. They stood with their heads lowered reverently, as if in perpetual tribute to the Heavenly Khan.

FINIS

Bibliography

Premodern Works

Bianzheng lun (*Essays in Defense of the Correct*) by Falin

Da Ci'en si sanzang fashizhuan (*Biography of the Tripitaka Master of the Dharma of the Great Ci'en Monastery*) by Huili and Yan Cong

Da Tang chuangye qiju zhu (*Court Diary from the Founding Days of the Great Tang*) by Wen Daya

Jiu Tang shu (*Old Book of the Tang*) by Liu Xu et al.

Suishu (*Book of the Sui*) by Wei Zheng et al.

Tang da zhaoling ji (*Imperial Edicts of the Tang*) compiled by Song Minqiu

Tang huiyao (*Tang Compendium of the Essential*) by Wang Pu

Xin Tang shu (*New Book of the Tang*) by Ouyang Xiu and Song Qi

Zhenguan zhengyao (*Essentials for Government from the Zhenguan Reign*) by Wu Jing

Zizhi tongjian (*Comprehensive Mirror for Aid in Government*) by Sima Guang et al.

Modern Works

Bingham, Woodbridge. *The Founding of the T'ang Dynasty: The Fall of Sui and Rise of T'ang, a Preliminary Survey*

Twitchett, Denis C., ed. *The Cambridge History of China, vol. 3: Sui and T'ang China*

Wechsler, Howard J. *Mirror to the Son of Heaven: Wei Cheng at the Court of T'ang T'ai-tsung*

Wright, Arthur F. *The Sui Dynasty*

Xiong, Victor Cunrui. *Emperor Yang of the Sui Dynasty: His Life, Times, and Legacy*

Xiong, Victor Cunrui. *Historical Dictionary of Medieval China*

Chronology

- **21st–17th c. BCE**: Xia dynasty
- **17th–11th c. BCE**: Shang dynasty
- **11th c.–771 BCE**: Western Zhou dynasty
- **770–256 BCE**: Eastern Zhou dynasty
  - 722–481 BCE: Spring and Autumn
  - 403–221 BCE: Warring States
- **221–209 BCE**: Qin dynasty
- **206 BCE–9 CE**: Western Han dynasty
- **9–23 CE**: Xin dynastye
- **25–220 CE**: Eastern Han dynasty
- **220–265**: Three Kingdoms
- **265–316**: Western Jin dynasty
- **317–420**: Eastern Jin dynasty
- **420–589**: Southern dynasties
  - 420–479: Song
  - 479–502: Qi
  - 502–557: Liang
  - 557–589: Chen
- **439–581**: Northern dynasties
  - 386–534: Northern Wei (North unified in 439)
  - 534–550: Eastern Wei
  - 535–556: Western Wei
  - 550–557: Northern Qi
  - 557–581: Northern Zhou

- **581–618: SUI DYNASTY**
  - **612:** Daye-8 Koguryŏ War.
  - **613:** Daye-9 Koguryŏ War;
    Yang Xuangan Rebellion.
  - **614:** Daye-10 Koguryŏ War.
  - **617:** Liu Wuzhou Rebellion;
    Li Yuan launched the Righteous Uprising and founded the Righteous Army.

- **618–907: TANG DYNASTY**
  - **618:** Emperor Yang Guang died;
    The Tang dynasty founded by Li Yuan;
    The Tang forces defeated by Xue Ju in west Shaanxi.

618: Li Shimin defeated Xue Rengao (Xue Ju's son).

619: Li Mi killed after briefly submitting to the Tang;
Song Jingang joined Liu Wuzhou;
Liu Wenjing executed for libel.

620: Song Jingang defeated by Li Shimin;
Liu Wuzhou and Song Jingang killed by Tujue;
Li Shimin's expedition against Wang Shichong (based in Luoyang).

621: Li Shimin defeated Dou Jiande (based in Hebei) and Wang Shichong,
and captured Luoyang;
Liu Heita Rebellion;
Xu Yuanlang Rebellion.

622: Liu Heita, initially defeated by Li Shimin, continued to harass the Tang
with Tujue's backing;
Li Jiancheng and Li Yuanji defeated Liu Heita.

623: Liu Heita and Xu Yuanlang killed;
The Tang defeated Tuyuhun.

626: The Xuanwu Gate Incident started by Li Shimin in which Li Jiancheng
and Li Yuanji were killed;
Li Yuan abdicated in favor of Li Shimin (Taizong);
Tujue invasion threatened Chang'an;
Li Shimin and Xieli (Tujue Khan) formed an alliance at the Bian Bridge.

627: Xuanzang started off on his journey to the Western Regions.

628: Civil War among the Tujue;
The Tang killed Liang Shidu and pacified the North;
Lu Zushang killed for declining an appointment (later rehabilitated).

629: Li Jing and Li Shiji led the war against Xieli of Tujue.

630: The Tang captured Xieli, and the Eastern Tujue fell;
Li Shimin accepted the title of "Heavenly Khan."

632: Li Shimin's visit to the Qingshan Palace, His birthplace.

634: Li Yuan suffered a stroke.

635: The first Christian mission to China arrived in Chang'an;
Li Yuan passed away in the Da'an Palace.

636: The Five Histories presented to the throne;
Li Shimin suffered a bowel disease;
Empress Zhangsun died at 35.

637: Li Shimin's long sojourn in Luoyang;
Li Shimin's edict ranking Daoism above Buddhism sparked a protest
led by Monk Zhishi.

638: Li Shimin returned to Chang'an;

Li Shimin issued the edict on Christianity.

639: Monk Falin jailed and banished.

640: Gaochang King Qu Wentai died;
Hou Junji conquered Gaochang.

641: Hou Junji and Xue Wanjun jailed, then released, after Cen Wenben and Wei Zheng petitioned on their behalf;
Princess Wencheng married off to Tubuo King Songzanganbu;
Li Shimin left for Luoyang;
Crown Prince Li Chengqian attempted to have his mentor Yu Zhining killed.

642: Li Tai presented the *Comprehensive Gazetteer* to the throne.

643: Li Shimin's confidant Wei Zheng died;
The hall of fame in the Lingyan Pavilion inaugurated;
Crown Prince Li Chengqian allied himself with Hou Junji;
Li Chengqian unseated after his plot against the throne was exposed;
Li Zhi set up as Crown Prince.

644: Li Shimin started preparations for war against Koguryŏ.

645: Master Xuanzang returned from the Western Regions and met with Li Shimin in Luoyang;
First Tang Koguryŏ War (April–October);

646: Zhang Liang condemned and executed.

647: Li Shimin suffered a stroke.

648: Li Shimin completed the *Models for the Emperor*;
Wang Xuance accomplished his mission to India;
The Tang conquered Qiuci;

649: Li Shimin passed away; and was later buried in Zhaoling;
Li Zhi succeeded to the throne.

907: Fall of the Tang dynasty.

- **960–1279:** Song dynasty
- **1271–1368:** Yuan dynasty
- **1368–1644:** Ming dynasty
- **1644–1911:** Qing dynasty

Glossary

Key figures are highlighted in bold.

Pronunciation

- a = a as in f**a**ther**s**
- c = zz as in pi**zz**a
- ch = ch as in **ch**ina
- e or ê = olo as in c**olo**nel without the *r* sound (except after i, u or ü, y)
- e (after i, u or ü, y) = e as in r**e**d
  e.g.: Ye \yeh\, Xue \shüeh\
- er = er as in dinn**er** (Am.)
- i = ee as in d**ee**d (except after sibilants: c, ch, s, shi, z, zh)
- i (after sibilants: c, ch, s, shi, z, zh) = the vowelized sound of the consonant
  e.g.: Li Zhi \lee jih\ ("jih" as in lo**dge**), Yuchi \yü-chih\ ("chih" not "chee")
- j = g as in **g**ee
- o = o as in f**o**reign
- q = ch as in **ch**eese (approx.)
- u = oo as in f**oo**d (except after j, q, x)
- u (after j, q, x) = ü (Ger. umlaut)
  e.g.: Qu \chü\ (not "choo")
- ü = ü (Ger. umlaut)
- x = ch as in **ich** (Ger.), or *sh* as in **sh**eep (approx.)
  e.g.: Xiyu \shee-yü\
- z = ds as in wor**ds**
- zh = j, as in **J**oe (approx.)

- Abraham (fl. 635): archdeacon of a group of Nestorians visiting China.
- An Qieluo \an chyeh-luo\ ("chyeh" is pronounced [chee'yeh]): Sui occultist.
- *Analects* (*Lunyu* \loon-yü\): collection of sayings by Confucius and his disciples and accounts of them.
- Ancestral Temple: place where the imperial ancestors were worshipped.
- *Annals of the Thirty States*: history by Xiao Fangdeng \sheeao fang-dêng\ (Liang).
- Anshi \an-shih\ City (SE of Haicheng, Liaoning).
- Anterior Basilica: largest hall in the Weiyang Palace, Han Chang'an.
- *Art of War of Grand Duke Jiang* \jeeang\: ancient work on warfare allegedly transmitted through Zhang Liang of the Western Han.

- Arunasva: Magadha king (r. 647–648).
- Ashina She'er \a-shih-na shê-er\ (604–655): Tang-Tujue general.
- Avalokiteśvara ("ś" = "sh"); Guanyin: Bodhisattva known for his compassion.
- Ba: Tang Prefecture (seat: Bazhong, Sichuan).
- Baibi: Sui place SE of Xinjiang, Shanxi.
- Baiyan City: Koguryǒ city SE of Dengta, Liaoning.
- Ban Gu (32–92 CE): Eastern Han historian.
- Bashang: place in the southeastern suburb of Chang'an.
- Battle of Jingxing \jeeng-sheeng\ (204 BCE).
- Bayegu (Bayïrqu): nomadic people in Mongolia.
- Beisha City: Koguryǒ-Tang city (in Dalian, Liaoning).
- *Benevolent King's Prajnaparamita Sutra*: Buddhist sutra about the Buddha's dialogue with a king representing other kings on how to protect their countries.
- Bin: Tang Prefecture (seat: NW of Xi'an, Shaanxi).
- Bo: Tang Prefecture (seat: Bozhou [Bozhou, Anhui]).
- Board (*bu*): see "Six Boards."
- Board of Rites (*libu* \lee-boo\): one of the Six Boards.
- Bodhiruci (fl. 6th c. CE): Buddhist monk from north India.
- Bokhara (the state of An): based in Bukhara, Uzbekistan.
- *Book of the Han* (*Hanshu*): Western Han history by Ban Gu.
- *Book of the Later Han* (*Hou Han shu*): Eastern Han history by Fan Ye (398–445).
- *Book of the Song* (*Songshu*): Liu-Song history by Shen Yue \shen yüeh\ (441–513).
- Breaking through the Enemy Array (*Pozhen yue*): Li Shimin's signature music.
- Buddha City: city north of Jimsar, Xinjiang.
- Caishu \tsai-shoo\ (late 11th c. BCE): W. Zhou noble; brother of the Duke of Zhou.
- Cen Wenben (595–645): Tang top official under Li Shimin.
- Central Plain: Henan.
- Chai Shao (d. 638): Li Shimin's brother-in-law.
- Chancellery: one of the three top-echelon decision-making bodies. It was headed by two Presidents.
- Chang He \chang hê\ (fl. 626): Tang commandant.
- Chang'an (Han): Han capital northwest of Sui-Tang Chang'an.
- Chang'an (Sui-Tang): Tang capital; renamed from Daxing City.
- Chang'an County: one of the two urban Counties of Chang'an.
- Changle, Princess of; Li Lizhi: first daughter of Li Shimin and Ms. Zhangsun.
- Chen (557–589): last of the Southern Dynasties, annexed by the Sui (cap.: Jiankang [Nanjing]).

- Chen Dade \chen da-dê\ (fl. 641): Tang official.
- Chen, Last Sovereign of (r. 582–589): last Chen sovereign.
- Cheng Gongying \chêng gong-yeeng \ (d. 646): occultist; executed.
- Cheng, Emperor (51–7 BCE; r. 33–7 BCE): Western Han sovereign.
- Cheng Zhijie \chêng jih-jyeh\ ("jyeh" is pronounced [jee'yeh]); Cheng Yaojin (589–665): general under Li Shimin.
- Cheng'en \chêng-en\ Basilica: hall in the Eastern Palace, Chang'an.
- Chengtian Gate: southern main entrance to the Palace City. It functioned as an important basilica.
- *chen*-prognostication: divinatory technique based on enigmatic texts and sayings.
- Chenxin \chen-sheen\; Heart Pleaser (d. 643): young entertainer; Li Chengqian's friend.
- Chief Administrator (*zhangshi* \jang-shih\): the executive officer under a Prince.
- Chief Minister (*xiang* \sheeang\): one of the decision-makers at the highest level.
- Chousang: place near Lingbao, Henan.
- **Chu Suiliang** (596–658 or 597–659): top Tang official under Li Shimin and Li Zhi; calligrapher.
- Chunqiu \choon-cheeoo\: see Spring and Autumn.
- Ci'en \tsih-en\ Monastery (Loving Grace Mon.): Buddhist monastery built by Li Zhi (Gaozong) in Chang'an.
- Cijian \tsih-jian\: place west of Luoyang.
- Circle (*dao*): administrative and territorial division comprised of a number of Prefectures and Commanderies. First ad hoc in nature, it became permanent under the Tang.
- *Classic of Filial Piety*: minor Confucian classic.
- Commandant (*zhonglang jiang* \jong-lang jeeang\): middle-ranking officer.
- Commandery (*jun* \jün\): administrative and territorial division higher than the County and lower than the Prefecture (*zhou*). Abolished in the early Sui, it was later revived under Emperor Yang as a substitute for the term "Prefecture."
- *Comprehensive Gazetteer* (*Kuodi zhi* \kuo-dee jih\): book on geography by Li Tai and others.
- Council of Ephesus (431): ecumenical council of Christian bishops that condemned Nestorianism.
- County (*xian* \sheean\): administrative and territorial division lower than a Commandery (*jun*) or Prefecture (*zhou*).
- Court for Agriculture: one of the Nine Courts.
- Court for Tributaries (*honglu si* \hong-loo sih\): one of the Nine Courts.
- Court of Judicial Review (*dali si* \da-lee sih\): one of the Nine Courts.

- Court of State Sacrifices (*taichang si* \tai-chang sih\): one of the Nine Courts.
- Court of the National Granaries (*sinong si* \sih-nong sih\): one of the Nine Courts.
- Court of Weaponry and Regalia (*weiwei*): one of the Nine Courts.
- Cui Renshi \tsuee ren-shih\ (fl. 648): Tang official.
- Cuiwei \tsuee-wei\ Palace (Jadeite Tenuity P.): renamed from the Taihe Palace.
- Daming \da-ming\ Palace (Great Brilliance P.): built by Li Shimin for His father northeast of Chang'an, it was finished by Li Zhi.
- Dao'an (312–385): Buddhist monk active during the Former Qin.
- Daoshu: Luoyang Ward known for housing occultists under the Sui.
- Daxing \da-sheeng\ City: capital of the Sui dynasty, founded in 583; renamed Chang'an under the Tang.
- Daxing Basilica: see Taiji Basilica.
- Daxing Palace: see Taiji Palace.
- Daye \da-yeh\ (Great Enterprise): reign period (605-618).
- Daye Basilica: large hall in the Palace City of Luoyang.
- Department of State Affairs (*shangshu sheng*): top executive agency at the center in charge of the Six Boards, usually headed by two Vice Premiers.
- Dié \dyeh\ ("dyeh" is pronounced [dee'yeh]): Tang Prefecture (seat: Diebu, East Gansu).
- Ding: Tang Prefecture (seat: Dingzhou, Hebei).
- Dingxiang \deeng-sheeang\: Sui-Tang Commandery (seat: NW of Horinger, Inner Mongolia).
- Dingzhou \deeng-jou\: seat of Ding Prefecture (in Hebei).
- Directorate for the Palace Buildings (*jiangzuo jian* \jeeang-dzuo jeean\): central agency in charge of court construction projects.
- Directorate of Education (*guozi jian* \guo-dzih jeean\): central government agency in charge of education.
- disenroll, to: to erase from the official roll and reduce to commoner status.
- Donglai: Sui Commandery (Yantai, Weihai, etc., Shandong).
- Dou Jiande \dou jeean-dê\ (573–621): late Sui warlord active in Hebei.
- Dou Jin (fl. 630): Tang official; builder.
- Dou, Ms. (569–613): wife of Li Yuan (Gaozu) of Xianbei descent; mother of Li Shimin (Taizong), Li Jiancheng, and Li Yuanji.
- Du Fuwei (d. 624): late Sui rebel leader active in the South; surrendered to Tang (619).
- Du He \doo hê\ (d. 643): son of Du Ruhui.
- **Du Ruhui** (585–630): leading politician under Li Shimin.

- Du Xingmin \doo sheeng-meen\ (fl. 634): Tang official.
- Du Yan (d. 628): Tang official; Du Ruhui's uncle.
- Duan Zhichong \duan jih-chong\ (fl. 647): petitioner.
- Duan Zhixuan \duan jih-shüan\ (598–642): general under Li Shimin.
- Duke of Tang: see Li Yuan.
- Duke of Zhou \jou\ (11th c. BCE): Western Zhou politician.
- Dunhuang: Sui-Tang Commandery in west Gansu.
- Eastern Capital: see Luoyang.
- Eastern Palace: residence of the Crown Prince east of the Taiji Palace; reference to the Crown Prince.
- Eastern Wei (534–557): one of the two dynasties that replaced the Northern Wei (cap.: Ye [Linzhang, Hebei]).
- Eight Chairs: two Vice Premiers of the Department of State Affairs, and Presidents of the Six Boards.
- Encampment Guard (*tunwei*), Left or Right: one of the Twelve/Sixteen Guards in the capital.
- *Essays in Defense of the Correct* (*Bianzheng lun* \beean-jêng loon\): collection of essays by Falin.
- Falin \fa-lin\ (572–640): Buddhist monk; banished.
- Fan Kuai (d. 189 BCE): Western Han general under Liu Bang.
- **Fang Xuanling** \fang shüan-ling\ (579–648): Early Tang top politician; close associate of Li Shimin.
- Faya \fa-ya\ (d. 629): Tang monk; executed.
- Feishan Palace: suburban palace built by Li Shimin in Luoyang.
- Feng Deyi \fêng dê-yee\ (568–627): Tang top official under Li Yuan and Li Shimin.
- Fengdu Market: largest urban market of Sui Luoyang; south of the Luo River.
- *fengshan*: highest form of thanks-giving ceremony conducted in Mount Tai.
- Fenyang \fen-yang\ Palace: Sui touring palace north of Taiyuan.
- First Emperor of Qin \cheen\ (259–210 BCE; r. 221–210 BCE): founder of the Qin dynasty; tyrant.
- Five Dynasties: Liang, Chen, Northern Qi, Northern Zhou, and Sui.
- Forbidden Park: enclosed imperial park north of the Palace City, Chang'an.
- Fu Fu'ai (d. 645): Tang officer.
- Fu Jian (338–385; r. 357–385): Former Qin emperor.
- Fu Yi (555–639): Tang grand astrologer and leading anti-Buddhist.
- Fuzhou: seat of Fu Prefecture (Fuxian, Shaanxi).
- Gaimou City: Koguryŏ-Tang city (Gaiping, Liaoning).

- Gan: Tang Prefecture (seat: Zhangye, Gansu).
- Gao Biaoren (fl. 631): Tang official; emissary to Yamato.
- Gao Deru (d. 617): Sui official.
- Gao Huizhen \gao huee-jen\ (fl. 645): Koguryŏ-Tang officer.
- Gao Junya \gao jün-ya\ (d. 617): Sui Deputy Vicegerent of Taiyuan.
- **Gao Shilian** \gao shih-leean\ (576–647): top official under Li Shimin; uncle and adoptive father of Empress Zhangsun and Zhangsun Wuji.
- Gao Yang (529–559; r. 550–559): founder of the Northern Qi.
- Gao Yanshou (fl. 645): Koguryŏ-Tang officer.
- Gao: small Spring and Autumn state in Shandong.
- Gaochang: kingdom (460–640; under the Qus from 497) in Turfan, Xinjiang; seat: Gaochang City (Turfan).
- Gaozhi \gao-jih\: city (Changwu, Shaanxi).
- Gaozong: see Li Zhi.
- Gaozu: see Li Yuan.
- Ge Hong \gê hong\ (283–363): Daoist; alchemist.
- General-in-chief (*da jiangjun*): top commanding officer.
- Gods of the Soil and Grain (Sheji \shê-jee\): the divinities of harvest, worshiped in their state altar inside the capital.
- Gongsun Chang (d. 646): occultist; committed suicide.
- Grand Commissioner of Pacification of Taiyuan Circle (*anfu dashi*): top leader of Taiyuan Circle.
- *Grand Scribe's Records* (*Shiji* \shih-jee\): history by Sima Qian.
- Gu Yi (d. 617): Sui general.
- Gua Prefecture (seat: Guazhou [SE of Anxi, Gansu]).
- Guāng Prefecture (seat: Guāngzhou [Yexian, Shandong]): Northern Qi area east of Qing Prefecture.
- Guangwu \guang-woo\, Emperor; Liu Xiu (6 BCE–57 CE; r. 25–57): founder of the Eastern Han dynasty.
- Guannei: Tang Circle (Sui Taiyuan Circle) that included most of Shaanxi and the Ordos in Inner Mongolia.
- Guanshu (late 11th c. BCE): Western Zhou noble; brother of the Duke of Zhou.
- Guanwen Basilica (B. for the Observation of Literature): library in the Palace City of Luoyang; built by Emperor Yang.
- Guanzhong \guan-jong\: Wei river valley and its neighboring areas in south Shaanxi; considered strategically most important.
- Guard (*wei*); Guard Command [*weifu*]: one of the 12 or 16 elite military units responsible for safeguarding the Palace, and the defense of the capital area.
- Guard Command (*weifu*): see "Guard."

- Guazhou: see Gua Prefecture.
- Guo Rong (d. 614): Sui court official.
- Guo Xiaoke \guo sheeao-kê\ (d. 649): Tang general.
- Han Xin \han sheen\ (d. 196 BCE): greatest early Han general.
- Hanzhong \han-jong\: area south of the Wei valley in south Shaanxi.
- Harsha (r. 606–647): Magadha king.
- Heavenly Khan (Qaghan) (*tian kehan*): title the leaders of nomadic and oasis powers created for Li Shimin (630).
- Hedong \hê-dong\: **1** area mainly comprised of Shanxi. **2** Sui County, southwest of Yongji, Shanxi, near the Tong Pass.
- Hegan Chengji \hê-gan chêng-jee\ (604–656): Li Chengqian's underling.
- Helan Chushi \hê-lan chu-shih\ (fl. 643): Tang officer; Hou Junji's son-in-law.
- hereditary-protective (*yin*) privileges: they allowed descendants of senior officials (rank 5 and above) to hold public offices.
- Hexi \hê-shee\ Corridor: area extending from west to central Gansu.
- Hibiscus Garden (Furong *yuan*): scenic area in the southeast corner of Chang'an.
- Hongfu Monastery: Buddhist monastery in Chang'an.
- Honghua \hong-hua\ (seat: Qingyang, Gansu): Sui Commandery.
- Hongsheng Palace (in suburban Daxing City): residence of Yang Lihua and her daughter Yuwen Êying.
- Hongyi \hong-yee\ Palace; Da'an Palace (west of the Palace City, Chang'an): residence of Li Shimin (before enthronement), Li Yuan (after abdication).
- **Hou Junji** \hou jün-jee\ (d. 643): Tang top general; executed for sedition.
- Huaiyuan \huai-yüan\ Garrison (based in Liaozhong, Liaoning).
- Huangfu Decan \huang-foo dê-tsan\ (fl. 634): Tang remonstrator.
- Huiluo Granary: Sui-Tang granary east of Luoyang.
- Hulao Pass (NW of Xingyang, Henan): important pass east of Luoyang.
- Huo Qubing \huo chü-beeng\ (140–117 BCE): Western Han general under Emperor Wu.
- Huotai Mountains (SE of Huozhou, Shanxi).
- Huoyi \huo-yee\: Sui city (Huozhou, Shanxi).
- Imperial City: enclosed government area south of the Palace City inside Chang'an.
- Institute for Literature (Wenxue *guan* \wen-shüeh guan\): **1** Li Shimin's think-tank founded in 621 with 18 academicians. **2** opened by Li Shimin for His son Li Tai in 636.
- Institute for the Advancement of Literature (Hongwen *guan*): renamed from the Institute for the Cultivation of Literature (see) in 626.

- Institute for the Cultivation of Literature (Xiuwen *guan* \sheeoo-wen guan\): top academic institution founded in 621.
- Institute of Historiography (*shiguan* \shih-guan\): set up under Li Shimin.
- Iron Plaque: certificate awarded for extraordinary merit; could be used to save its recipient from an execution.
- Jade Gate Pass (Yumen \yü-men\ P.) (in west Gansu): strategic pass in the northwest.
- Ji \jee\ County (seat: in Beijing).
- Jia Yi (200–168 BCE): Western Han official; essayist.
- Jiang Shiren \jiang shih-ren\ (fl. 648): Tang officer.
- Jiangdu \jeeang-doo\ (Yangzhou, Jiangsu): main urban center in the lower Yangzi.
- Jianwen, Emperor (r. 549–551): Liang sovereign and successor to Emperor Wu.
- Jiao Prefecture (seat: Jiaozhou [Hanoi]).
- Jiaozhou \jeeao-jou\ (Hanoi): seat of Jiao Prefecture.
- *jiazi* \jeeah-dzih\: first number in the sexagenary cycle of the Chines calendar that designates a day or a year; deemed to be of great significance.
- Jie \jyeh\ ("jyeh" is pronounced [jee'yeh]): last king of the Xia dynasty; considered one of the worst rulers in history.
- Jiexiu \jyeh-sheeoo\ ("jyeh" is pronounced [jee'yeh]) (Jiexiu, south of Taiyuan, Shanxi).
- *jinshi* \jeen-shih\ (advanced scholar): top academic degree; rose in prestige during the Tang.
- Jinyang \jeen-yang\ Palace: Sui-Tang palace complex in Taiyuan.
- Jiucheng Palace: Tang Palace 300 *li* west of Chang'an; Renshou in Sui.
- Kangju \kang-jü\: state based in Samarkand inhabited by Sogdians.
- Khotan (Hetian): oasis state based in Yutian, Xinjiang.
- Koguryǒ: ancient Koreans active in north Korea and south Manchuria; their kingdom.
- Kong Yingda (574–648): Tang official; Confucian scholar.
- Kunyang \koon-yang\ (Yexian, Henan): locale of a major battle in 23 CE where Liu Xiu (future Emperor Guangwu) defeated Wang Mang's much larger army.
- Li Baiyao (565–548): Tang official; historian.
- **Li Chengqian** \lee chêng-cheean\ (618–645): Crown Prince (to 643) under Li Shimin.
- Li Chunfeng \lee choon-fêng\ (602–670): Tang astrologer; occultist.
- Li Daoyu \lee dao-yü\ (fl. 646): Tang official.
- Li Daozong \lee dao-dzong\ (600–653): Tang general and Prince; nephew of Li Yuan.

- Li Gui (d. 619): late Sui warlord; declared himself Emperor of Liang (618) in the northwest.
- Li Hun \lee hoon\ (d. 613): Sui official; son of Li Mu; executed.
- Li Ji: see Li Shiji.
- **Li Jiancheng** \lee jeean-chêng\ (589–626): first Crown Prince of the Tang; eldest son of Li Yuan and Ms. Dou; brother and rival of Li Shimin; killed in the Xuanwu Gate Incident.
- Li Jing (571–649): top general under Li Yuan and Li Shimin; great strategist.
- Li Junxian \lee jün-sheean\ (648): Tang general.
- Li Ke (619–653): Li Shimin's non-heir son.
- **Li Mi** \lee mee\ (583–619): Sui rebel leader; commander of the Wagang Army.
- Li Min (pet name: Hong) (568–613): Sui official; husband of Yuwen Êying; executed.
- Li Mu \lee moo\ (510–586): founding elder of the Sui dynasty.
- Li Shentong (d. 630): Early Tang Prince and general; cousin of Li Yuan.
- **Li Shiji** \lee shih-jee\ (594–669); Xu Shiji; Li Ji: top Tang general; served Li Mi before joining the Tang; followed Li Shimin in fighting Dou Jiande, Liu Heita, and Wang Shichong; leader of campaigns against Eastern Tujue (630) and Koguryŏ (667–668).
- **Li Shimin** \lee shih-meen\; Taizong \tai-dzong\ (599–649; r. 626–649): second Emperor of the Tang; Duke of Dunhuang; Prince of Qin; son of Li Yuan and Ms. Dou; named Heavenly Khan (Qaghan) in 630.
- Li Shou (fl. 628): Tang official.
- **Li Tai**; Prince of Wei (619–653): second son of Li Shimin and Ms. Zhangsun; Li Chengqian's rival.
- Li Yin: late Western Han official.
- Li You (early 620s–643): Li Shimin's non-heir son; started rebellion; forced to commit suicide.
- Li Yuàn (d. 626): second uncle of Li Shimin.
- **Li Yuan** \lee yüan\; Gaozu \gao-dzoo\ (566–635; r. 618–626): Sui Duke of Tang; founding Emperor of the Tang dynasty; father of Li Shimin.
- Li Yuanchang (d. 643): Li Yuan's non-heir son; Li Shimin's half brother; forced to commit suicide.
- **Li Yuanji** \lee yuan-jee\ (603–626): Prince of Qi; son of Li Yuan and Ms. Dou; supporter of Li Jiancheng; killed in the Xuanwu Gate Incident.
- **Li Zhi** \lee jih\; Gaozong (628–683; r. 649–683): Tang Emperor; Li Shimin's third son by Empress Zhangsun.
- Li, Ms. (d. 646): Zhang Liang's last wife; executed.
- Liang \leeang\ (Xiao-Liang) (502–557) (cap.: Jiankang [Nanjing]): Southern dynasty replaced by the Chen.

- Liang Prefecture (seat: Liangzhou [Wuwei, Gansu]).
- Liang Shi \leeang shih\: Tang general under Li Shimin (Taizong).
- Liang Shidu \leeang shih-doo\ (d. 628): Tang rebel leader active in north Shaanxi and the Ordos.
- Liangyi \leeang-yee\ Basilica: hall on the central axis of the Taiji Palace, Chang'an.
- Liangzhou \leeang-jou\ (Wuwei, Gansu): seat of Liang Prefecture.
- Liao Prefecture (seat: Liaodong City).
- Liao River (Hun River in Liaoning).
- Liaodong: **1** area in west Liaoning. **2** Liaodong City.
- Liaodong City: Koguryǒ City (Liaoyang, Liaoning); conquered by the Tang (645).
- Licheng \lee-chêng\ (Jinan, Shandong).
- Lingyan Pavilion (*ge* \gê\) (Mist-transcending P.): located in Chang'an's Palace City; converted into the Tang hall of fame (643).
- Linhu Basilica (Lakeside B.): hall in the Taiji Palace.
- Linyi \leen-yee\: state in south Vietnam.
- Linyu \leen-yü\ Pass (west of Qinhuangdao, Hebei).
- Liu Bang \leeoo bang\ (256–195 BCE; r. 202–195 BCE): Gaozu of Han; founder of the Han dynasty.
- Liu Dewei \leeoo dê-wei\ (582–652): Tang official.
- Liu Heita (d. 623): rebel leader active in Shandong; initially follower of Dou Jiande.
- **Liu Wenjing** (568–619): Tang senior official; friend of Li Shimin (Taizong); executed by Li Yuan.
- **Liu Wuzhou** \leeoo woo-jou\ (d. 622): Sui rebel leader based in north Shanxi supported by Tujue.
- Liyang \lee-yang\: city near Xunxian, north Henan, southeast of Anyang.
- Lizheng \lee-jêng\ Basilica: hall in the Taiji Palace.
- Long Tuqizhi \too-chee-jih\: king of Yanqi (r. –644).
- Long Wood Gates (Changlinmen), Right and Left: two gates on the west and east sides of the Eastern Palace.
- Longmen: place. **1** south of Luoyang. **2** (Hejin, Shanxi) on the east bank of the Yellow River, bordering on Shaanxi.
- Longxi \long-shee\ (seat: near Longxi Gansu): Commandery from the 3rd century to the Sui.
- Longyou (mainly Gansu): Tang Circle.
- Lord Lao; Laozi \lao-dzih\; Li Er: legendary founder of Daoism.
- Lord on High (Shangdi): highest divinity in Chinese tradition.
- Lü Cai \lü tsai\ (fl. 632): Tang official.

- Lu Shuang (fl. 629): husband of Zheng Renji's daughter.
- Lu Zushang (d. 628): Tang official; executed by Li Shimin.
- Lü, Empress (d. 180 BCE): wife of Liu Bang; ruled Han China after Liu's death (195 BCE).
- Lu, Ms.: Fang Xuanling's wife.
- Luokou (Gongyi, Henan): site of the Luokou Granary, the main grain storage facility near Luoyang.
- Luoyang Palace: Palace City in Luoyang.
- Luoyang (Luoyang, Henan): Sui-Tang Eastern Capital.
- Ma Wenju \ma wen-jü\ (fl. 645): Tang officer.
- Magadha: north India kingdom.
- *Mahaprajna-paramita-sutra:* Buddhist sutra.
- Maitreya Buddha: the future Buddha.
- Mang Hills (north of Luoyang).
- Mangdang Mountains: they straddle Henan, Shandong, Jiangsu, and Anhui.
- Mashou \ma-shou\, Mount (near Liaodong City).
- Mayi \ma-yee\ (seat: Mayi [Shuozhoushi, Shanxi]): Sui Commandery.
- Mentor (*shuzi* \shoo-dzih\): high-ranking official in charge of edifying the crown Prince.
- Mgar Stong-btsan (d. 667): Tubo top official.
- Ming, Emperor (28–75 CE; r. 57–75 CE): Eastern Han sovereign.
- Ming River: it rose in the Taihang Mountains in Shanxi and flowed into south Hebei.
- Mingde \ming-dê\ Gate: southern main entrance of Chang'an.
- *Models for the Emperor* (*Difan*): book by Li Shimin for His son Li Zhi.
- Mohe \moh-hê\: non-Han people active in central and north Manchuria and beyond.
- *Mr. Zuo's Commentary to the Chunqiu* (*Chunqiu Zuozhuan*): Confucian classic attributed to Zuo Qiuming.
- Mu of Qin \cheen\, Duke (r. 659–621 BCE): sovereign of the local state of Qin.
- Muye \moo-yeh\ (Xinxiang, Henan): locale of a battle in c. 1046 BCE where the Zhou army under King Wu defeated the Shang army.
- Nārāyaṇasvāmin (fl. 648–649): Indian occultist.
- National History: history of the current dynasty.
- National University (*guoxue* \guo-shüeh\).
- Nestorius (fl. 428–431): founder of Nestorianism.
- Nine Courts: central government agencies lower than the Six Boards. Each Court was headed by a Director (*qing* \ching\).

- Ning Prefecture (seat: Ningxian, Gansu).
- North, the: the Yellow River valley.
- Northern Qi (550–577) (cap.: Ye [Linzhang, Hebei]): Northern dynasty that succeeded the Eastern Wei.
- Northern Wei (386–534) (cap.: Luoyang [493–]): first Northern dynasty, founded by the Tuoba.
- Northern Zhou (557–581) (cap.: Chang'an): Northern dynasty that succeeded the Western Wei and annexed the Northern Qi.
- Paekche \pak-cheh\ (–660): state in southwest Korea; annexed by the Tang.
- Palace City: enclosed palace area in Chang'an or Luoyang.
- Palace Domestic Service (*neishi sheng*): palace agency staffed by eunuchs.
- Palace Style: poetic style developed at the Liang court; criticized for being ornate and trivial.
- **Pei Ji** \pei jee\ (561–632): Li Yuan's friend; Tang senior official; banished from Chang'an under Li Shimin.
- Pei Ju \pei jü\ (547–627): leading Tang official under Li Yuan.
- Pei Xingzhuang \pei sheeng-juang\ (fl. 642): Tang official.
- Plume Hunt (Yulie \yü-lyeh\)("lyeh" is pronounced [lee'yeh]): rhapsody by Yang Xiong (Western Han).
- *Precepts for Women* (Nüze): book compiled by Empress Zhangsun.
- Prefecture (*zhou* \jou\): administrative and territorial division higher than the Commandery (*jun* \jün\) or the County; abolished by Emperor Yang; revived by the Tang.
- Pu Prefecture (seat: southwest of Yongji, Shanxi).
- Pujin Bridge: it ran across the Yellow River west of Hedong.
- Pyongyang (present-day Pyongyang): Koguryŏ capital.
- Qi \chee\ Prefecture: **1** (in Shandong). **2** (west of Xi'an in Shaanxi).
- Qi, Prince of: see Li Yuanji.
- Qianshui \cheean-shui\ Moor (northeast of Changwu, Shaanxi).
- Qianyang \cheean-yang\ Basilica: largest building in Sui Luoyang, destroyed by Li Shimin. See Qianyuan.
- Qianyuan \cheean-yüan\ Basilica: main hall in the Palace City, Tang Luoyang; Qianyang under the Sui.
- Qibiheli \chee-bee-hê-lee\ (d. 677): Tang-Tiele general.
- Qidan \chee-dan\ (Khitan): non-Han people active in an area that includes Tongliao, Chifeng, etc., Inner Mongolia.
- Qin Shiying \cheen shih-yeeng\ (d. 643): Daoist occultist; executed.
- Qin Shubao \cheen shoo-bao\ (d. 638): general under Li Shimin.

- Qin, Prince of: see Li Shimin.
- Qin: ancient state, mostly corresponding to Shaanxi.
- Qing Prefecture. **1** (seat: Qingzhou [Yidu, Shandong]): Northern Qi area. **2** (seat: Qingyang, Gansu): Tang area.
- Qingshan \cheeng-shan\ Palace (140 *li* west of Chang'an): Li Shimin's birthplace and childhood home.
- Qiuci \cheeoo-tsih\: oasis state based in Kucha, Xinjiang.
- Qu Wentai \chü wen-tai\ (d. 640; r. 623–640): penultimate king of Gaochang.
- Qu Zhisheng \chü jih-shêng\: last king of Gaochang (r. 640).
- Quan Gaisuwen \chüan gai-soo-wen\; Yuan Gaisuwen (Yŏn Kaesomun) (603–666): Koguryŏ dictator.
- Quan Wanji \chüan wan-jee\ (d. 643): Tang censor; Chief Administrator under Li You; killed.
- Queshu \chüeh-shoo\ Valley (Sparrow and Rat V.): west of Jiexiu, Shanxi.
- Qutu Tong \chü-too tong\ (557–628): Sui general; Tang senior official.
- RA: Righteous Army.
- *Record of Rites* (*Liji* \lee-jee\): Confucian classic.
- *Rectification of Meanings* (*Zhengyi* \jêng-yee\): authoritative subcommentaries on the Confucian Classics by Kong Yingda et al.
- Renzhi \ren-jih\ Palace (Benevolence and Wisdom P.): touring palace built by Li Yuan in Tongchuan, 300 *li* north of Chang'an; enlarged by Li Shimin as Yuhua Palace.
- Righteous Army (RA): rebel army organized by Li Yuan (Gaozu) in 617.
- Sadāpralāpa: weeping Bodhisattva known for his persistent quest for the truth.
- Sang Xianhe \sang sheean-hê\ (fl. 617): Qutu Tong's subordinate.
- *Secret Records*: an esoteric book.
- Secretariat: top-echelon decision-making body, headed by two Presidents.
- Shan Xiongxin \shan sheeong-sheen\ (d. 621): Wang Shichong's general; Li Shiji's friend.
- Shang Prefecture (seat: Shangzhou, Shaanxi).
- Shang Yang (395–338 BCE): reformer of the state of Qin.
- Shangdang \shang-dang\ (seat: Shangdang [Changzhi, Shanxi]): Sui Commandery.
- Shanggu (seat: Yixian, Hebei): Sui Commandery southwest of Beijing.
- Shaolin Monastery (in the Song Mountains).
- Shen Yue \shen yüeh\ (441–513): Qi-Liang historian.
- Shenji \shen-jee\ (d. 646): adopted son of Zhang Liang; executed.
- Shibi \shih-bee\ Khan (Qaghan) (d. 619): Eastern Tujue leader.

- *shidian* \shih-deean\: sacrificial rite in honor of Confucius.
- Shun \shoon\: legendary good sovereign of far antiquity.
- Shuntian Gate: see Chengtian Gate.
- Shuofang: see Xia Prefecture.
- Shusun Tong \shoo-soon tong\ (fl. 205–190s): Western Han ritual scholar.
- Silibi \sih-lee-bee\ Khan; Li Simo (fl. 640s): Tujue leader (Qaghan); Tang general.
- Silla \shee-la\: state in southeast Korea, friendly to Tang under Li Shimin.
- Sima Qian \sih-ma cheean\: Western Han historian.
- Sir Vacuous (Zixu \dzih-shü\): rhapsody by Sima Xiangru (Western Han).
- Six Boards: six top executive agencies under the Department of State Affairs: Personnel, Revenue, Rites, Works, Justice, and War.
- Song (Liu-Song) (420–479) (cap.: Jiankang [Nanjing]): Southern dynasty replaced by the Liang.
- **Song Jingang** (d. 620): late Sui warlord; joined Liu Wuzhou (619); killed.
- Song Laosheng (d. 617): Sui general.
- Song Mountains (east of Luoyang, Henan).
- Song Prefecture (seat: Jiacheng [Songpan, north Sichuan]).
- Song: Spring and Autumn state in Shandong.
- Songzanganbu (Srong-btsan Sgam-po) (d. 650s): Tubo king; married Princess Wencheng.
- South, the: the Yangzi River valley, especially the lower Yangzi area.
- South Mountains (south of Chang'an).
- Spring and Autumn (Chunqiu \choon-cheeu\) (8th–5th c. BCE): historical period.
- Stellar Lodges (*xiu* \sheeoo\): 28 celestial divisions along the Zodiac and celestial equator such as Well, Woman, Ghost, etc. They are matched with earthly regions such as Qin, Yan, Chu, etc. for divination purposes.
- Su Prefecture (seat: Jiuquan, Gansu).
- Sudhanakumāra: disciple of the Buddha; made 53 virtuous friends.
- Sui (581–618) (cap.: Daxing City): dynasty prior to the Tang.
- Sun Daiyin (fl. 645): Koguryŏ-Tang officer.
- Sun Simiao \soon sih-meeao\ (581–682): famed medical doctor.
- Sun, Master; Sunzi \soon-dzih\: late Spring and Autumn strategist.
- Supervisor of the Household (*zhanshi* \jan-shih\): senior official in charge of edifying the crown Prince, higher in rank than a Mentor.
- Sweet Springs (Ganquan \gan-chüan\): rhapsody by Yang Xiong (Western Han).
- Taihe \tai-hê\ Palace (in the South Mountains): see Cuiwei Palace.
- Taiji \tai-jee\ Basilica: main hall in the Palace City of Tang Chang'an; known as Daxing Basilica in the Sui.

- Taiji Palace: main palace in the Palace City of Tang Chang'an; known as Daxing Palace in the Sui.
- Taiyuan Circle (seat: Taiyuan [SW of Taiyuan, Shanxi]: Sui region with its core area in Shanxi.
- Taiyuan: main urban center in Shanxi; southwest of present-day Taiyuan.
- Taizong \tai-dzong\, see Li Shimin.
- Tan Daoji (d. 436): Liu-Song general.
- Tang (618–907): dynasty that replaced the Sui; founded by Li Yuan (Gaozu).
- *Tang Code* (*Tanglü*): essentially a body of laws codified in the Zhenguan reign period.
- Tang Jian \tang jeean\ (579–656): Tang official.
- Tao Hongjing (456–536): Daoist; alchemist.
- Tiele \tieh-lê\: northern nomadic people of Turkic descent.
- Ting Prefecture (seat: Buddha City [north of Turfan, Xinjiang]).
- Tong Pass: strategic pass north of Weinan County, Shaanxi, and south of the Yellow River.
- Tong Yehu (Tong Yabghu) Khan (Qaghan) (–628): Western Tujue leader.
- Tubo: ancient Tibetans and their state.
- Tujue \too-jüe\: nomadic people of Turkish descent active in Mongolia and Central Asia.
- Tuli \too-lee\ (602–631): minor Eastern Tujue leader; Xieli's nephew.
- Tuoba Wei: Northern Wei.
- Tuoba: a branch of the Xianbei.
- Tuyuhun \too-yü-hoon\: nomadic people active mainly in Qinghai and east Gansu.
- Two Capitals (Liangjing): **1** Chang'an and Luoyang. **2** rhapsody by Ban Gu (Eastern Han) about the two cities.
- Uighurs: nomadic people of Turkic descent in Mongolia in Tang times.
- Upper Forest (Shanglin): rhapsody by Sima Xiangru (Western Han).
- *Venerated Documents* (*Shangshu*): Confucian classic also known as the *Book of History*.
- *Veritable Record of the Current Emperor*: by Fang Xuanling, Xu Jingzong, and others.
- Vicegerent (*liushou* \leeoo-shou\): ad hoc position whose holder exercised power in the capital or a major city on behalf of the Emperor.
- Wagang \wa-gang\ Army: Sui rebel army under Li Mi, active in Henan.
- Wang Bao (fl. 6th c.): Liang-Northern Zhou poet.
- Wang Bodang (d. 619): Li Mi's general.
- Wang Gui (571–639): Tang official under Li Jiancheng and Li Shimin.

- Wang Kangda (d. 617): general under Li Yuan.
- Wang Rengong (d. 617): Sui Commandery governor of Mayi.
- **Wang Shichong** (d. 621): Sui official; declared himself Emperor of Zheng \jêng\ (619); defeated by Li Shimin.
- Wang Wan (fl. 621): Wang Shichong's nephew.
- Wang Wei (d. 617): Sui Deputy Vicegerent of Taiyuan.
- Wang Xizhi \wang shee-jih\ (303–361): greatest Chinese calligrapher.
- Wang Xuance \wang shüan-tsê\ (fl. 643–661): Tang emissary to India.
- Wang Yuanzhi \wang yüan-jih\ (510–635): Mount Mao Daoist; occultist.
- Wei Dao'er (Lishanfei) (d. 618): Sui rebel leader active in Hebei.
- Wei Kai: Northern Qi official.
- Wei Lingfu (d. 643): Daoist occultist; executed.
- Wei Ting (590–647): Tang official in charge of transporting grain prior to the Tang Koguryŏ War.
- **Wei Zheng** \wei jêng\ (580–643): trusted adviser and confidant to Li Shimin, known for his candor and courage. Previously he had worked for Li Mi and Li Jiancheng.
- Weiyang \wei-yang\ Palace: largest palace in Han Chang'an.
- Wen Yanbo (573–637): Tang official under Li Shimin.
- Wen, Emperor; Wendi. **1** (202–157 BCE; r. 180–157 BCE): Western Han sovereign. **2** né Yang Jian \yang jeean\ (541–604; r. 581–604): founder of the Sui; father of Emperor Yang.
- Wencheng, Princess (623\25–680): Tang Princess married to the Tubo King Songzanganbu.
- Western Market: one of the two markets in Chang'an.
- Western Park (west of Luoyang): a vast enclosed area with a number of palace complexes; built by Yang Guang.
- Western Regions (Xiyu \shee-yü\): Xinjiang, or vast region that included Xinjiang and areas to its west (Central Asia, West Asia, India, etc.).
- Western Wei (535–556) (cap.: Chang'an): one of the two dynasties that replaced the Northern Wei.
- Wu, Emperor; Wudi. **1** (r. 141–87 BCE): Western Han sovereign. **2** (r. 502–549): Liang sovereign.
- Wu, King (Yŏngnyu) (d. 642; r. 618–642): Koguryŏ king.
- Wude \woo-dê\ (Martial Virtue): reign period (618–626).
- Wude Basilica: large hall east of the Taiji Palace, Chang'an, inhabited by Li Yuanji until his death (626).
- Wugu City (in Fengcheng, Liaoning): Koguryŏ city.
- Xi \shee\: non-Han people active near Chifeng, Inner Mongolia.

- Xi Prefecture (seat: Gaochang City): converted from the Kingdom of Gaochang.
- Xia \sheea\ Prefecture (seat: Shuofang [west of Hengshan, north Shaanxi]).
- Xianbei \sheean-bei\: non-Han people that arose in the 2nd century CE. They founded several dynasties in the North later.
- Xiande \sheean-dê\ Basilica: main hall of the Eastern Palace.
- Xiang \sheeang\ Prefecture (seat: in Anyang, north Henan).
- Xianling \sheean-leeng\: Gaozu Li Yuan's tomb park west of Chang'an.
- Xianren \sheean-ren\ Palace: in the Western Park in the western suburb of Luoyang.
- Xianyang \sheean-yang\: ancient name of Chang'an (Daxing City).
- Xiao Xian \sheeao sheean\ (583–621): Liang royal; rebel leader in the south.
- **Xiao Yu** \sheeao yü\ (575–648): Sui-Tang top official.
- Xiaowen \sheeao-wen\, Emperor (467–499; r. 471–499): Northern Wei sovereign.
- Xieli \shyeh-lee\ ("shyeh" is pronounced [shee'yeh]) (d. 634): Eastern Tujue leader (620–30), defeated by Li Shimin.
- Xihe \shee-hê\ (seat: Xihe [Fenyang, Shanxi]): Sui Commandery.
- Xin Chujian \sheen choo-jeean\: Tang official under Li Yuan.
- Xiongnu \sheeong-noo\: northern nomadic people active in Mongolia; Huns.
- Xu Hui \shü huee\ (627–650): Li Shimin's concubine.
- Xu Jingzong \shü jeeng-dzong\ (592–672): Tang official and historian.
- Xu Shiji \shü shih-jee\: see Li Shiji.
- Xu Yuanlang \shü yüan-lang\ (d. 623): Tang rebel leader active in Shandong.
- Xuan \shüan\, Emperor. **1** (91–48 BCE; r. 114–48 BCE): Western Han sovereign. **2** (559–580; r. 578–579): Northern Zhou sovereign; Yuwen Êying's father.
- Xuandu \shüan-doo\ Abbey: leading Daoist institution in Daxing-Chang'an.
- Xuanwu \shüan-wu\ Gate (Dark Warrior G.): central northern entrance of the Taiji Palace; opened onto the Forbidden Park; held key to the security of the Palace.
- Xuanwu Gate Incident: On July 2, 626, Li Shimin and his associates assassinated Li Jiancheng and Li Yuanji.
- **Xuanzang** \shüan-dzang\ (602–664): Buddhist master; traveled to India and brought back 657 Buddhist works in Sanskrit.
- Xue Dading \da-deeng\ (fl. 617): Hedong gentleman.
- Xue Ju \shüeh jü\ (d. 618): late Sui warlord based in east Gansu.
- Xue Rengao \shüeh ren-gao\ (d. 618): late Sui warlord; son of Xue Ju; defeated and executed.
- Xue Wanjun \shüeh wan-jün\ (d. early 640s): Tang general.
- Xueyantuo \shüeh-yan-tuo\ (Syr Tardush): nomadic people in Mongolia.
- Xun Xiang \shün sheeang\ (fl. 620): Song Jingang's general.

- Yan Hongliang (d. 643): Li You's associate.
- Yan Liben \yan lee-bên\ (d. 673): Tang painter; brother of Yan Lide.
- Yan Lide \yan lee-dê\ (d. 656): Tang official; builder; brother of Yan Liben.
- Yan Prefecture (seat: Yanzhou [north of Yanzhou, SW Shandong]).
- Yan: ancient state in Hebei and south Manchuria.
- Yang Guang: see Emperor Yang.
- Yang Jian: see Emperor Wen.
- Yang Lihua: Emperor Wen of Sui's daughter; Emperor Xuan's wife; Yuwen Êying's mother.
- Yang Su (d. 606): Sui leading general; father of Yang Xuangan.
- Yang Tong (d. 619; r. 618–619): grandson of Emperor Yang of Sui (Yang Guang); Prince of Yue; set up by Wang Shichong as Emperor.
- Yang Wengan (d. 624): Tang official; rebelled against Li Yuan (624).
- Yang Xuangan \yang shüan-gan\ (d. 613): Sui official; rebel leader; son of Yang Su.
- Yang Yichen (d. 617): Sui top general.
- Yang Yin (d. 560): Northern Qi top official.
- Yang You (605–619; r. 617–618): Emperor Gong of Sui; grandson of Emperor Yang (Yang Guang); Prince of Dai.
- **Yang, Emperor** (Yangdi; né Yang Guang) (569–618; r. 604–618): second Sui sovereign. The dynasty collapsed on His watch.
- Yangzhou \yang-jou\: Jiangdu.
- Yanqi \yan-chee\ (Qarasahr) (cap.: near Yanqi, Xinjiang): oasis state.
- Yao Junsu \yao jün-soo\: Sui general; subordinate to Qutu Tong.
- Yao: legendary good sovereign of far antiquity.
- Ye \yeh\ (SW of Linzhang, Hebei): capital of the Northern Qi.
- Yehu \yeh-hoo\ Khan (Qaghan), Si Yehu (d. 632): leader of Western Tujue.
- Yi Prefecture (seat: Yizhou [Chengdu, Sichuan]).
- Yin Ashu: Consort Yin's father.
- Yin Kaishan (d. 622): Tang general under Li Shimin.
- Yin Shishi \yeen shih-shih\ (d. 617): Sui general.
- **Yin, Virtuous Consort** (fl. 620s): Li Yuan's consort; opponent of Li Shimin.
- Ying Prefecture (seat: in Liaoyang, Liaoning).
- Yining \yee-neeng\ (Righteous Peace): reign period (617–618).
- Yiqiu Palace \yee-cheeoo\: small palace inside the Eastern Palace.
- *Yisi* \yee-sih\ *Divination*: book on divination by Li Chunfeng.
- Yiwu (cap.: Yiwu [Hami, Xinjiang]): oasis state west of the Jade Gate Pass.

- *Yogācārabhūmi-śāstra*: Buddhist treatise on the 17 stages leading to nirvana; translated by Xuanzang and others.
- You Prefecture (seat: Youzhou [Beijing]).
- Youzhou \you-jou\ (in Beijing): seat of You Prefecture in north Hebei; known as Zhuo Commandery under Emperor Yang.
- Yu Shiji \yü shih-jee\ (d. 618): top official under Emperor Yang of Sui; brother Yu Shinan.
- **Yu Shinan** \yü shih-nan\ (558–638): Tang official, calligrapher; Li Shimin's literary friend.
- **Yu Zhining** \yü jih-neeng\ (588–665): highest-ranking Tang official in charge of edifying Li Chengqian.
- Yuan, Emperor (r. 552–555): Liang sovereign.
- **Yuchi Jingde** \yü-chih jeeng-dê\ (585–658): Li Shimin's general; played a key role in the Xuanwu Gate Incident.
- Yuhua \yü-hua\ Palace (Jade Flower P.) (in the Phoenix Valley, Yuhua Mountains): originally called Renzhi; enlarged and renamed under Li Shimin.
- **Yuwen Êying** \yü-wen ê-yeeng\ (574–613): Emperor Wen of Sui's granddaughter; daughter of Northern Zhou Emperor Xuan and Yang Lihua.
- **Yuwen Shiji** \yü-wen shih-jee\ (d. 642): senior official of the Sui and Tang (from 619); son of Yuwen Shu.
- Yuwen Shu \yü-wen shoo\ (d. 616): Sui top general, father of Yuwen Shiji.
- Yuwen Ying (d. 624): Tang official.
- Zang \dzang\, King (Pojang) (d. 682; r. 642–668): Koguryŏ King.
- Zhang Baozang \jang bao-dzang\ (fl. 636): Tang physician.
- **Zhang, Fair Lady** (fl. 620s): Li Yuan's favorite consort; opponent of Li Shimin; Li Jiancheng's lover.
- Zhang Gongjin (584–632): general under Li Shimin.
- Zhang Jian \jang jeean\ (591–650): Tang general; official.
- Zhang Junyi \jang jün-yee\ (d. 645): Tang officer.
- **Zhang Liang** \jang leeang\ (d. 646): Tang top general, official under Li Shimin; executed.
- Zhang Qian \jang cheean\: Western Han emissary sent by Emperor Wu in the late 2nd century BCE to Central Asia.
- Zhang Sizheng \jang sih-jêng\ (d. 643): Li Chengqian's underling.
- Zhang Xuansu \jang shüan-soo\ (d. 664): Tang remonstrator; Li Chengqian's mentor.
- Zhangnan \jang-nan\ (near Wucheng, Shandong).
- Zhangqiu Zituo \jang-cheeoo dzih-tuo\: Northern Qi Confucian; executed for attack on Buddhism.

- **Zhangsun** \jang-soon\, **Empress** (601–636): wife of Li Shimin; sister of Zhangsun Wuji; adopted daughter of Gao Shilian.
- **Zhangsun Wuji** \jang-soon woo-jee\, (d. 659): leading politician under Li Shimin; elder brother of Empress Zhangsun; adopted son of Gao Shilian.
- Zhangye \jang-yeh\ (in central Gansu).
- Zhao Yuankai (fl. 638): Tang official.
- Zhaoling \jao-leeng\ (140 *li* west of Chang'an): Li Shimin's tomb park. Empress Zhangsun and Li's close associates were buried there.
- Zheng \jêng\ and Wey, sound of: decadent music (Zheng and Wey were two Spring and Autumn states in the Central Plain).
- Zheng Renji \jêng ren-jee\: Sui official.
- Zhenguan \jen-guan\ (Honorable Outlook): reign period (627–649).
- Zhezhi \jê-jih\ City (NE of Jungchuan, Gansu): base of Xue Rengao when he was defeated (618).
- Zhishi \jih-shih\ (600–637): Buddhist monk.
- Zhishi Sili \jih-shih sih-lee\ (fl. 620s–640s): Tang general; initially Tujue officer under Xieli.
- Zhiyong \jih-yong\ (fl. Chen-Sui): calligrapher.
- Zhòu \jou\: last king of the Shang dynasty; one of the worst rulers in history.
- Zhuang \juang\ of Chu, King (r. 613–591 BCE): sovereign of the state of Chu.
- Zhuang, Master (Zhuangzi \juang-dzih\) (c. 369–286 BCE): Warring States Daoist philosopher.
- Zhuangyan \juang-yan\ Monastery: one of the two largest Buddhist monasteries in Chang'an.
- Zhubi \joo-bee\, Mount (SW of Liaoyang, Liaoning).
- Zhuo \juo\ (seat: Jixian [Beijing]): Sui Commandery in north Hebei.
- Zhuque \joo-chüeh\ Gate: southern entrance of the Imperial City, Chang'an.
- Zhuquemen \joo-chüeh-mên\ Avenue: main north-south street of Chang'an.

Heavenly Khan

ISBN: 978-986-6286-66-7

DOI: 10.6140/AP.9789866286667

Publishing Date: August, 2014

Price: US $10

Author: Victor Cunrui Xiong

Executive Editor: Huang-Yu Chao

Cover & Layout Designer: Mei-Hsiu Lin

Typesetting: Kailun Wang

General Manager: Chris Cheng

Manager: Ya-Chu Fan

Publishing Specialist: Kevin Yang

Publisher: Airiti Press Inc.

      18F, No. 80, Sec. 1, Chenggong Rd., Yonghe

      Dist., New Taipei City 234, Taiwan

      Tel: +886-2-2926-6006

      Fax: +886-2-2923-5151

      E-mail: press@airiti.com